MEDICINAL CHEMISTRY-III

B.Pharm, Sixth Semester

According to the syllabus based on **'Pharmacy Council of India'**

Prof. (Dr.) V.N. Indulatha
B.Pharm, M.Pharm, Ph.D.
Vice Principal/ Professor
Sree Abirami College of Pharmacy, Coimbatore

Dr. Rakesh Kumar
M.Pharm, Ph.D.
Principal,
Vaish Institute of Pharmaceutical Education and Research, Rohtak

Dr. Neha Tiwari
M.Pharm, Ph.D.
Associate Professor
Khyati College of Pharmacy, Ahmedabad

THAKUR PUBLICATION PVT. LTD., LUCKNOW

* Ahmedabad * Bengaluru * Bhopal * Bhubaneswar * Chennai * Dehradun * Ernakulam
* Hyderabad * Jaipur * Jalandhar * Kolkata * Nagpur * Patna * Pune * Rohtak *

Medicinal Chemistry-III

- Prof. (Dr.) V.N. Indulatha
- Dr. Rakesh Kumar
- Dr. Neha Tiwari

Published by:

Thakur Publication Pvt. Ltd.

HO: Abhishekpuram, 60 Feet Road, Jankipuram, Lucknow-226021
Ph.9235318597/96/95/94/91/22/17, 9335318517 Landline : 0522-3571915

Website: www.tppl.org.in
Email: thakurpublication@gmail.com

Books are Available for Online Purchase at: **tppl.org.in**
Download old Question papers from: **www.questionpaper.org.in**

ISBN No. 978-93-89627-60-2 **₹230/-**
First Edition 2020
Reprint 2021
Reprint Edition 2025

Printed at:
Savera Printing Press
Tirupatipuram, Jankipuram Extension near AKTU, Lucknow-226 031
E-mail: lkospp@gmail.com, Mobile No. 9235318506/07

"Dedicated

to

*my **Beloved Students**"*

- Prof. (Dr.) V. N. Indulatha

"Dedicated

to

*my **Beloved Joint Family**"*

- Dr. Rakesh Kumar

"Dedicated

to

*my **Father***

&

*my **Husband**"*

- Dr. Neha Tiwari

Preface

It gives us immense pleasure to place before the **B.Pharm Sixth Semester** pharmacy students the book on **"Medicinal Chemistry-III"**.

This book has been written strictly in accordance with the current syllabus prescribed by Pharmacy Council of India, for B.Pharm students. Keeping in view the requirements of students and teachers, this book has been written to cover all the topics in an easy-to-comprehend manner within desired limits of the prescribed syllabus, and it provides the students fundamentals of various antibiotics, anti-fungal, anti-malarial, anti-protozoal and anti-tubercular agents, anthelmintics, and drug design and combinatorial chemistry which are required by them during their pharmaceutical career.

All efforts have been made to keep the text error-free and to present the subject in a student friendly and easy to understand. However, any suggestions and constructive comments would be highly appreciated and incorporated in the future edition.

Please e-mail us at, **thakurpublication@gmail.com**

Website, **www.tppl.org.in**

Acknowledgement

I would like to express my sincere thanks and gratitude to all my respected teachers as well as my students who brought me upto this level. I am really thankful to **Dr. P Periyaswamy**, **Dr. Kunthavi Devi**, **Dr. R. Senthil Kumar**, **Dr. P. Balamurugan**, **Dr. P. Umadevi** and **Dr. P. Sucharitha,** Directors of Sree Abirami Charitable Trust, for the oppurtunity to serve in their institution. My heartfelt thanks to our beloved Principal, **Prof. Dr. M. Senthil Kumar**, Sree Abirami College of Pharmacy, Coimbatore, for his constant encouragement. I would also like to thank my parents, my husband and my family for the moral support given to me to serve best in my carrier.

- Prof. (Dr.) V. N. Indulatha

Along with hard work, the support of people present in our surrounding is also precious. I would really like to express my gratitude to those people who have helped and supported me throughout my work. But above all, I would like to thank, God for all his blessing for leading me through trials and fears to success, for showing me the light even in times of great darkness and for giving me strength to come this far.

It is my proud privilege to acknowledge with deep sense of gratitude and devotion, the keen personal interest and in valuable guidance rendered to me by esteemed and revered teacher, guide and illuminating supervisor, **Prof. (Dr.) Shailendra Patil, Professor, Dean, SVN Institute of Pharmaceutical Sciences, Sagar, MP** for instilling in me the qualities of being a researcher. His constant support and enthusiasm has brought this work of mine to its present form. His invaluable suggestion, constructive criticism and directions have cleared the horizons for me whenever I was in the darkness of confusion and dilemma. It is a great honor to work under his guidance.

I am gratefully acknowledging Hon'ble President and Management of Vaish Education Society, Rohtak for all the support and encouragement:

I would like to express my gratitude for his unconditional day and night help in writing this book to **Dr. Aakash Deep**, Assistant Professor in the Department of Pharmacy in Choudhary Bansilal University, Bhiwani and **Dr. Anurag**, Meerut Institute of Engineering and Technology, Bhagpat. I am equally thankful to my dear colleagues **Dr. Ramchander Khatri**, Assistant Controller of Examination in DPSRU, Delhi, **Mr. Sunil Kumar**, **Mr. Tanuj Hooda**, **Amit Lather**, **Mr. Harsh Goyal** for their help in the compilation of this book.

Now I feel very proud to thanks my lovely joint family for the mental, financial and moral support in my research work in all the circumstances. I am grateful for the affection and love of my mother Smt. Ompati Devi, my sisters, Sunita, Anita **and Diksha.**

I gratefully acknowledge my brothers Mr. Sanjay Kumar and Jeewan for their moral support. I like to thank my beloved better half Mrs. Shaweta and daughter Shreya and my son Aayush for their kind support and sacrifice while writing of this book.

- Dr. Rakesh Kumar

I would like to express my gratitude to many people who saw me through this book and to all those who provided support. I wish to place on record my heartfelt thanks to everyone who have made this book possible.

I am very much thankful to **Dr. Pragnesh Patani**, **Principal (I/c), A- One Pharmacy College** for his kind co-operation and constant encouragement.

I record my profound sense of gratitude to my esteemed mentors **Prof. (Dr.) Ranjit Singh, Director, School of Pharmaceutical Sciences, Shobhit University, Gangoh, Saharanpur** and **Prof. (Dr.) Ashutosh Mishra, Principal, Acharaya Narendra College of Pharmacy, Babhnan, Gonda, Uttar Pradesh** for their constant guidance, supervision, unflagging interest, critical comments and valuable suggestions.

Transcending all this, the unbounded affection, sweet love and constant inspiration of my family members who made it possible to fulfill this task and mere thanks would not be sufficient for it.

Milestones in life are achieved not by individual efforts, but by blessings and guidance of elders, nears & dears. My final debt is to all dear ones whose unruffled patience, silent encouragement and desires to see my success have evened in this denouement.

Above all, I bow my head before the Almighty God with whose grace and beatitude, I moved through this venture.

- Dr. Neha Tiwari

Syllabus

Module 01 **10 Hours**

Antibiotics

Historical background, Nomenclature, Stereochemistry, Structure activity relationship, Chemical degradation classification and important products of the following classes.

β-Lactam antibiotics

- Penicillin, Cepholosporins, β- Lactamase inhibitors, Monobactams.

Aminoglycosides

- Streptomycin, Neomycin, Kanamycin.

Tetracyclines

- Tetracycline, Oxytetracycline, Chlortetracycline, Minocycline, Doxycycline.

Module 02 **10 Hours**

Antibiotics

Historical background, Nomenclature, Stereochemistry, Structure activity relationship, Chemical degradation classification and important products of the following classes.

Macrolide

- Erythromycin Clarithromycin, Azithromycin.

Miscellaneous

- Chloramphenicol*, Clindamycin.

Pro-drugs

- Basic concepts and application of prodrugs design.

Antimalarials

- Etiology of malaria.

Quinolines

- SAR, Quinine sulphate, Chloroquine, Amodiaquine, Primaquine phosphate, Pamaquine, Quinacrine hydrochloride, Mefloquine.
- Biguanides and dihydro triazines
- Cycloguanil pamoate, Proguanil.

Miscellaneous

- Pyrimethamine, Artesunete, Artemether, Atovoquone.

Module 03 **10 Hours**

Anti-Tubercular Agents

Synthetic Anti-Tubercular Agents

- Isoniozid, Ethionamide, Ethambutol, Pyrazinamide, Para amino salicylic acid.

Anti-Tubercular Antibiotics

- Rifampicin, Rifabutin, Cycloserine Streptomycine, Capreomycin sulphate.

Urinary Tract Anti-Infective Agents

Quinolones

- SAR of quinolones, Nalidixic Acid, Norfloxacin, Enoxacin, Ciprofloxacin, Ofloxacin, Lomefloxacin, Sparfloxacin, Gatifloxacin, Moxifloxacin.

Miscellaneous

- Furazolidine, Nitrofurantoin*, Methanamine.

Antiviral Agents

- Amantadine hydrochloride, Rimantadine hydrochloride, Idoxuridine trifluoride, Acyclovir*, Gancyclovir, Zidovudine, Didanosine, Zalcitabine, Lamivudine, Loviride, Delavirding, Ribavirin, Saquinavir, Indinavir, Ritonavir.

Module 04 **08 Hours**

Antifungal Agents

Antifungal Antibiotics

- Amphotericin-B, Nystatin, Natamycin, Griseofulvin.

Synthetic Antifungal Agents

- Clotrimazole, Econazole, Butoconazole, Oxiconazole Tioconozole, Miconazole, Ketoconazole, Terconazole, Itraconazole, Fluconazole, Naftifine hydrochloride, Tolnaftate.

Anti-Protozoal Agents

- Metronidazole, Tinidazole, Ornidazole, Diloxanide, Iodoquinol, Pentamidine Isethionate, Atovaquone, Eflornithine.

Anthelmintics

- Diethylcarbamazine citrate, Thiabendazole, Mebendazole, Albendazole, Niclosamide, Oxamniquine, Praziquantal, Ivermectin.

Sulphonamides and Sulfones

- Historical development, chemistry, classification and SAR of Sulfonamides: Sulphamethizole, Sulfisoxazole, Sulphamethizine, Sulfacetamide, Sulphapyridine, Sulfamethoxaole, Sulphadiazine, Mefenide acetate, Sulfasalazine.

Folate Reductase Inhibitors

- Trimethoprim*, Cotrimoxazole.

Sulfones

- Dapsone.

Module 05 **07 Hours**

Introduction to Drug Design

- Various approaches used in drug design.
- Physicochemical parameters used in quantitative structure activity relationship (QSAR) such as partition coefficient, Hammet's electronic parameter, Tafts steric parameter and Hansch analysis.
- Pharmacophore modeling and docking techniques.

Combinatorial Chemistry

- Concept and applications of combinatorial chemistry: solid phase and solution phase synthesis.

Contents

Chapter 5: Antibiotics-Miscellaneous

Chapter 6: Pro-drugs

Chapter 7: Antimalarials

Chapter 8: Anti-Tubercular Agents

Chapter 9: Quinolones and Urinary Tract Anti-Infective Agents

Chapter 13: Anthelmintics

Chapter 14: Sulphonamides, Sulfones, and Folate Reductase Inhibitorss

Chapter 15: Introduction to Drug Design

Chapter 16: Combinatorial Chemistry

CHAPTER 1 Antibiotics-Beta Lactam Antibiotics

1.1. ANTIBIOTICS

1.1.1. Introduction

The word **antibiotic** was derived from the word **antibiosis** which means **against life**. Historically, antibiotics were believed to be organic compounds produced by a microorganism toxic to other microorganisms. Due to this belief, an antibiotic was initially defined as a substance produced by a microorganism, which can prevent the growth of, or are fatal to other microorganisms even at low concentrations. But this definition has been modified at the present time for including antimicrobials produced by synthetic means either partially or wholly.

Antibiotics can either kill other bacteria or inhibit their growth. Those antibiotics which kill bacteria are termed as **bactericidal** and those which inhibit bacterial growth are termed **bacteriostatic**. Even though antibiotics are referred to as antibacterial agents, still they are differentiated as antibacterials, antifungals, and antivirals to indicate the type of microorganisms against which they act.

1.1.1. Classification

Antibiotics can be classified as follows:

1) **Based on their Chemical Structure**
   i) **Antibiotics**
      a) **β-Lactam Antibiotics:** Penicillins, Cephalosporins, Monobactams, Carbapenems, etc.
      b) **Aminoglycosides:** Streptomycin, Gentamycin, Framycetin, Neomycin, etc.
      c) **Macrolides:** Erythromycin, Roxithromycin, Clarithromycin, Azithromycin, etc.
      d) **Tetracyclines:** Oxytetracycline, Doxycycline, Minocycline, etc.
      e) **Nitrobenzene Derivatives:** Chloramphenicol, etc.
      f) **Polypeptide Antibiotics:** Polymyxin-B, Colistin, Bacitracin, Tyrothricin, etc.
      g) **Polyene Antibiotics:** Nystatin, Hamycin, Amphotericin-B, etc.
      h) **Miscellaneous Agents:** Rifampicin, Lincomycin, Vancomycin, Fusidic acid, Cycloserine, Viomycin, Griseofulvin, etc.
   ii) **Chemotherapeutic Agents Other than Antibiotics**
      a) **Sulphonamides and Related Agents:** Sulfadiazine, Sulfamethoxazole, Sulfones (Dapsone), *Para*-Aminosalicylic Acid (PAS), etc.
      b) **Diaminopyrimidines:** Pyrimethamine.
      c) **Quinolones and Fluoroquinolones:** Nalidixic acid, Norfloxacin, Ciprofloxacin, Ofloxacin, etc.

d) **Nitrofuran Derivatives:** Nitrofurantoin, Furazolidone, etc.
e) **Nitroimidazoles:** Metronidazole, Tinidazole, etc.
f) **Imidazole Derivatives:** Miconazole, Clotrimazole, Ketoconazole, Fluconazole, etc.
g) **Nicotinic Acid Derivatives:** Isoniazid, Pyrazinamide, Ethionamide, etc.
h) **Miscellaneous Agents:** Ethambutol, Thiacetazone, Clofazimine, etc.

2) **Based on their Mechanism of Action**
   i) **Inhibit Cell Wall Synthesis:** Penicillins, Cephalosporins, Cycloserine, Vancomycin, and Bacitracin.
   ii) **Cause Leakage from Cell Membranes:** Polypeptides (Polymyxins, Colistin, and Bacitracin) and Polyenes (Amphotericin B, Nystatin, and Hamycin).
   iii) **Inhibit Protein Synthesis:** Tetracyclines, Chloramphenicol, Erythromycin, Clindamycin, and Linezolid.
   iv) **Cause Misreading of m-RNA Code and Affect Permeability:** Aminoglycosides (Streptomycin, Gentamicin, etc.).
   v) **Inhibit DNA Gyrase:** Fluoroquinolones (Ciprofloxacin, etc.).
   vi) **Interfere with DNA Function:** Rifampin and Metronidazole.
   vii) **Interfere with DNA Synthesis:** Acyclovir and Zidovudine.
   viii) **Interfere with Intermediary Metabolism:** Sulphonamides, Sulphones, PAS, Trimethoprim, Pyrimethamine, and Ethambutol.

3) **Based on their Range of Action**
   i) **Broad Spectrum Antibiotics:** These are effective against gram +ve and gram –ve bacteria, rickettsia, and chlamydia **e.g.,** Tetracycline, Chloramphenicol, etc.
   ii) **Relative Broad Spectrum Antibiotics:** These are effective against gram +ve and gram –ve bacteria **e.g.,** Ampicillin group, Cephalosporins, Rifamycins, etc.
   iii) **Narrow Spectrum Antibiotics**
      a) These are effective against gram +ve bacteria, **e.g.,** Penicillin, Erythromycin group, and Vancomycin.
      b) These are also effective against gram –ve bacteria, **e.g.,** Streptomycin and other aminoglycoside antibiotics, Colistin, Polymyxin-B.
      c) **Antifungal Antibiotics:** Hamycin, Nystatin, Griseofulvin, etc.
      d) **Anticancer Antibiotics:** Actinomycin, Bicomycin, Mitomycin, Mithramycin, etc.

4) **Based on Types of Organisms Against which they are Primarily Active**
   i) **Antibacterial:** Penicillins, Aminoglycosides, Erythromycin, etc.
   ii) **Antifungal:** Griseofulvin, Amphotericin B, Ketoconazole, etc.
   iii) **Antiviral:** Acyclovir, Amantadine, Zidovudine, etc.
   iv) **Antiprotozoal:** Chloroquine, Pyrimethamine, Metronidazole, Diloxanide, etc.
   v) **Anthelmintic:** Mebendazole, Pyrantel, Niclosamide, Diethylcarbamazine, etc.

5) **Based on their Type of Action**
   i) **Primarily Bacteriostatic:** Sulphonamides, Erythromycin, Ethambutol, Tetracyclines, Chloramphenicol, and Clindamycin Linezolid.
   ii) **Primarily Bactericidal:** Penicillins, Aminoglycosides, Cephalosporins, Vancomycin, Nalidixic acid, Polypeptides, Ciprofloxacin, Rifampin, Isoniazid, Pyrazinamide, Metronidazole, and Cotrimoxazole.

6) **Based on their Source**
   i) **Fungi:** Penicillin, Griseofulvin, and Cephalosporin.
   ii) **Bacteria:** Polymyxin B, Tyrothricin, Colistin, Aztreonam, and Bacitracin.
   iii) **Actinomycetes:** Aminoglycosides, Macrolides, Tetracyclines, Polyenes, and Chloramphenicol.

1.2. β-LACTAM ANTIBIOTICS

1.2.1. Introduction

The β-lactam antibiotics belong to a broad category in which all the antibiotics have a β-lactam nucleus in their molecular structure, i.e., members of this antibiotic class possess a highly reactive 3-carbon and 1-nitrogen ring. The β-lactam antibiotics include penicillin derivatives (penams), monobactams, carbapenems and cephalosporins (cephems). They are the most widely used among all the antibiotics and act by inhibiting the cell wall synthesis of the bacterial organism.

The β-lactam antibiotics are generally given with β-lactamase inhibitors (**e.g.,** clavulanic acid) because the bacteria obtain resistance to β-lactam antibiotics by producing β-lactamase enzyme which attacks the β-lactam ring.

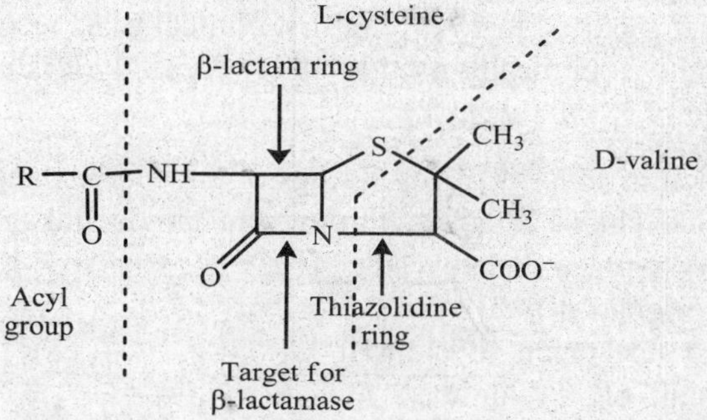

Figure 1.1: Antimicrobials that Interfere with Bacterial Nucleic Acids

1.2.2. Nomenclature

Based on their core ring structures, the β-lactam antibiotics are named as follows:

1) β-Lactams fused to saturated five-membered rings:
   i) **Penams:** β-Lactams containing thiazolidine rings.
   ii) **Carbapenams:** β-Lactams containing pyrrolidine rings.
   iii) **Oxapenams or Clavams:** β-Lactams fused to oxazolidine rings.
2) β-Lactams fused to unsaturated five-membered rings:
   i) **Penems:** β-Lactams containing 2,3-dihydrothiazole rings.
   ii) **Carbapenems:** β-Lactams containing 2,3-dihydro-1H-pyrrole rings.
3) β-Lactams fused to unsaturated six-membered rings:
   i) **Cephems:** β-Lactams containing 3,6-dihydro-2H-1,3-thiazine rings.
   ii) **Carbacephems:** β-Lactams containing 1,2,3,4-tetrahydropyridine rings.
   iii) **Oxacephems:** β-Lactams containing 3,6-dihydro-2H-1,3-oxazine rings.
4) **Monobactams: β-Lactams not fused to any other ring.**

1.2.3. Classification

- β-lactam Antibiotics
  - Penicillins: Penicillin G, PenicillinV, Methicillin, Nafcillin, Oxacillin, Cloxacillin, Dicloxacillin, Amoxicillin, Carbenicillin, Ticarcillin, Piperacillin, Mezlocillin, Cefoxitin, Azocillin
  - Cephalosporins
    - 1st Generation: Ampicillin, Cefadroxil, Cephalexin, Cephalothin, Cephapirin, Cephradine
    - 2nd Generation: Cefazolin, Cefamandole, Cefonicid, Cefmetazole, Cefotetan, Cefuroxime
    - 3rd Generation: Cefaclor, Cefoperazone, Ceftizoxime, Ceftazidime, Ceftriaxone, Cefixime, Moxalactam
    - 4th and 5th Generation: Cefepime, Cefozopran, Cefpirome, Cefquinome, Ceftobiprole, Ceftaroline, Fosamil
  - Carbapenems: Biapenem, Ertapenem, Doripenem, Impenem, Panipenem
  - Monobactams: Aztreonam, Tigemonam, Carumonam, Nacardicin A

Figure 1.2: Classification of β-Lactam Antibiotics

1.2.4. Penicillin

Penicillin is the **first antibiotic** which was discovered in **September 1928** by **Sir Alexander Fleming** (an English Bacteriologist). He accidentally obtained this antibiotic from a fungus dwelling in soil, called *Penicillium notatum*; however, its invention was first reported in **1929**, the first clinical trials were conducted on humans in **1940**, and was clinically used in **1941**. Presently it is obtained from a high yielding mutant of *P. chrysogenum*.

The nucleus of penicillin consists of fused rings of thiazolidine and *β*-lactam, and these rings have side chains attached through an amide linkage (**figure 1.3**). Penicillin G (PnG) with a benzyl side chain (at R) is the original penicillin to be used clinically. The side chain of natural penicillin can be split off by amidase to yield 6-amino-penicillanic acid, and then other side chains can be attached to yield different semi-synthetic penicillins having exclusive antibacterial properties and different pharmacokinetic profiles.

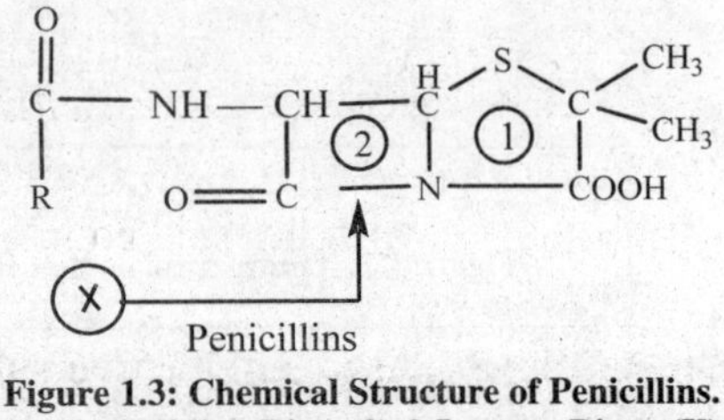

Figure 1.3: Chemical Structure of Penicillins. 1) Thiazolidine Ring; 2) β-Lactam Ring; (X) Bond which is Broken by Penicillinase.

Thiazolidine ring has a carboxyl group attached, to which salt formation occurs with Na^+ and K^+ ions. The stability of these salts is more stable than that of the parent acid. Sodium PnG is highly water-soluble, is stable in the dry state; however, its solution form rapidly deteriorates at room temperature, though it remains stable for 3 days at 4°C. Therefore, PnG solutions are recommended to prepare fresh.

1.2.4.1. Historical Background

Some historical aspects of penicillin are as follows:

1) **Alexander Fleming** was born on 6 August, 1881 in Scotland in a farming family. He studied at Regent Street Polytechnic after his family moved to London in 1895.

2) He joined St. Mary's medical school and became research assistant to famous **Sir Almroth Wright**, after he got distinction in 1906.
3) He completed his MBBS degree with gold medal in 1908 from the University of London and worked as a lecturer at St. Mart till 1914.
4) He served as captain during the World War-I and worked in battlefield hospitals in France. After the war, he returned to St. Mary in 1918 and got elected as Professor of Bacteriology in 1928.
5) In **1921**, he discovered natural antiseptic enzyme and named it as **lysozyme**. This substance existed in tissues and secretions like mucus, tears and egg-white but it did not have much effect on the strongly harmful bacteria.
6) In **1928** while experimenting on influenza virus in his laboratory in the basement of St. Mary's Hospital in London, he accidentally observed that a common fungus inhibits the growth of organism.
7) On September 28, 1928, he left one of his culture petri dishes with its lid opened for a few weeks. Consequently, a fungal spore landed on it, thus contaminating the culture. After returning, he noticed that his ***Staphylococcus*** culture was contaminated with the fungus.
8) However, he did not throw away the petri dish, instead examined it carefully. He observed that there was an inhibited bacterial growth around the mould (fungal colony).
9) He established that the mould was releasing an antibacterial substance that was spreading in the nearby area and lysing the bacteria, thus the bacterial colonies were dying.
10) He grew a pure culture and discovered that it was a Penicillium mould, which is now known as ***Penicillium notatum***.
11) He anticipated that Penicillium mould must be secreting an antibacterial substance, which he isolated in crude form of the active substance and named it **penicillin**.
12) This newly discovered active substance (penicillin) was effective even when diluted up to 800 times.
13) But the substance was also unstable and Alexander Fleming was not able to perform its isolation and purification. Therefore, he concluded that due to its instability, penicillin cannot be used clinically.
14) **Florey** and **Chain** in **1938** isolated pure form of penicillin, i.e., penicillenic by the processes of freeze-drying and chromatography.
15) **Fleming**, **Florey**, and **Chain** shared the Nobel Prize for this medicinal work on penicillin in **1945**.

1.2.4.2. Nomenclature

Penicillins are named as follows:

1) **Chemical Abstract:** Penicillins are described as 4-thia-l-azabicyclo-[3.2.0]-heptanes. Benzylpenicillin is described as 6-(2-phenylacetamido)-3,3-dimethyl-7-oxo-4-thia-l-azabiclo-[3.2.0]-hept-2-ane-2-carboxylic acid.

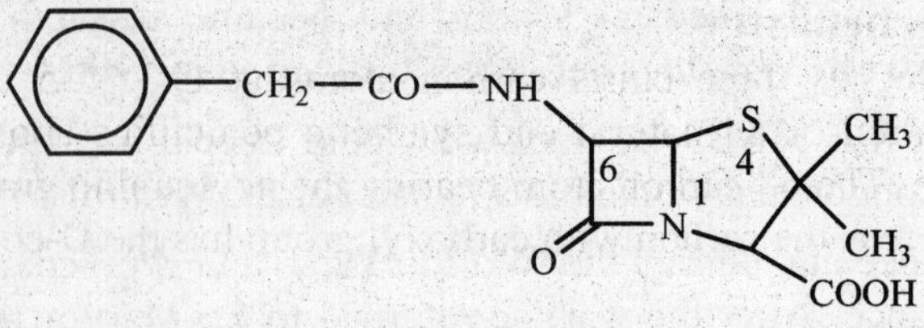

USP

2) **Penam:** The unsubstituted bicyclic ring system of penicillin is given the name penam, according to which the penicillins are described as 6-acylamino-2,2-dimethylpenam-3-carboxylates.

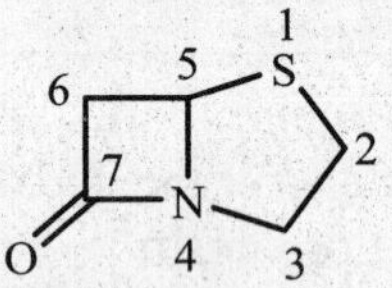

Penam

3) **Penicillanic Acid Derivatives**

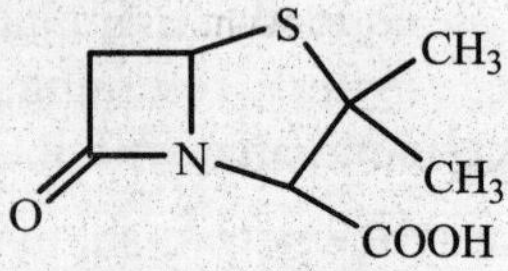

Penicillanic acid

4) **Methicillin is 2,6-Dimethoxy Benzamido Penicillanic Acid**

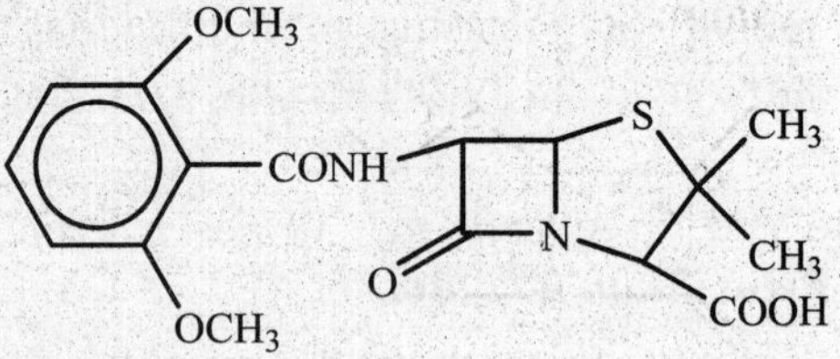

5) **Configuration:** Hydrogen atoms on the β-lactam ring, the acylamino groups are β, the carboxy group is α.

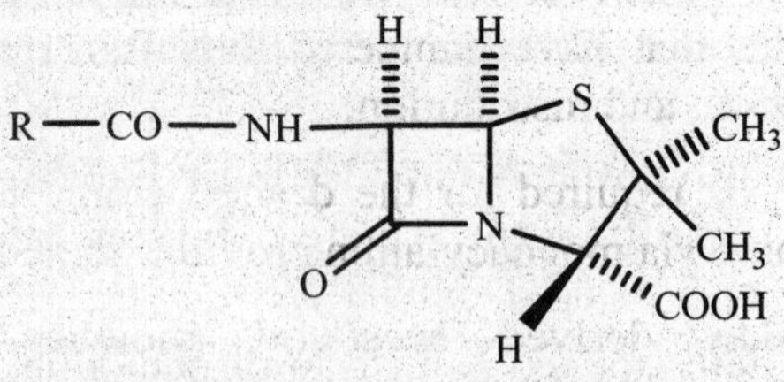

3S : 5R : 6R

6) **Penicillin Derivatives:** Semicillin is described as D-α-(sulfoamino) benzyl penicillin.

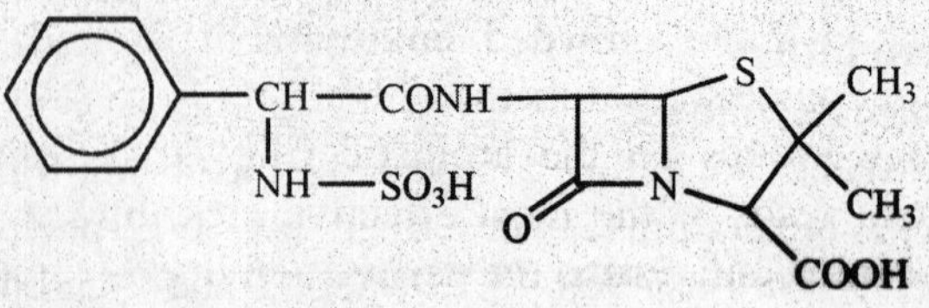

1.2.4.3. Stereochemistry

Penicillin molecule has three chiral carbon atoms at C-3, C-5 and C-6. The absolute configuration of all natural and synthetic penicillins about these three centres is the same. The 6th carbon atom bearing the acyl amino group has the L-configuration, whereas the carbon with carboxyl group has the D-configuration.

Thus, the acyl amino group and carboxyl group are *trans* to each other, with the former in α and the latter in β orientation relative to penam ring.

The absolute stereochemistry of penicillins was designated as **3S:5R:6R**. The atoms constituting 6-aminopenicillanic acid are biosynthetically derived from L-cysteine and D-valine amino acids.

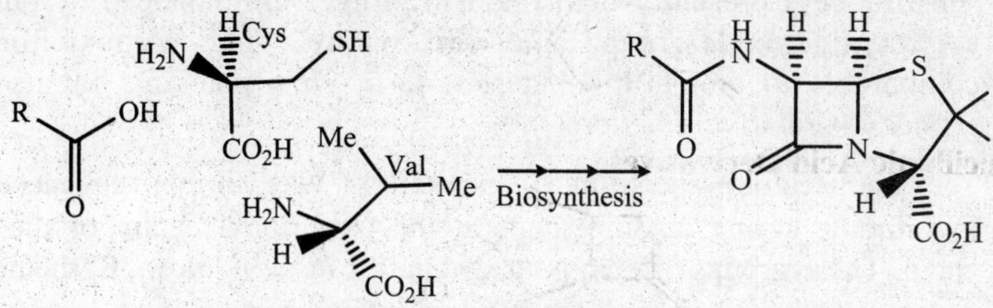

1.2.4.4. Structure-Activity Relationship

The SAR of penicillin involves substitution of the following groups at the following positions of carbon atom:

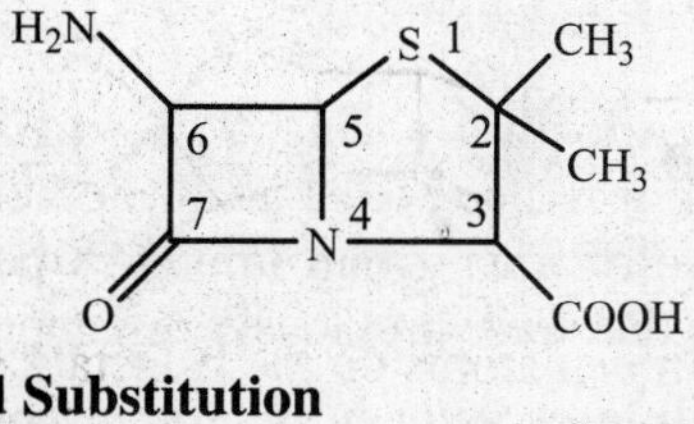

1) **C-6 Amino West-End Substitution**
   i) Design and development of the west-end substituents strengthened various weaknesses that have hampered penicillin's activity, stability, resistance, absorption, and distribution.

   ii) C-6 amine moiety is required for the desired antibacterial activity, but substitution of amine via monoacylation provides more potent congeners.

   iii) Only carboxamido derived west-end moieties are tolerated; sulphonation or phosphoramide-containing substituents lack antibacterial activity. Similarly, imide- or carbamate-containing west-end moieties are inferior.

   iv) Agents that were stable to penicillinase enzymes were formed by introducing a more crowded environment around β-lactam moiety. Methicillin contains 2,6-dimethoxy benzamido west-end and the position of methoxy groups on the aromatic ring is important; the bis ortho arrangement leads to the most effective crowding around the β-lactam carbonyl centre, and retains the desired activity.

The oxacillins have a 5-methyl-3-phenyl-4-isoxazolyl west-end substituent that results in a crowded environment around the β-lactam ring. In these compounds, the methyl and phenyl substituents are positioned near to the β-lactam system. Removal of any of the two groups increases susceptibility to penicillinases.

v) The antibacterial spectrum of penicillins was enhanced by designing more hydrophilic west-end substituents that can enhance the potency against gram-negative pathogens. Ampicillin contains a D-α-aminophenylacetamido west-end and is recognised as amino penicillins. Substituents on the phenyl ring are harmful either due to decreased hydrophilicity or due to adverse polar effects if an ionisable substituent is present. These opposing forces are balanced by putting a *para*-hydroxyl group onto the phenyl ring. Amoxicillin is comparable to ampicillin in terms of *in vitro* potency, but its oral efficacy is relatively better.

vi) The antibacterial spectrum of penicillins was further enhanced by introducing strong acidic groups at the α-carbonyl centre of the side chain. These groups offered potency against *P. aeruginosa.* Carbenicillin possesses α-carboxyphenylacetamido west-end substituent.

vii) Acylation of the ampicillin west-end amine functionality with polar groups forms cyclic urea derivatives, i.e., ureido penicillins (azlocillin) containing a five-membered cyclic urea joined to the α-amino substituent of ampicillin via N-acylation.

The activity of azlocillin against *P. aeruginosa* is more than that of carbenicillin, and it is also potent against other gram-negative pathogenic species. Presence of urea group improves penetration into these gram-negative species that were previously resistant to penicillins.

2) **Substitutions at Sulphur:** Sulphur atom is placed at position 1 of penicillin to retain the desired antibacterial activity.
3) **C-2 Substituents:** The geminal dimethyl group at C-2 is characteristic of the penicillin.
4) **C-3 Substituents:** Derivatisation of the C-3 carboxylic acid group is not tolerated unless the free penicillin carboxylic acid can be generated *in vivo*. Doubly activated penicillin esters, such as alkanoyloxyalkyl congeners undergo rapid *in vivo* cleavage and generate active penicillin, **e.g.,** pivampicillin and becampicillin.
5) **Variation at N-4:** Nitrogen atom at the ring junction is essential for antibacterial activity. It contributes to the reactivity of β-lactam carbonyl centre.

1.2.4.5. Chemical Degradation

In strongly acidic solutions (pH<3), penicillin undergoes a complex series of reactions and produce various inactive degradation products. Penicillinase enzyme hydrolyses the β-lactam ring and produces inactive **penicilloic acid**.

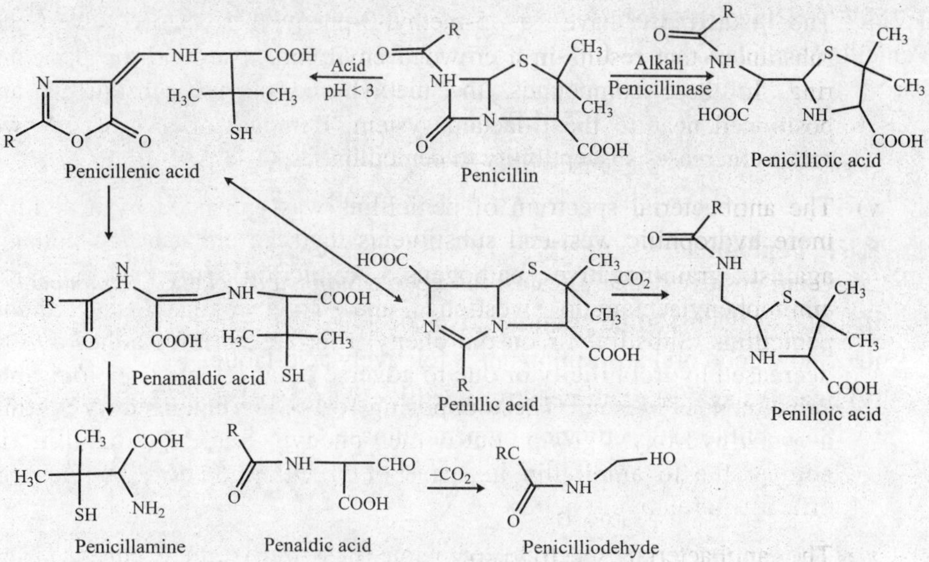

Figure 1.4: Chemical Degradation of Penicillin's

Acid-catalysed degradation of penicillin in stomach leads to its poor oral absorption. Thus, efforts to obtain penicillin with improved pharmacokinetic and microbiologic profile require to find acyl functionalities that minimise sensitivity of β-lactam ring to acid hydrolysis, and also maintain the antibacterial activity.

On substituting an electron-withdrawing group at the α-position of benzyl penicillin, the penicillin gets stabilised to acid-catalysed hydrolysis. The increased stability offered by such electron-withdrawing groups decreases the reactivity of the side chain amide carbonyl oxygen atom towards participation in β-lactam ring opening to form penicillenic acid.

1.2.4.6. Mechanism of Action

Penicillin acts in the following ways:

1) **Inhibition of Cell Wall Synthesis by Blocking Transpeptidation:** Penicillin acts as an alternative substrate and binds to Penicillin Binding Protein (PBP) receptor present on the surface of bacterial cell wall. PBP is the receptor for substrate peptidoglycan precursor in bacteria. After binding, penicillin inhibits transpeptidase that further inhibits cell wall synthesis.

2) **Activation of Autolytic Enzymes:**
   i) Penicillin activates the autolytic enzymes of bacteria. These enzymes after activation destroy bacteria by creating lesions on them.
   ii) Autolysins, present in bacterial cell wall, maintain the appropriate shape and size of cell and also facilitate cell division. Activity of autolysin is regulated by cell wall and teichoic acid.
   iii) Penicillin destroys the bacterial cell wall and disintegrates teichoic acid, thus activating autolysin and lysing the bacterial cell.

1.2.4.7. Classification

Penicillins are classified as follows:

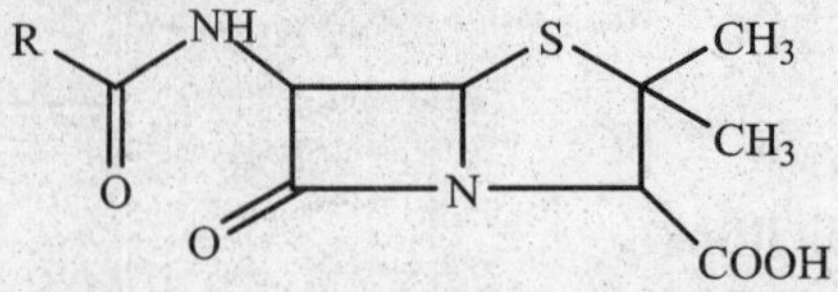

1) **Early Penicillins**
   - i) Gram-positive potency against susceptible *Staphylococci* and *Streptococci.*
   - ii) Active against some gram-positive cocci.
   - iii) Show good oral absorption but is relatively acid-labile.
   - iv) Inactive against gram-negative bacilli.
   - v) Susceptible to deactivation by penicillinase.

Penicillin G 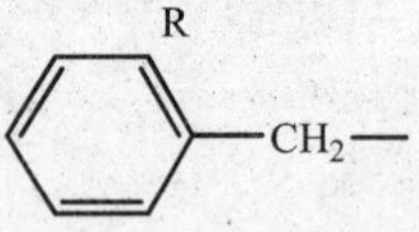

Penicillin V 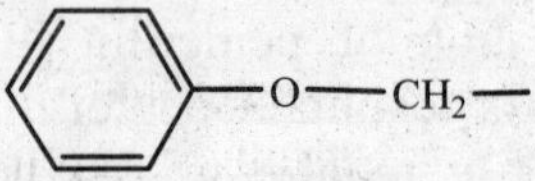

Phenethicillin 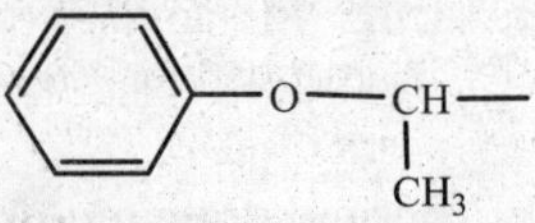

2) **Penicillinase-Resistant Penicillins:**
   - i) Reduced susceptibility to penicillinase.
   - ii) Active against microorganisms resistant to early penicillins.
   - iii) Oxacillins show good oral activity.
   - iv) Inadequate spectrum against many gram-negative species.

Methicillin 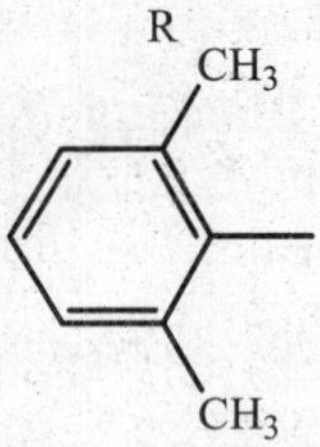

Oxacillins 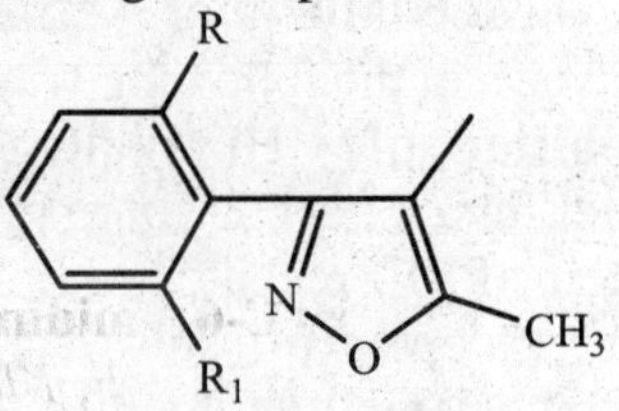

R, R_1 = H, Halogen

3) **Broad-Spectrum Penicillins**
   - i) Shows enhanced spectrum of activity against some gram-negative bacteria.
   - ii) Retains gram-positive potency.
   - iii) Shows good oral absorption.
   - iv) Ampicillin can be given via intravenous and intramuscular route.
   - v) Amoxycillin is an exceptional oral agent.
   - vi) Prodrug esters (of ampicillin) enhance the systemic drug levels.
   - **vii) Ineffective against *Pseudomonas aeruginosa.***

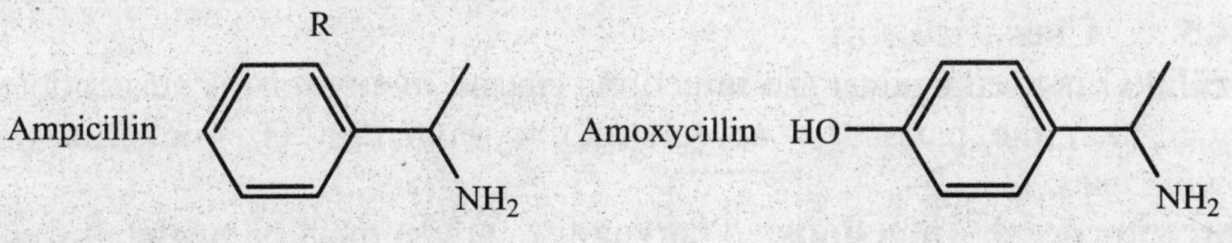

4) **Anti-Pseudomonal Penicillins**
   i) Shows enhanced spectrum of activity against many pathogenic gram-negative bacteria.
   ii) Reduced gram-positive potency.
   iii) Active against *P. aeruginosa.*
   iv) Shows good oral absorption.
   v) Prodrug esters of carbenicillin enhance systemic drug levels.

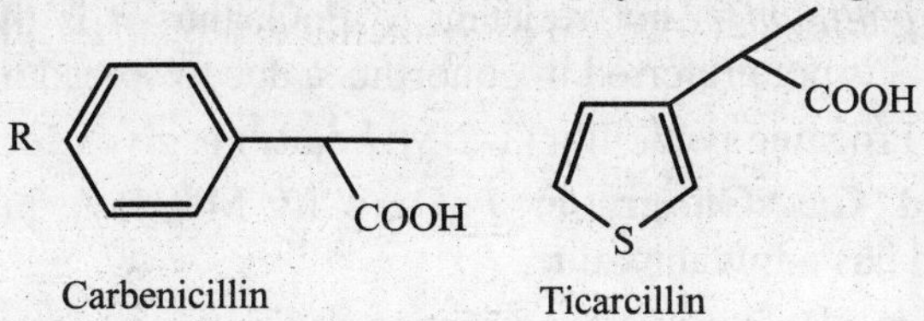

5) **Broad-Spectrum Ureido Penicillins**
   i) Shows enhanced spectrum of activity against *P. aeruginosa*, expanded activity against *Klebsiella*, *Serratia*, and *Proteus*.
   ii) Potent against gram-positive bacteria, but not effective against penicillinase producers.
   iii) Exhibits a good pharmacokinetic profile.

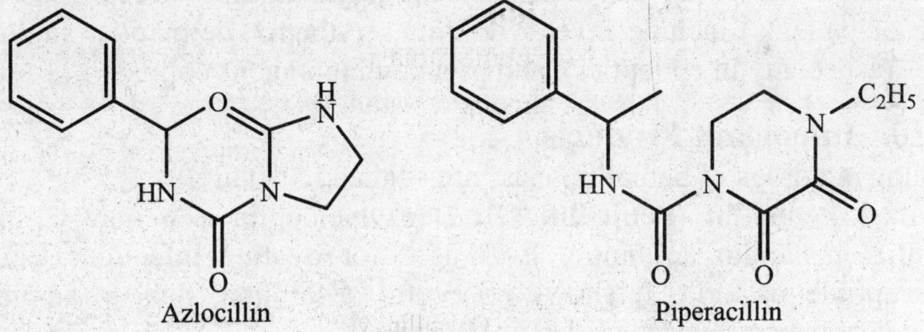

6) **Penicillin with a C-6 Amidino West-End**
   i) Active against *E. coli*, *Klebsiella*, *Shigella*, *Salmonella*, and many other resistant species.
   ii) Inactive against *P. aeruginosa*.
   iii) Prodrug esters enhance the systemic drug levels.

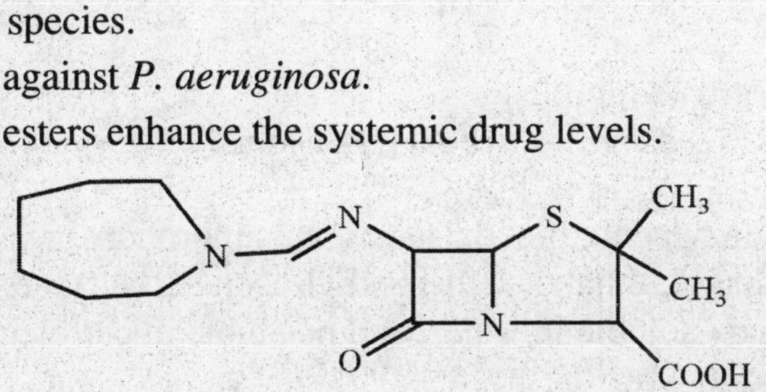

Mecillinam

1.2.4.8. Uses

Penicillin G is used against the infections caused by organisms susceptible to it, provided that the patient is not allergic to Penicillin G. Penicillin has the following uses:

1) **Streptococcal Infections:** Pharyngitis, otitis media, scarlet fever, and rheumatic fever respond to ordinary doses of PnG given for 7-10 days. Sub-Acute Bacterial Endocarditis (SABE) caused by *Streptococcus viridans* or *Streptococcus faecalis* is treated with high doses (10-20 MU i.v. daily) of PnG along with gentamicin for 2-6 weeks.
2) **Pneumococcal Infections:** PnG (3-6 MU i.v.) is given in every 6 hours.
3) **Meningococcal Infections:** These conditions are treated with intravenous injection of high doses.
4) **Syphilis:** *T. pallidum* is not resistant to PnG, thus it is the drug of choice. However, PnG is not preferred in gonorrhoea due to spread of resistant strains.
5) **Diphtheria:** Procaine penicillin (1-2 MU daily) is given for 10 days.
6) **Tetanus and Gas Gangrene:** PnG (6-12 MU/day) kills the causative organism and has adjuvant value.
7) Penicillin G is also the drug of choice for anthrax, actinomycosis, trench mouth, rat bite fever, and infections caused by *Listeria monocytogenes* and *Pasteurella multocida*.

1.2.4.9. Adverse Effects

Common adverse drug reactions of penicillins (observed in ≥1% of patients) include diarrhoea, hypersensitivity, nausea, rash, neurotoxicity, urticaria, and superinfection (including candidiasis). Infrequent adverse effects (observed in 0.1-1% of patients) include fever, vomiting, erythema, dermatitis, angioedema, seizures (especially in epileptics), and pseudomembranous colitis.

1.2.4.10. Important Products

The following drugs of penicillin class are studied in detail:

1) **Benzyl Penicillin (Penicillin G):** Benzylpenicillin is a narrow spectrum natural penicillin antibiotic. It is used for treating infections caused by susceptible bacteria. It shows poor oral absorption, thus is administered intravenously or intramuscularly.

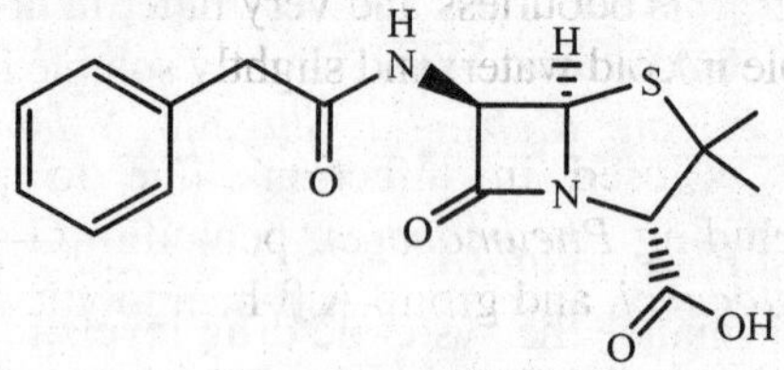

Benzylpenicillin

Properties: Benzylpenicillin exists as an amorphous white powder. It is soluble in methanol, ethanol, ether, ethyl acetate, benzene, chloroform, and acetone; sparingly soluble in water; and insoluble in petroleum ether.

Uses: Benzylpenicillin is used in septicaemia, meningitis, pericarditis, endocarditis, and severe pneumonia caused by penicillin G-susceptible microorganisms.

2) **Phenoxy Methyl Penicillin (Penicillin V):** Penicillin V is obtained from natural sources. It is better than other penicillin because it is not affected by the action of gastric juices.

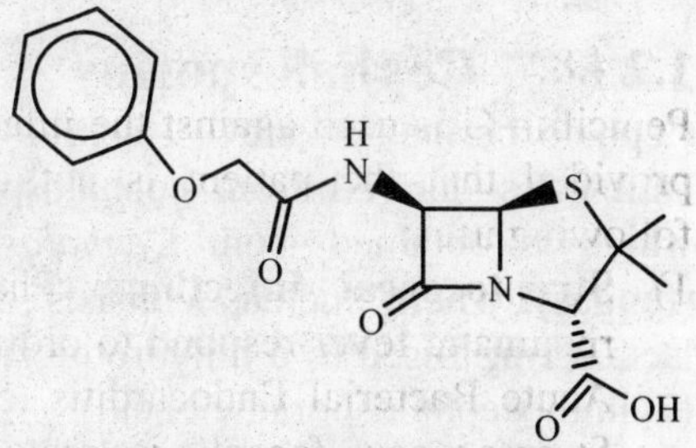

Phenoxy Methyl Penicillin

Properties: Penicillin V exists as a white crystalline powder. It has a bitter taste and is odourless. It is highly soluble in water; soluble in polar organic solvents; and practically insoluble in vegetable oils and liquid petrolatum.

Uses: Penicillin V is used in mild to moderately severe infections (**e.g.,** dental infection, middle ear infections, rheumatic fever, scarlet fever, heart infections, skin infections, and upper and lower respiratory tract infections).

3) **Ampicillin:** Ampicillin is a broad spectrum penicillin antibiotic of semi-synthetic origin. It is not hydrolysed by various β-lactamases, and it shows bactericidal activity.

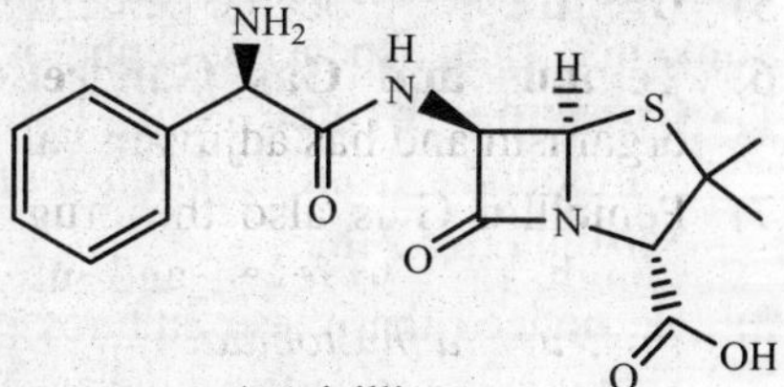

Ampicillin

Properties: Ampicillin exists as a white, odourless, crystalline, anhydrous powder. It is soluble in methanol; sparingly soluble in water and ethanol; and insoluble in ether, ethyl acetate, petroleum ether, benzene, and chloroform.

Uses: Ampicillin is used in gastrointestinal infections, respiratory infections, UTIs, and meningitis caused by *E. coli*, *P. mirabilis, Enterococci*, *Shigella*, *S. typhosa* and other *Salmonella*, non-penicillinase-producing *N. gonorrhoeae*, *H. influenza*, and *Staphylococci*.

4) **Cloxacillin:** Cloxacillin is a chlorinated derivative of oxacillin and a semi-synthetic antibiotic.

Properties: The sodium salt of cloxacillin exists as a white crystalline hygroscopic powder. It is odourless and very bitter in taste. It is freely soluble in water; highly soluble in cold water; and slightly soluble in chloroform.

Uses: Cloxacillin is used in infections due to penicillinase-producing *Staphylococci*, including *Pneumococci*, penicillin G-sensitive and penicillin G-resistant *Staphylococci*, and group A β-haemolytic *Streptococci*.

5) **Carbenicillin:** Carbenicillin is a semi-synthetic, broad spectrum penicillin. Since it gets affected by gastric juices and penicillinase enzyme, it is administered via parenteral route.

Properties: Carbenicillin exists as a white coloured, water-soluble powder.

Uses: Carbenicillin is used in acute and chronic infections of upper and lower urinary tract, and asymptomatic bacteriuria caused by certain strains of bacteria.

1.2.5. Cephalosporins

Cephalosporins are semi-synthetic antibiotics derived from cephalosporin-C, which is obtained from *Cephalosporium* (fungus). Their nucleus consists of a β-lactam ring fused to a dihydrothiazine ring (7-aminocephalosporanic acid). A large number of semi-synthetic compounds are produced by adding different side chains at position 7 of β-lactam ring (this alters the spectrum of activity) and position 3 of dihydrothiazine ring (this affects the pharmacokinetic profile). Cephalosporins are categorised into 4 generations. This categorisation has a sequence of development, and also considers the overall antibacterial spectrum and potency.

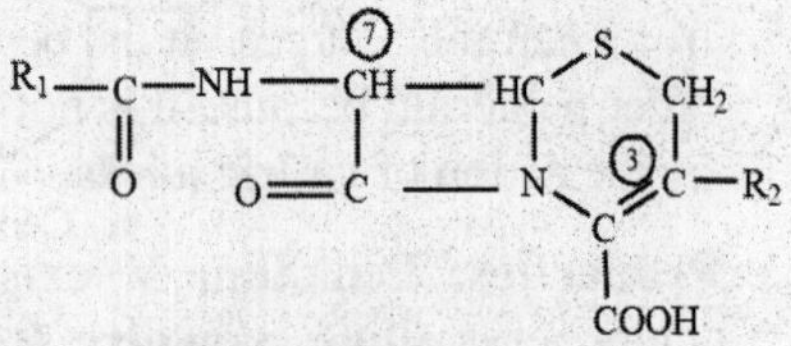

Cephalosporin

1.2.5.1. Historical Background

Some historical aspects of cephalosporin are as follows:

1) **Giuseppe Brotzu** (an Italian scientist) first isolated cephalosporin compounds from *Cephalosporium acremonium* cultures from a sewer in Sardinia in **1948**.
2) He noticed that these cultures produced substances that were effective against *Salmonella typhi* (causative agent of typhoid fever) and had β-lactamase.
3) Cephalosporin C was isolated by **Guy Newton** and **Edward Abraham** at the Sir William Dunn School of Pathology at the University of Oxford.
4) Modification of the 7-Amino Cephalosporanic Acid (7-ACA) side chains led to the development of antibiotic agents.
5) **Eli Lilly** launched the first agent **cephalothin** (cefalotin) in **1964**.
6) Alarmed by the need to keep ahead of rapidly mutating bacterial strains, researchers since developed 4th generation cephalosporins.
7) **Eli Lilly** introduced Keflex (generic name Cephalexin) in January **1971**.
8) In January **1996**, a progressive reintroduction of cephalosporins including the novel 4th generation cephalosporin (cefepime) was made.
9) In February **2003**, Ranbaxy laboratories launched their high-end cephalosporin or cefprozil under the brand name Refzil.
10) In 2005, despite the risk that a patient with history of penicillin allergy will experience a reaction to a 1st generation cephalosporin not more than 0.5%, 2nd generation cephalosporin not more than 0.2% and a 3rd generation cephalosporin practically nil in at least 25 studies.
11) In February **2010**, U.S researchers announced that most of the patients with a history of penicillin allergy can safely take cephalosporins.

1.2.5.2. Nomenclature

Cephalosporins are named as follows:

1) **Chemical Abstracts:** Cephalothin is 3-(acetoxy methyl)-8-oxo-7-(2-thienly) **acetamido-5thia-l-aza-bicyclo-oct-2ene-2carboxylic acid.**

2) **Cepham Derivatives:** Cepham is the unsubstituted bicyclic lactam.

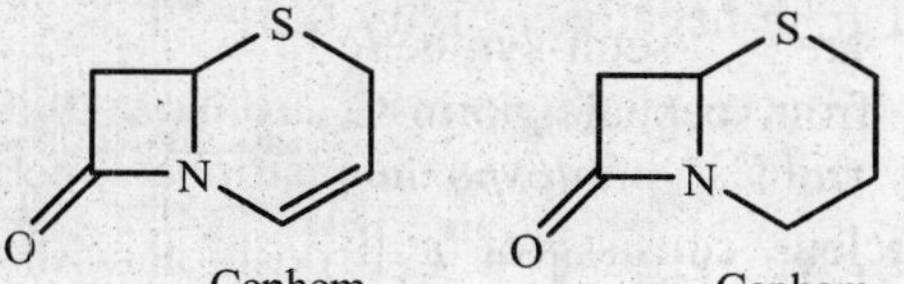

1.2.5.3. Structure-Activity Relationship

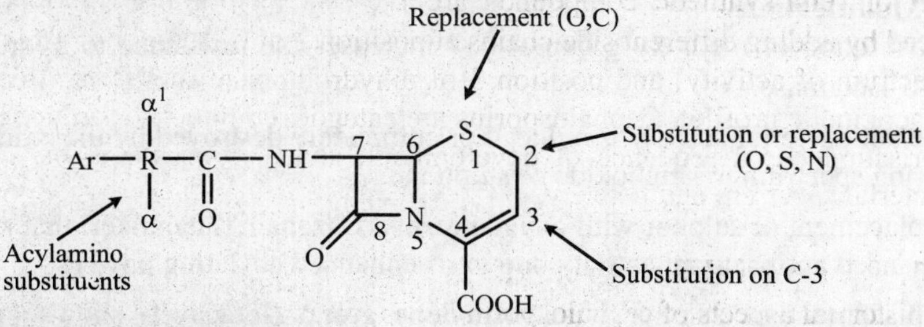

7-Acylamio Substitution

1) Addition of amino group and hydrogen atom at α and α_1 position forms a basic compound that gets protonated under acidic conditions of stomach. Ammonium ion improves the stability of β-lactam ring, thus rendering cephalosporins orally active. Acylation of the amino group increases the activity of cephalosporins against gram-positive bacteria and decreases the activity against gram negative bacteria.
2) When new acyl groups are derived from carboxylic acids, cephalosporins show a good spectrum of antibacterial action for gram-positive bacteria.
3) Substitutions on the aromatic ring phenyl (that increases lipophilicity) increase gram-positive activity and reduce gram-negative activity.
4) Phenyl ring in the side chain can be replaced with other heterocycles having improved spectrum of activity and pharmacokinetic profile (thiophene, tetrazole, furan, pyridine, and aminothiazoles).
5) The stability of L-isomer of an α-amino α_1-hydrogen derivative of cephalosporins was 30-40 times more than that of D-isomer. Adding methoxy oxime at α and α_1 position increases the stability to 100-fold. Presence of catechol groups also enhances activity against *Pseudomonas aeruginosa*, and retains some gram-positive activity, which is unused for a catechol cephalosporin.
6) These compounds penetrate into the cell by using the bacterial ion β-dependent ion transport system. When the lipophilicity of the side chain and effects of polar α-substituents (OH, NH_2, SO_3H, and COOH) are increased, the gram negative activity reduces.

Modification in the C-3 Substitution

The pharmacokinetic and pharmacodynamics properties of cephalosporins depend on C-3 substituents. Modification at C-3 position reduces cephalosporins degradation.

1) **The benzoyl ester improves the gram-positive activity, but reduces the gram-negative activity.**

2) Pyridine, imidazole replaced acetoxy group by azide ion yields a derivative with diminished gram-negative activity.
3) Displacement of 3-acetoxy group with aromatic thiols enhances the gram-negative activity and also improves the pharmacokinetic properties.
4) Replacement of acetoxy group at C-3 position with CH_3 and Cl results in orally active compounds.

Other Modifications

1) Substitution of methoxy group at C-7 increases the resistance to hydrolysis by β-lactamase.
2) The antibacterial activity is reduced or completely destroyed by the oxidation of ring spectrum to sulphoxide or sulphone.
3) Replacement of sulphur with oxygen forms oxazepam (latamoxet) that shows enhanced antibacterial activity due to its enhanced acylating power.
4) Replacement of sulphur with methylene group (loracavet) shows greater chemical stability and a longer half-life.
5) The carboxyl group at C-4 can be converted into ester prodrugs to enhance the bioavailability of cephalosporins, and also to make them orally active.
6) The olefinic linkage at C-3 and C-4 influences the antibacterial activity and their activity is lost due to the ionisation of double bond to 2nd and 3rd positions.

1.2.5.4. Chemical Degradation

Cephalosporins in comparison to penicillins are more stable to hydrolytic degradation. However, they undergo various chemical and enzymatic conversions, whose specific nature depends on the side-chain at C-7 and the substituent on C-3.

If a good leaving group is present at C-3, spontaneous expulsion of the 3'-substituent occurs due to hydrolysis of C-N bond of β-lactam nucleus by a nucleophile or β-lactamase. Thus, stability of desacetyl cefotaxime to hydrolysis is more in comparison to that of cefotaxime.

If a leaving group is not present at C-3, the cephalosporins are more acid-stable and orally active. Hence, absorption of cephalexin with a methyl group at C-3 is much better than that of cephaloglycin with a acetoxymethyl group at C-3. Both these compounds however have phenylglycyl side-chain at the C-7. The nature of substituents at C-7 helps in determining the facility with which the reactive β-lactam bond is hydrolysed or broken either chemically or enzymatically, thus leading to degradation of cephalosporin C.

Given below are some conditions under which cephalosporin degrade:

1) **In Strong Acid Solution:** In the presence of esterase/acid, cephalosporin-C gives desacetyl cephalosporin and an inactive desacetyl cephalosporin (lactone).

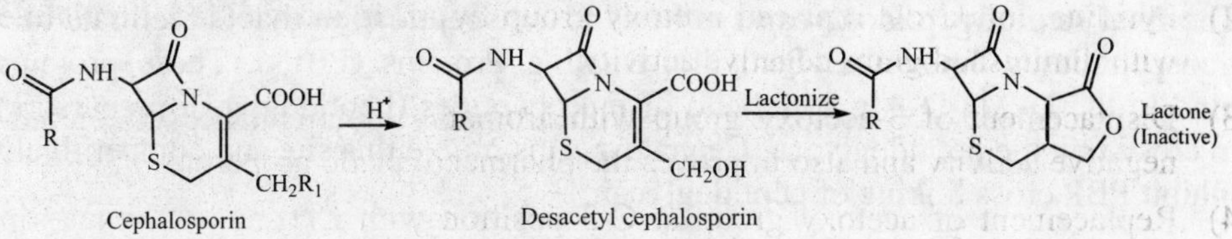

2) **In the Presence of β-Lactamase:** Cephalosporin C is degraded into cephalosporic acid, anhydrodesacetyl cephalosporic acid, and desacetyl cephalosporic acid by β-lactamase or cephalosporanase enzyme. These acidic products undergo further breakdown into many other fragmented and rearranged products.

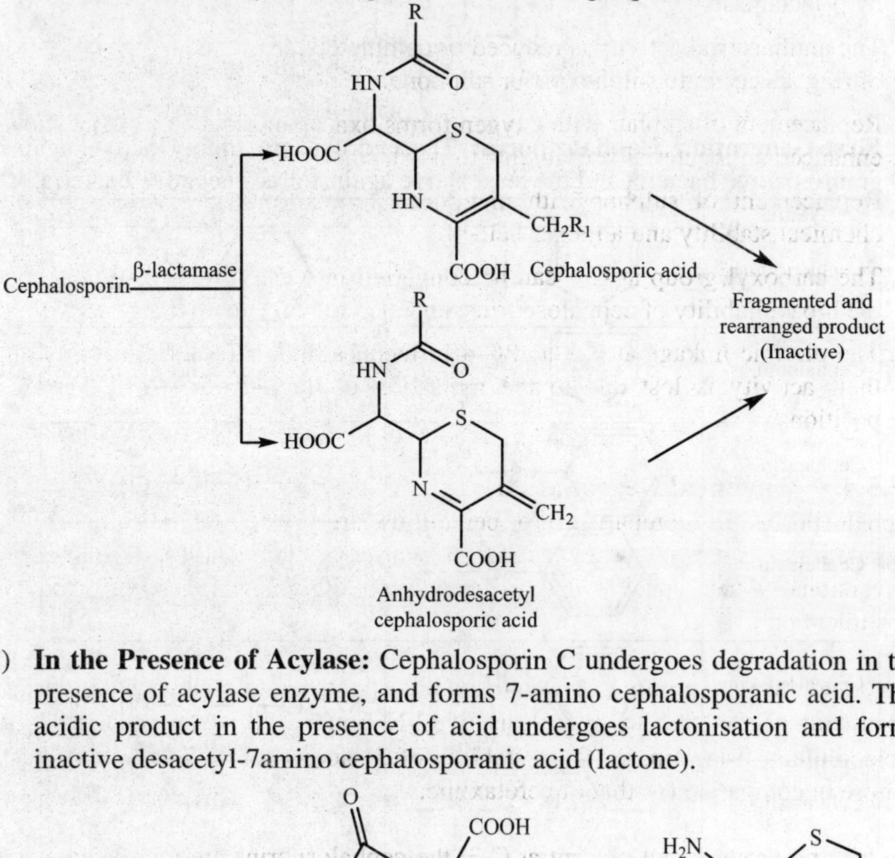

3) **In the Presence of Acylase:** Cephalosporin C undergoes degradation in the presence of acylase enzyme, and forms 7-amino cephalosporanic acid. This acidic product in the presence of acid undergoes lactonisation and forms inactive desacetyl-7amino cephalosporanic acid (lactone).

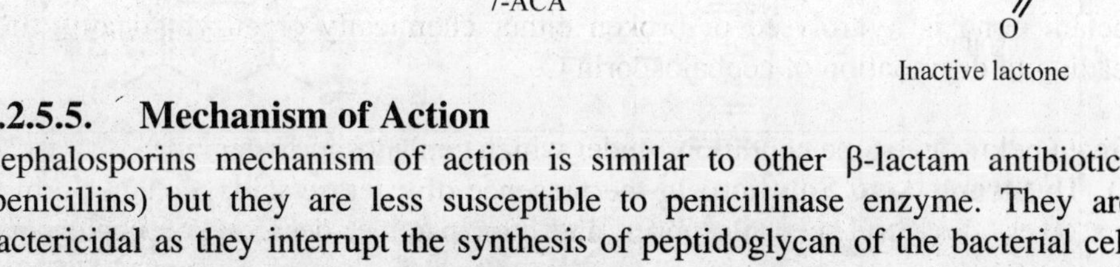

1.2.5.5. Mechanism of Action

Cephalosporins mechanism of action is similar to other β-lactam antibiotics (penicillins) but they are less susceptible to penicillinase enzyme. They are bactericidal as they interrupt the synthesis of peptidoglycan of the bacterial cell wall. The peptidoglycan layer is important for structural integrity of the cell wall.

The final step of peptidoglycan synthesis is transpeptidation that is facilitated by transpeptidases, known as Penicillin-Binding Proteins (PBPs). These proteins bind to the D-Ala-D-Ala at the end of muropeptides (peptidoglycan precursors) to cross-link the peptidoglycan. Cephalosporins mimic this site and competitively inhibit PBP cross linking of peptidoglycan.

1.2.5.6. Classification

Cephalosporins are classified into the following generations:

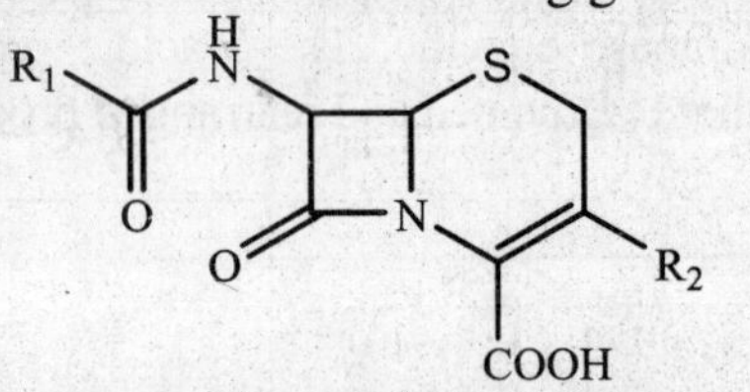

1) **First-Generation Cephalosporin:** These drugs are highly active against gram-positive bacteria and the least active against gram-negative bacteria.

Names	R_1	R_2
Cephaloridine	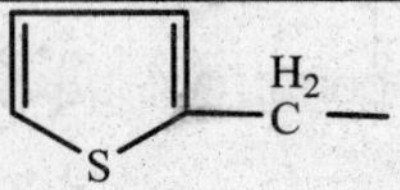	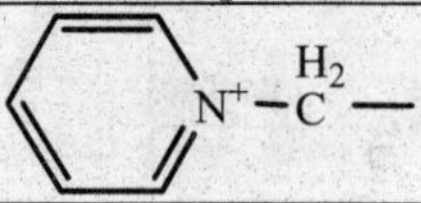
Cephalothin	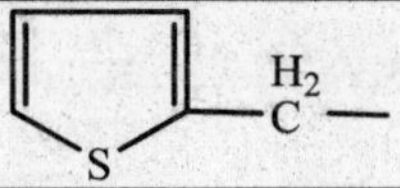	$-H_2C-O-C(=O)-CH_3$
Cephapirin	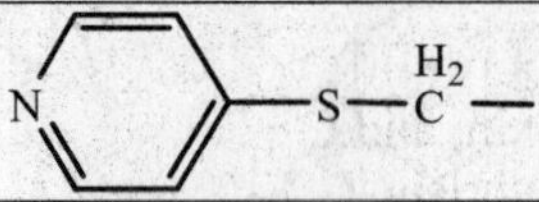	$-H_2C-O-C(=O)-CH_3$
Cephalexin	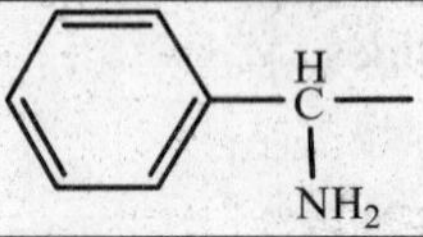	$-CH_3$
Cephaloglycine	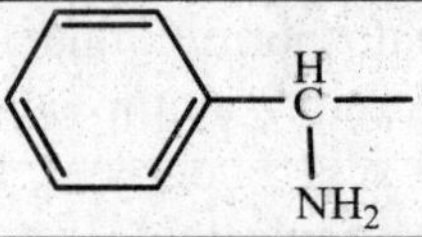	$-H_2C-O-C(=O)-CH_3$
Cefadroxil	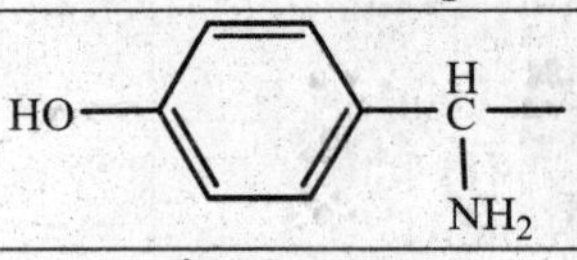	$-CH_3$
Cephradine		$-CH_3$
Cefazolin	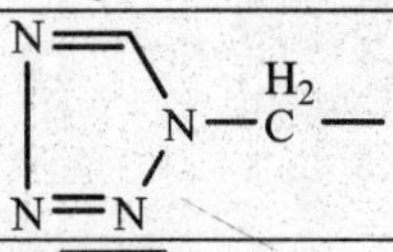	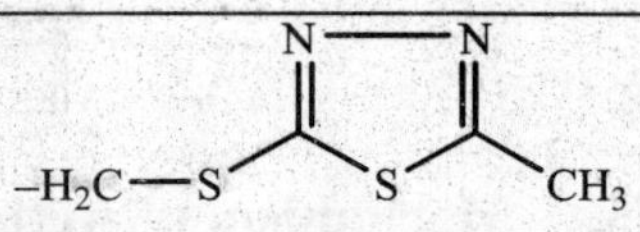
Cephradine		$-CH_3$

2) **Second-Generation Cephalosporin:** These drugs in comparison to the first-generation drugs are more active against gram-negative bacteria.

Names	R_1	R_2
Cefamandole	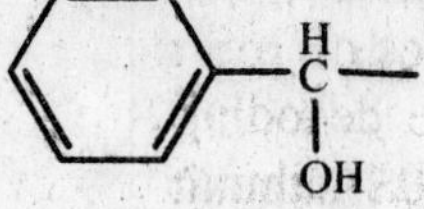	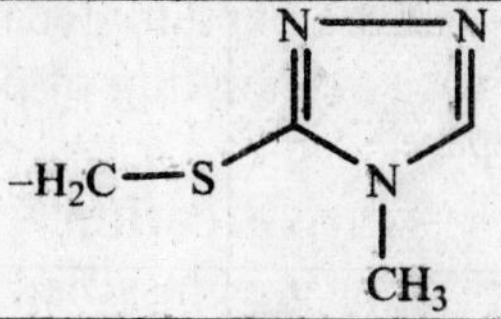
Cefoxitin	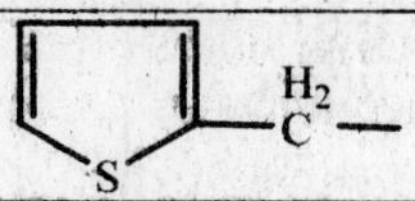	$-H_2C-O-C(=O)-NH_2$
Cefuroxime	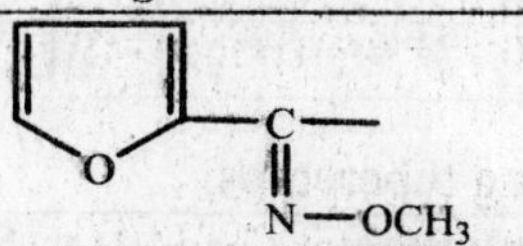	$-H_2C-O-C(=O)-NH_2$
Cefaclor	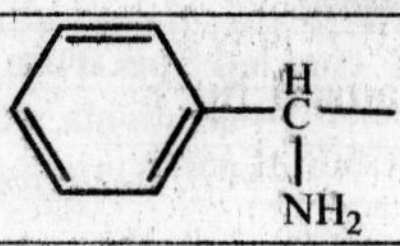	–Cl
Cefonicid	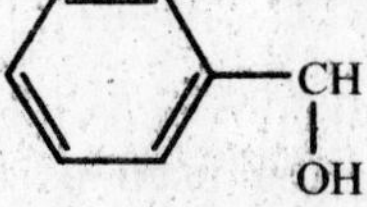	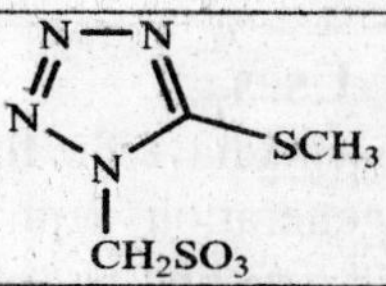

3) **Third-Generation Cephalosporin:** These drugs in comparison to the first-generation drugs are less active against gram-positive bacteria, but have an expanded activity spectrum o against gram-negative bacteria.

Names	R_1	R_2
Ceftizoxime	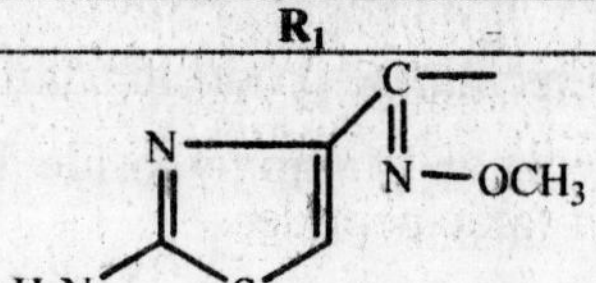	–H
Cefotaxime	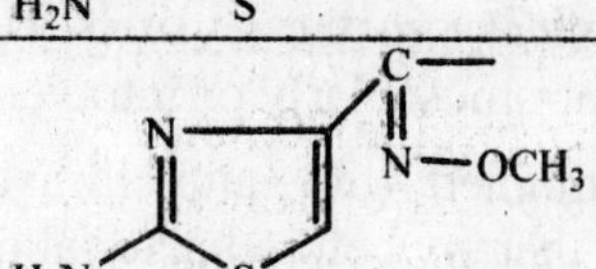	$-H_2C-O-C(=O)-CH_3$
Ceftazidime	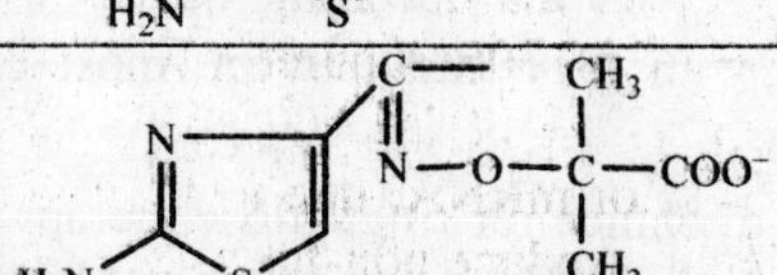	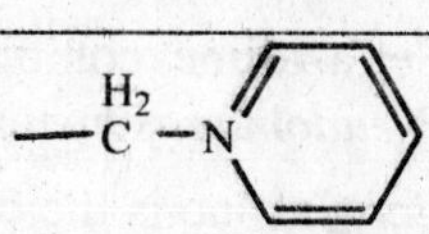
Ceftriaxone	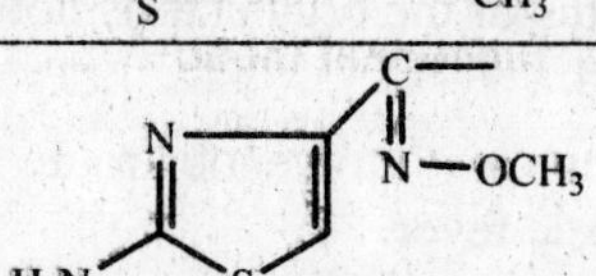	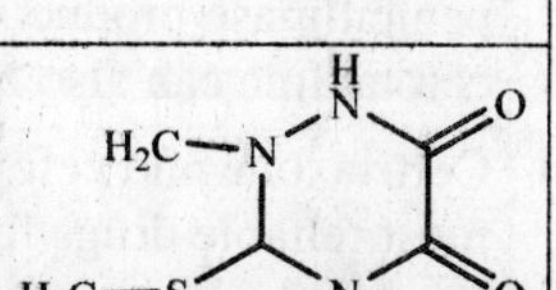
Cefmenoxime	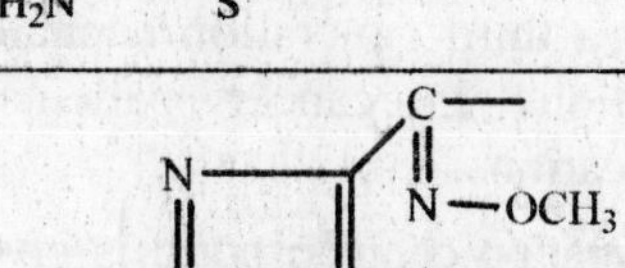	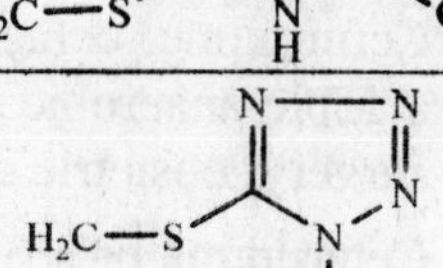

4) **Fourth Generation:** These drugs are **extended spectrum antibiotics**, and are resistant to β-lactamases.

Names	R_1	R_2
Cefepime	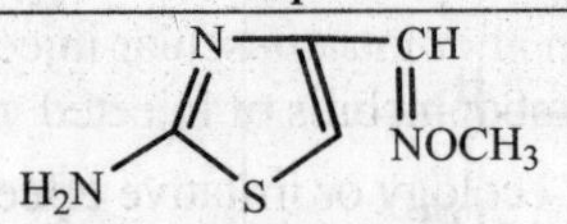	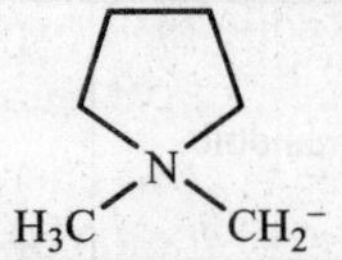
Cefpirome	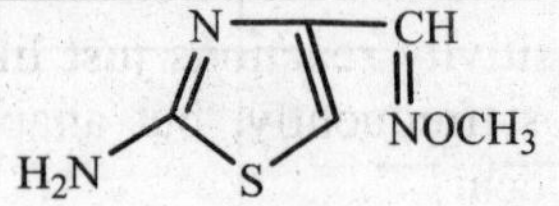	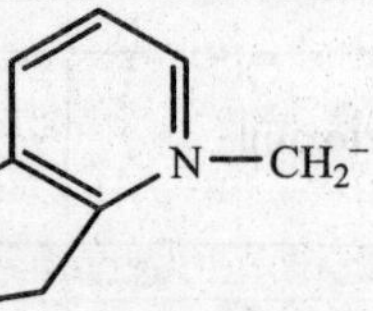

5) **Fifth Generation**

Cephalosporin	Dose	Route	Dosing Interval	Spectrum
5th Generation (Extended Spectrum)				
Ceftaroline	600mg	IV	12 hours	Pneumonia, skin and soft tissue infections.
Ceftobiprole	500mg	IV	12 hours	Methicillin-resistant Staphylococcus aureus.

1.2.5.7. Uses

Cephalosporins have the following uses:

1) First generation cephalosporins can be used as an alternative to PnG in allergic patients (but not who had anaphylactic reaction).
2) Cefuroxime, cefotaxime, and ceftriaxone are used in respiratory, urinary, and soft tissue infections caused by gram-negative organisms, especially *Klebsiella*, *Proteus*, *Enterobacter*, and *Serratia*.
3) Cephalosporins are used in penicillinase-producing *Staphylococcal* infections.
4) Cephalosporin combined with an aminoglycoside is used in Septicaemias caused by gram-negative organisms.
5) Cefazolin is given in surgical prosthesis such as artificial heart valves, artificial joints, etc. either intramuscularly or intravenously.
6) Cefotaxime/ceftriaxone combined with ampicillin or vancomycin is given intravenously for empirical therapy before bacterial diagnosis.
7) Ceftazidime combined with gentamicin is the most effective therapy for *Pseudomonas meningitis*.
8) Ceftriaxone is the drug of choice for single dose therapy of gonorrhoea if the penicillinase producing status of the organism is not known. Cefuroxime and cefotaxime can also be used.
9) Ceftriaxone and cefoperazone via intravenous route are the fastest acting and most reliable drugs for enteric fever.
10) Cefuroxime, cefaclor, or a third generation cephalosporin is used in mixed aerobic-anaerobic infections in cancer patients undergoing colorectal surgery, obstetric complications.
11) **Ceftazidime or a 3rd generation cephalosporin is given either alone or with an aminoglycoside in prophylaxis and treatment of infections in neutropenic patients.**

1.2.5.8. Adverse Effects

In general, cephalosporins are well-tolerated, but are more toxic than penicillins. They show the following adverse effects:

1) Many individuals experience pain after intramuscular injection of cephalosporins (especially of cephalothin). Thrombophlebitis of injected vein can also occur.
2) Diarrhoea due to alteration of gut ecology or irritative effect commonly occurs on oral administration of cephradine and parenteral administration of cefoperazone.
3) Cephalosporins cause hypersensitivity reactions just like penicillin, but to a lesser extent. Rashes occur most frequently, but anaphylaxis, angioedema, asthma, and urticaria may also occur.
4) Cephaloridine causes nephrotoxicity, thus is no more in use. Cephalothin and other cephalosporins cause a low-grade nephrotoxicity.
5) Cephalosporins with a methylthiotetrazole or similar substitution at C-3 (cefoperazone and ceftriaxone) cause bleeding due to hypoprothrombinaemia (commonly in patients with cancer, intra-abdominal infection, or renal failure).
6) Ceftazidime and some other cephalosporins rarely cause neutropenia and thrombocytopenia.

1.2.5.9. Important Products

The following drug of Cephalosporins class are studied in detail:

1) **Cephalexin:** Cephalexin is a semi-synthetic antimicrobial cephalosporin. It is less potent than cephaloridine or cephalothin. It is active against gram-positive as well as gram-negative bacteria.

   Properties: Cephalexin exists as a white or cream coloured, crystalline powder with a characteristic odour. It is slightly soluble in alcohol and chloroform; and soluble in water.

   Uses: Cephalexin is used in respiratory tract infections caused by *Streptococcus pneumoniae* and *Streptococcus pyrogens*; in otitis media caused by *Haemophilus influenzae*, *Streptococcus pneumoniae*, *Streptococcus pyogenes*, *Staphylococcus aureus*, and *Moraxella catarrhalis*; in skin infections caused by *Staphylococcus aureus* and/or *Streptococcus pyogenes*; in bone infections caused by *Staphylococcus aureus* and/or *Proteus mirabilis*; and in genitourinary tract infections, such as acute prostatitis, caused by *Escherichia coli*, *Klebsiella pneumoniae*, and *Proteus mirabilis*.

2) **Cephaloridine:** Cephaloridine is derived from cephalosporin C and is its 1st generation semi-synthetic derivative. It is different from other cephalosporins as it occurs as a Zwitter ion.

   Properties: Cephaloridine exists as a white coloured crystalline powder which is either odourless or have a slight odour of pyridine. It is soluble in water; and insoluble in most organic solvents.

   Uses: Cephaloridine is used in lower respiratory tract infections. It is highly effective in pneumococcal pneumonia. It is clinically and bacteriologically **successful in *Staphylococcal* and *Streptococcal* infections.**

3) **Cephalothin:** Cephalothin is a semi-synthetic, 1st generation cephalosporin antibiotic and also a β-lactam with bactericidal activity.

Properties: Cephalothin exists as a white crystalline odourless powder. It is soluble in water; and insoluble in most organic solvents.

Uses: Cephalothin is used for preventing infections during surgery and for treating various infections related to blood, bones, joints, respiratory tract, skin, and urinary tract.

1.2.6. Monobactams

Monobactams are a structurally-related class of β-lactam antibiotics. They are resistant to β-lactamases. Monobactams are active against β-lactamase producing gram-negative bacteria (*Enteric*, *Pseudomonas*, and *Serratia*). They show extended spectrum of activity against gram-negative bacteria than penicillin. However, they are inactive gram-positive bacteria and anaerobes. Individuals allergic to penicillin are non-allergic to monobactams. Monobactams binds to PBPs and inhibit transpeptidase activity. This causes filamentation of bacteria, thus killing them later.

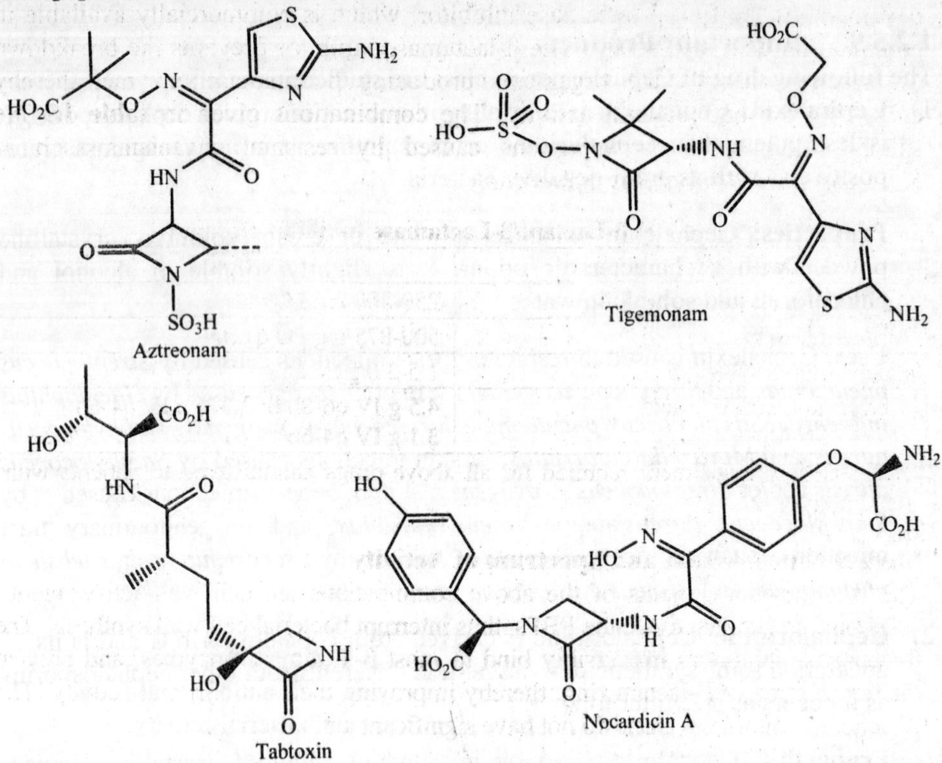

Figure 1.5: Monobactams

Aztreonam is the most common **example** of monobactam. It is a monocyclic β-lactam antibiotic isolated from *Chromobacterium violaceum*. It is resistant to β-lactamases and is used in infections related to the meninges, bladder, and kidneys caused by gram-negative bacteria. **It may cause a superinfection with gram-positive organisms.**

Mechanism of Action
Aztreonam is bactericidal and inhibits the bacterial cell wall synthesis due to its high affinity for Penicillin Binding Protein 3 (PBP3). It binds to PBP3 and inhibits the third and last stage of bacterial cell wall synthesis. Cell lysis is mediated by bacterial cell wall autolytic enzymes (such as autolysins). Aztreonam may also interfere with an autolysin inhibitor.

Uses
Aztreonam is used in urinary tract infections, lower respiratory tract infections, septicemia, skin and skin-structure infections, intra-abdominal infections, and gynaecologic infections caused by susceptible gram-negative microorganisms.

1.2.7. β-Lactamase Inhibitors
β-Lactamase inhibitors are **enzymes produced by gram-positive and gram-negative bacteria that inactivate β-lactam antibiotics by opening the β-lactam ring.**

When penicillin is inactivated by penicillinases or β-lactamases enzymes produced by bacteria, resistance develops to it. Several attempts have been made to prevent degradation of penicillin by this enzyme. Then clavulanic acid was developed as the first β-lactamase inhibitor, which is commercially available in combination with a β-lactam. The β-lactamase inhibitor prevents the breakdown of β-lactam ring by the organisms producing β-lactamase enzyme, thereby enhancing the antibacterial activity. The combinations given in **table 1.1** are suitable alternatives for infections caused by resistant organisms such as *S. aureus* and *Haemophilus influenzae*.

Table 1.1: β-Lactam/β-Lactamase Inhibitor Dosages

Drug Combinations	Doses
Amoxicillin-clavulanic acid	250-500 mg PO q8h
Ampicillin-sulbactam	500-875 mg PO q12th
Piperacillin-tazobactam	1.5-3.0 g IV q6h
Ticarcillin-clavulanic acid	4.5 g IV q6-8h or 3.375 g IV q4-6h 3.1 g IV q4-6h

Note: Dosage adjustment required for all above drugs administered to patients with renal impairment.

Mechanism of Action and Spectrum of Activity
The β-lactam components of the above combinations are cell wall-active agents. They bind to and inactivate the PBPs, thus interrupt bacterial cell wall synthesis. The β-lactamase inhibitors irreversibly bind to most β-lactamase enzymes, and prevent the degradation of β-lactam ring, thereby improving their antibacterial activity. The β-lactamase inhibitors alone do not have significant antibacterial activity.

Clinical Uses
The β-lactam/β-lactamase inhibitors are used in polymicrobial infections based on their broad spectrum of activity. They are mainly used in intra-abdominal infections, gynaecologic infections, and skin and soft tissues infections (including human and animal bites), foot infections in diabetic patients, and respiratory tract infections **(including aspiration pneumonia, sinusitis, and lung abscesses).**

Adverse Events

Addition of the β-lactamase inhibitor to the penicillins has not resulted in any new or major adverse events. The major adverse effects associated with oral administration of β-lactam/β-lactamase inhibitor combinations are hypersensitivity reactions and gastrointestinal side effects (nausea and diarrhoea).

The combinations of β-lactamase inhibitors are physically incompatible with parenteral aminoglycosides. Each penicillin in the combinations has been associated with the inactivation of aminoglycosides *in vitro*. The clinical significance of this interaction is unknown.

Names	Structures	Subclasses	Partner β-Lactams
Clavulanic acid	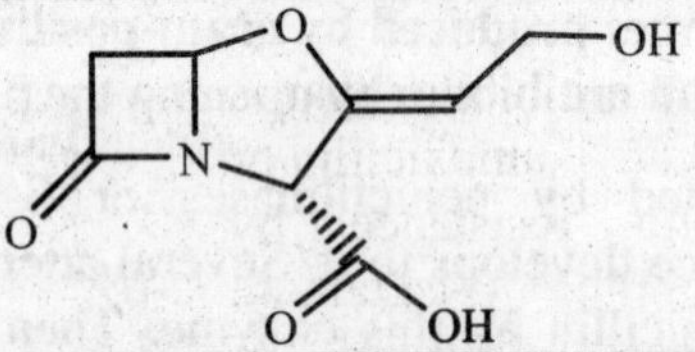	Clavam	Amoxicillin
Sulbactam	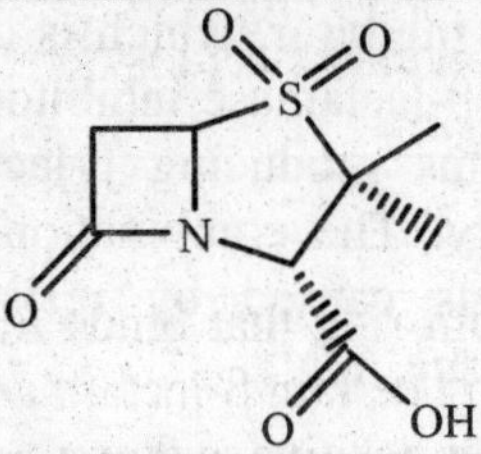	Penicillanic acid sulfone	Ampicillin
Tazobactam	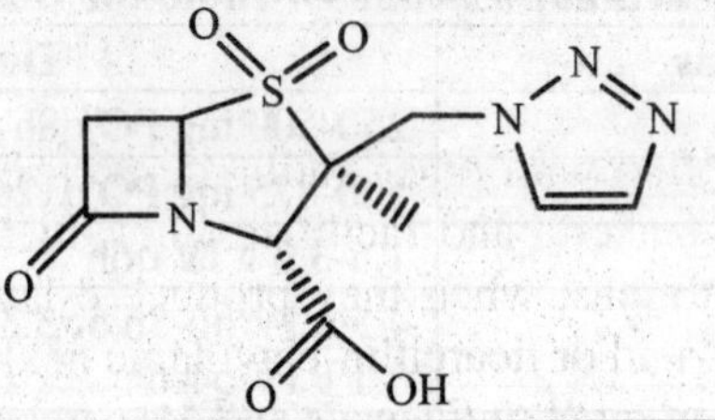	Penicillanic acid sulfone	Piperacillin ceftolozane
Avibactam	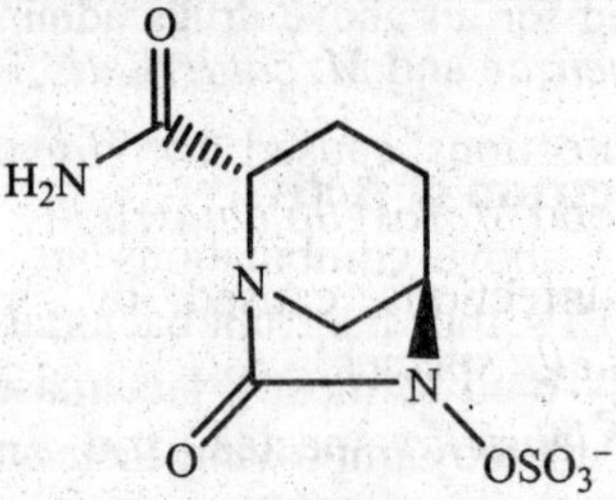	DBO	Ceftazidime
Relebactam	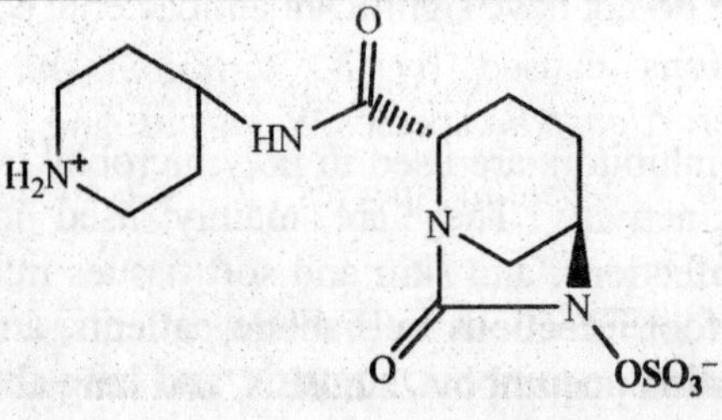	DBO	Imipenem

RG6080	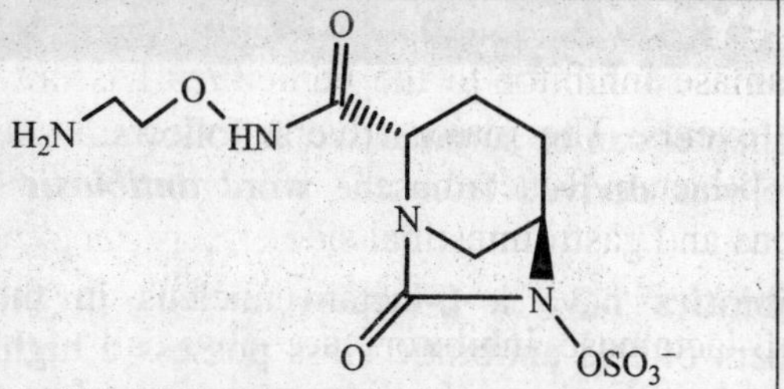	DBO	Not selected
RPX7009	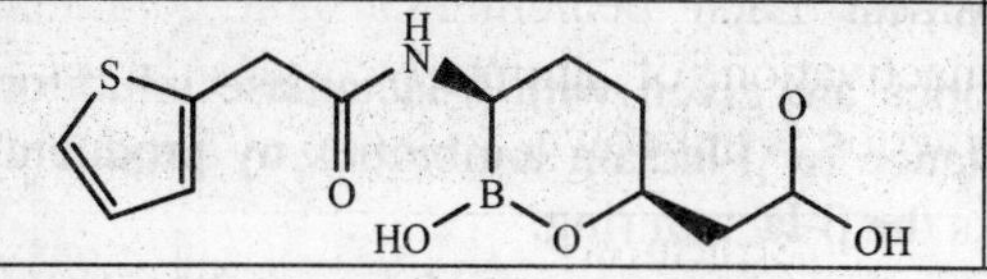	Boronic acid	Meropenem

Clavulanic Acid

Clavulanic acid is a β-lactamase inhibitor that is used in combination with amoxicillin or ticarcillin to fight antibiotic resistance by preventing their degradation by β-lactamase enzymes, broadening their spectrum of susceptible bacterial infections. Clavulanic acid is derived from *Streptomyces clavuligerus*.

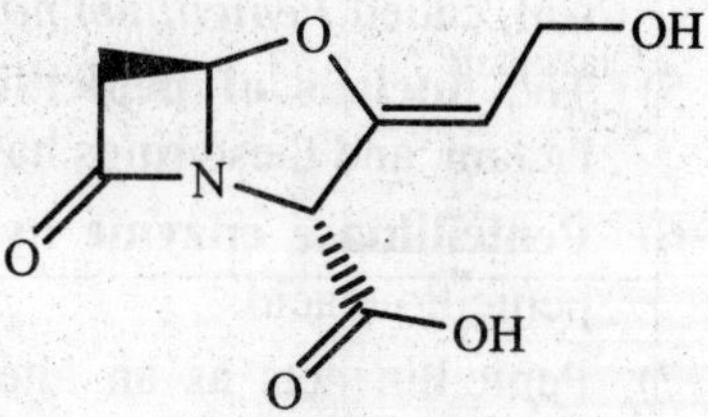

Clavulanic Acid

Mechanism of Action

Clavulanic acid contains a β-lactam ring that binds irreversibly to β-lactamases and prevents them from inactivating certain β-lactam antibiotics that are effective in the treatment of susceptible gram-positive and gram-negative infections.

Uses

Clavulanic acid in combination with other antibiotics prevents the development of drug-resistant strains of bacteria and facilitates their therapeutic antibacterial effects. The following conditions, when they produce β-lactamases, are treated with amoxicillin-clavulanic acid or ticarcillin-clavulanic acid combination:

1) Acute otitis media caused by *H. influenzae* and *M. catarrhalis*,
2) Sinusitis caused by *H. influenzae* and *M. catarrhalis*,
3) Lower respiratory tract infections caused by ***Haemophilus influenzae***, *S. aureus*, *Klebsiella* species, and *Moraxella catarrhalis*,
4) Skin and skin-structure infections caused by *Staphylococcus aureus*, *Escherichia coli*, and *Klebsiella* species,
5) UTI caused by *E. coli*, *Klebsiella* species, and *Enterobacter* species, *S. marcescens*, or *S. aureus*,
6) Gynaecologic infections caused by *P. melaninogenicus*, *Enterobacter* species, *E. coli* species, *Klebsiella* species, *S. aureus*, and *S. epidermidis*,
7) Septicaemia caused by *Klebsiella* species, *E. coli* species, *S. aureus*, or *Pseudomonas* species,
8) Bone and joint infections caused by *S. aureus*, and
9) **Intra-abdominal infections caused by *E. coli*, *K. pneumoniae*, or *B. fragilis*.**

1.3. SUMMARY

The details given in the chapter can be summarised as follows:

1) The word **antibiotic** was derived from the word ***antibiosis*** which means against life.
2) The **β-lactam antibiotics** have a β-lactam nucleus in their molecular structure, i.e., members of this antibiotic class possess a highly reactive 3-carbon and 1-nitrogen ring.
3) The β-lactam antibiotics are given with β-lactamase inhibitors because the bacteria obtain resistance to β-lactam antibiotics by producing β-lactamase enzyme which attacks the β-lactam ring.
4) **Penicillin** is the first antibiotic which was discovered in September 1928 by Sir Alexander Fleming (an English Bacteriologist) from a fungus dwelling in soil, called *Penicillium notatum.*
5) The **nucleus of penicillin** consists of fused rings of thiazolidine and *p*-lactam, and these rings have side chains attached through an amide linkage.
6) **Penicillinase enzyme** hydrolyses the β-lactam ring and produces inactive penicilloic acid.
7) Penicillin acts as an alternative substrate and binds to Penicillin Binding Protein (PBP) receptor present on the surface of bacterial cell wall.
8) **Autolysins**, present in bacterial cell wall, maintain the appropriate shape and size of cell and also facilitate cell division.
9) Penicillin destroys the bacterial cell wall and disintegrates teichoic acid, thus activating autolysin and lysing the bacterial cell.
10) **Benzylpenicillin** is a narrow spectrum natural penicillin antibiotic.
11) **Ampicillin** is a broad spectrum penicillin antibiotic of semi-synthetic origin.
12) **Penicillin V** is obtained from natural sources.
13) **Cloxacillin** is a chlorinated derivative of oxacillin and a semi-synthetic antibiotic.
14) **Carbenicillin** is a semi-synthetic, broad spectrum penicillin.
15) **Cephalosporins** are semi-synthetic antibiotics derived from cephalosporin-C, which is obtained from *Cephalosporium* (fungus).
16) The **nucleus of cephalosporins** consists of a β-lactam ring fused to a dihydrothiazine ring (7-aminocephalosporanic acid).
17) **Giuseppe Brotzu** (an Italian scientist) first isolated cephalosporin compounds from *Cephalosporium acremonium* cultures from a sewer in Sardinia in 1948.
18) In the presence of esterase/acid, cephalosporin-C gives desacetyl cephalosporin and an inactive desacetyl cephalosporin (lactone).
19) Cephalosporin C is degraded into cephalosporic acid, anhydrodesacetyl cephalosporic acid, and desacetyl cephalosporic acid by β-lactamase or cephalosporanase enzyme.
20) Cephalosporin C undergoes degradation in the presence of acylase enzyme, and forms 7-amino **cephalosporanic acid.**
21) **Cephalexin is a semi-synthetic antimicrobial cephalosporin.**

22) **Cephaloridine** is derived from cephalosporin C and is its 1st generation semi-synthetic derivative.

23) **Cephalothin** is a semi-synthetic, 1st generation cephalosporin antibiotic and also a β-lactam with bactericidal activity.

24) **Monobactams** are a structurally-related class of β-lactam antibiotics. They are resistant to β-lactamases.

25) **Aztreonam** is a monocyclic β-lactam antibiotic isolated from *Chromobacterium violaceum*.

26) **β-Lactamase inhibitors** are enzymes produced by gram-positive and gram-negative bacteria that inactivate β-lactam antibiotics by opening the β-lactam ring.

27) **Clavulanic acid** is a β-lactamase inhibitor that is used in combination with amoxicillin or ticarcillin to fight antibiotic resistance by preventing their degradation by β-lactamase enzymes, broadening their spectrum of susceptible bacterial infections.

28) Clavulanic acid is derived from *Streptomyces clavuligerus*.

1.4. EXERCISE

1.4.1. True or False

1) The nucleus of penicillin consists of fused rings of thiazolidine and *β*-lactam.
2) Autolysins, present in bacterial nucleus, maintain the appropriate shape and size of cell and also facilitate cell division.
3) Ampicillin is a narrow spectrum penicillin antibiotic of natural origin.
4) Cephalosporins are semi-synthetic antibiotics derived from cephalosporin-C, which is obtained from *Cephalosporium.*
5) Giuseppe Brotzu isolated cephalosporin compounds from *Cephalosporium acremonium* cultures from a sewer in Sardinia in 1948.
6) Cephaloridine is derived from cephalosporin C and is its 3rd generation semi-synthetic derivative.
7) Monobactams are a structurally-related class of β-lactam antibiotics.
8) Clavulanic acid is derived from *Streptomyces clavuligerus.*

1.4.2. Fill in the Blanks

9) Penicillin was discovered by Sir Alexander Fleming from ________.
10) Penicillinase enzyme hydrolyses the β-lactam ring and produces inactive ________.
11) ________ is a narrow spectrum natural penicillin antibiotic.
12) The nucleus of cephalosporins consists of a β-lactam ring fused to a ______.
13) Cephalosporin C undergoes degradation in the presence of acylase enzyme, and forms ________.
14) ________ are resistant to β-lactamases.
15) Aztreonam is a monocyclic β-lactam antibiotic isolated from ________.

Answers

1) False	2) False	3) False	4) True	5) True	6) False
7) True	8) True	9) *Penicillium notatum*		10) Penicilloic acid	
11) Benzylpenicillin		12) Dihydrothiazine ring		13) 7-amino cephalosporanic acid	
14) Monobactams		15) *Chromobacterium violaceum*			

1.4.3. Very Short Answer Type Questions

1) Classify antibiotics based on their range of action.
2) Give the classification of β-lactam antibiotics.
3) Draw the chemical structure of penicillin.
4) What are cephalosporins?
5) Give the first generation classification of cephalosporins.
6) Give the mechanism of action and uses of any one penicillin product.
7) Why β-lactam antibiotics are given with β-lactamase inhibitors?

1.4.4. Short Answer Type Questions

1) Give the complete classification of antibiotics.
2) Enlist few uses of penicillin. Also give its mechanism of action.
3) Write the classification and chemical degradation of penicillin.
4) Discuss the SAR of cephalosporins.
5) Give the mechanism of action and uses of any two cephalosporins.

1.4.5. Long Answer Type Question

1) Write an exhaustive note on penicillins.
2) Discuss the SAR of penicillin.
3) Briefly write about the chemical degradation process of cephalosporins.
4) Give a detailed review on β-lactamase inhibitors.

CHAPTER 2 Antibiotics-Aminoglycosides

2.1. AMINOGLYCOSIDES

2.1.1. Introduction

Aminoglycoside is a molecule or a portion of a molecule composed of amino-modified sugars. It has a hexose ring, either streptidine (in streptomycin) or 2-deoxystreptamine (other aminoglycosides), and various amino sugars are attached to this ring by glycosidic linkages. It is water-soluble, stable in solution, and more active at alkaline pH.

Some of the aminoglycosides (**e.g.,** amikacin, arbekacin, gentamicin, kanamycin, neomycin, netilmicin, paromomycin, rhodostreptomycin, streptomycin, tobramycin, and apramycin) are antibiotics and show activity against certain bacteria types. They are widely used against gram-negative enteric bacteria in bacteremia and sepsis. Along with vancomycin or penicillin, they are used for treatment of endocarditis and tuberculosis.

2.1.2. Historical Background

Waksman discovered **streptomycin** from the culture of *Streptomyces griseus*. Streptomycin was the **first aminoglycoside-amincyclitol antibiotic** and was effective in the treatment of tuberculosis. For this discovery, **Waksman** was awarded the Nobel Prize in Medicine in 1952.

After 5 years of streptomycin discovery in **1949**, **Waksman** introduced the **second aminoglycoside** antibiotic, i.e., **neomycin**. Toxicity issues associated with neomycin and emerging streptomycin resistance led to the discovery of additional aminoglycosides in the 1950s and early 1960s with the group of Umezawa, Japan reporting kanamycin and gentamicin by **Weinstein** at Schering, both of which found clinical use. Neomycin and kanamycin/gentamicin classes of aminoglycoside are the two most common structural classes of aminoglycoside antibiotic. They share a central 2-deoxyaminocyclitol ring substituted with sugars at position 4, 5 (neomycin) or position 4, 6 (kanamycin/gentamicin).

In the late 1960s, resistance to kanamycin was reported and found to be associated with enzymatic modification of the drugs. Emergence of resistance ended the clinical utility of kanamycin and launched a two decade search for new natural and semi-synthetic agents that were not susceptible to resistance mechanisms, **e.g.,** bramycin, amikacin, and netilmicin. However, the breadth of resistance is difficult to overcome with new agents and the availability of newer antibacterial agents with a similar microbial spectrum such as the **fluoroquinolones in the 1970s, has served to marginalise the clinical use of aminoglycosides.**

2.1.3. Nomenclature

Aminoglycosides derived from bacteria of *Streptomyces* genus are named with the suffix *-mycin,* while those derived from *Micromonospora* genus are named with the suffix *-micin.*

This nomenclature system, however, is not specific for aminoglycosides. **For example,** vancomycin is a glycopeptide antibiotic; erythromycin, produced from *Saccharopolyspora erythraea* (earlier misclassified as *Streptomyces*) and its synthetic derivatives, i.e., clarithromycin and azithromycin, are macrolides. All differ in their mechanisms of action.

2.1.4. Structure-Activity Relationship

Aminoglycosides comprise of two or more amino sugars joined to a highly substituted 1,3-diaminocyclohexane (aminocyclitol) centrally placed ring via glycoside linkage. This ring is 2-deoxystreptamine in all aminoglycosides, except in streptomycin and dihydrostreptomycin, where it is streptidine. Thus,

1) In kanamycin and gentamicin, two amino sugars are attached to 2-deoxystreptamine.
2) In streptomycin, two amino sugars are attached to streptidine.
3) In neomycin, three amino sugars are attached to 2-deoxystreptamine.

Aminoglycoside antibiotics thus contain two important structural features:

1) Amino sugar portion, and
2) Centrally placed hexose ring (either 2-deoxystreptamine or streptidine).

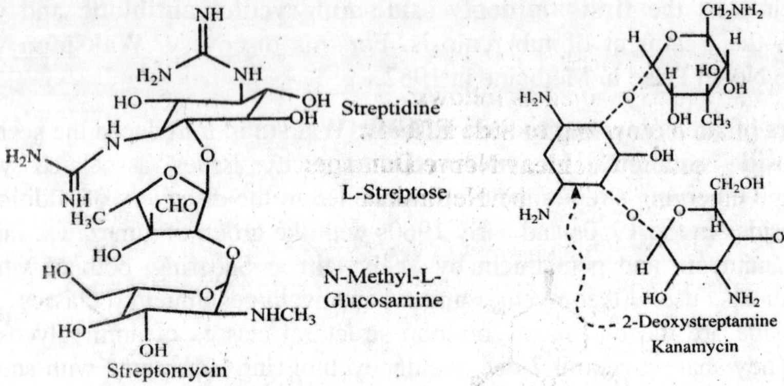

1) **SAR of Amino Sugar Portion**
   i) The amino function at C-6 and C-2 are the major target sites for bacterial inactivating enzymes.
   ii) Methylation at C-6 does not decrease the activity, rather increases enzymatic resistance.
   iii) Cleavage of 3-hydroxyl or 4-hydroxyl or both the groups has no effect on the activity.

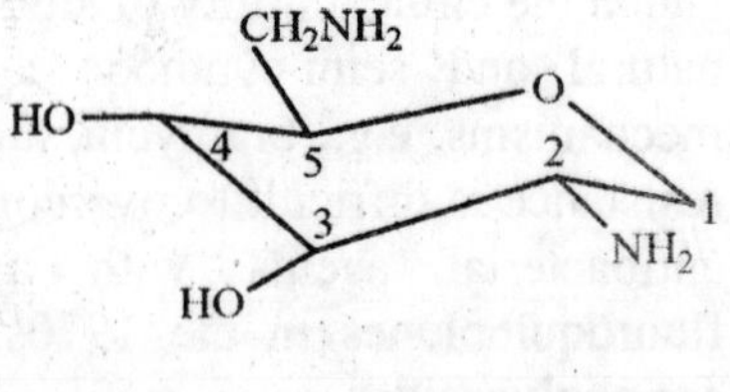

2) **SAR of Centrally Placed Hexose Ring (Aminocyclitol Ring)**
   i) Modifications at C-1 amino group have been tested. Acylation (e.g., amikacin) and ethylation (e.g., 1-N-ethylsisomicin) of C-1 amino group does not increase the antibacterial activity, but helps to retain it.
   ii) In sisomicin series, 2-hydroxylation and 5-deoxygenation increases the inhibition of bacterial inactivating enzymes. Thus, only a few modifications of the central ring are possible which do not obstruct the activity spectrum of aminoglycosides.

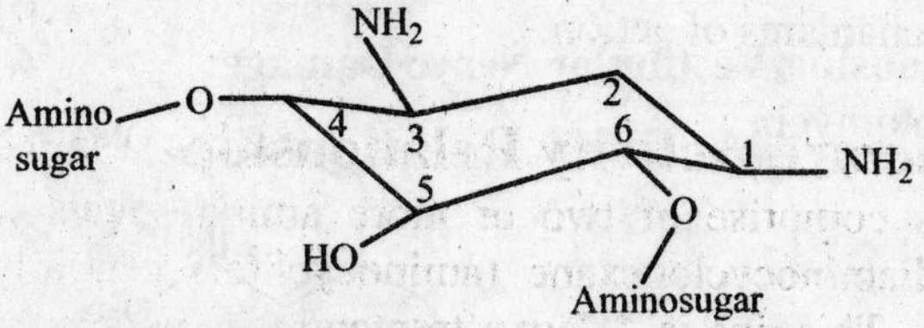

2.1.5. Mechanism of Action

Aminoglycosides bind to specific 30S sub-unit ribosomal proteins (S12 in the case of streptomycin) and **inhibit protein synthesis** in any one of the following **three ways:**

1) They interfere with the initiation complex of peptide formation,
2) They misread the mRNA which causes incorporation of incorrect amino acids into the peptide, thus forming a non-functional or toxic protein, and
3) They irreversibly break the polysomes into non-functional monosomes, and the overall effect is lethal for the cell.

2.1.6. Classification

Aminoglycosides are classified as follows:

1) **Classification According to Side Effects:**
   i) **Drugs Causing Cochlear Nerve Damage:**
      a) Amikacin b) Netilmicin

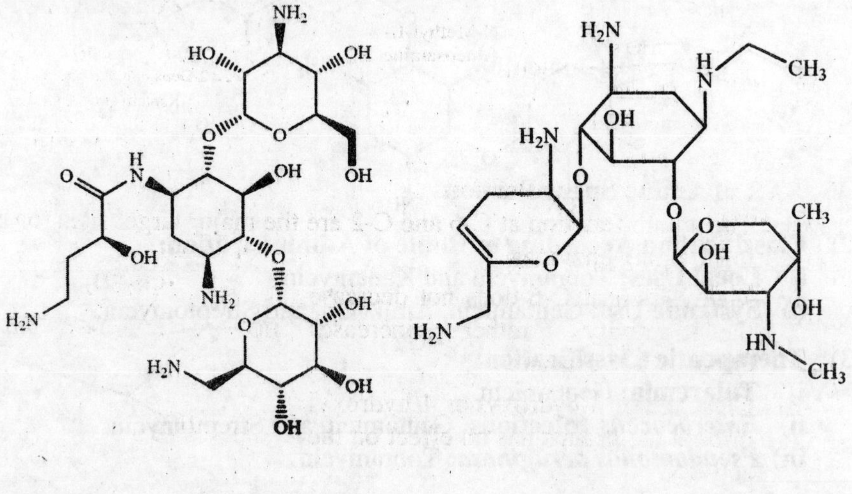

c) Kanamycin

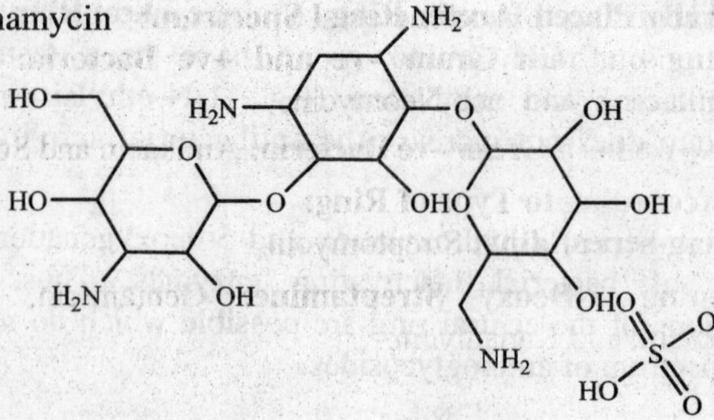

ii) **Drugs Causing Vestibular Nerve Damage:**

a) Streptomycin

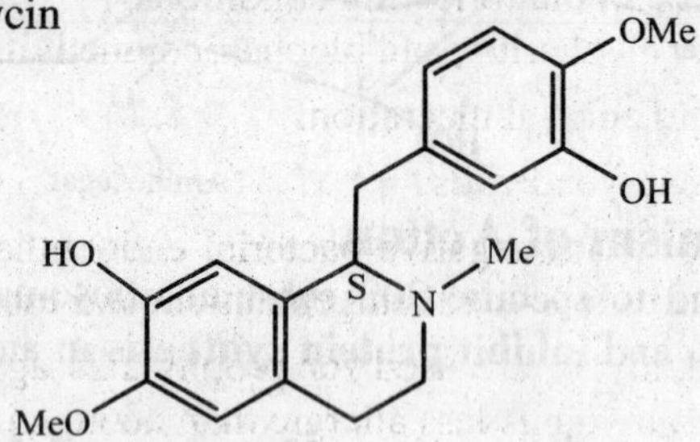

b) Tobramycin

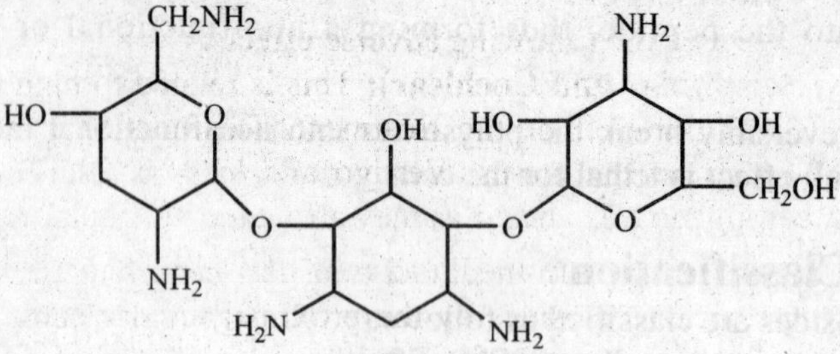

c) Gentamicin

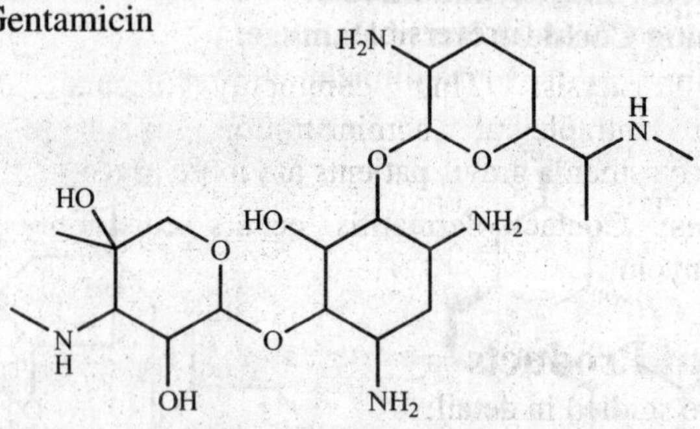

2) **Classification According to Route of Administration:**

i) **Local Uses:** Tobramycin and Kanamycin.

ii) **Systemic Use:** Gentamicin, Amikacin, and Streptomycin.

3) **Therapeutic Classification:**

i) **Tularemia:** Gentamicin.

ii) ***Enterococcus* Infections:** Gentamicin and Streptomycin.

iii) ***Pseudomonas aeruginosa*:** Tobramycin.

4) **Classification According to Antibacterial Spectrum:**
   i) **Drugs Acting on both Gram –ve and +ve Bacteria:** Gentamicin, Tobramycin, Kanamycin, and Neomycin.
   ii) **Drugs Acting on both Gram –ve Bacteria:** Amikacin and Streptomycin.
5) **Classification According to Type of Ring:**
   Drugs Containing Streptidine: Streptomycin.
6) **Drugs Containing 2-Deoxy Streptamine:** Gentamicin, Tobramycin Neomycin Amikacin, and Kanamycin.

2.1.7. Uses

Aminoglycosides are used in the following conditions:
1) Acute conjunctivitis, blepharitis, and blepharocojunctivitis.
2) Bacterial keratitis and corneal ulceration.
3) Dacryocystitis and dacryoadenitis.
4) Amikacin is used for gram-negative bacterial endophthalmitis as its toxicity to intraocular structures is lesser than gentamicin and tobramycin.
5) Tobramycin and neomycin are used for prophylaxis against infections after ocular surgery. Tobramycin is less allergic than neomycin.

2.1.8. Adverse Effects

Aminoglycosides produce the following adverse effects:
1) **Ototoxicity (Vestibular and Cochlear):** This is related to high peak plasma levels and to the duration of the treatment. Deafness is irreversible and affects the foetuses in the uterus. Vertigo and loss of balance (in patients receiving streptomycin) also occur as they affect the vestibular apparatus.
2) **Nephrotoxicity:** The calcium-mediated transport processes are disrupted by the retention of aminoglycosides by the proximal tubular cells. As a result, kidney damage occurs ranging from mild, reversible renal impairment to severe, acute tubular necrosis (irreversible).
3) **Neuromuscular Paralysis:** This commonly occurs after direct intraperitoneal or intrapleural administration of large doses of aminoglycosides. Myasthenia gravis patients are more at risk
4) **Allergic Reactions:** Contact dermatitis occurs commonly on topical application of neomycin.

2.1.9. Important Products

The following drugs are studied in detail:
1) Streptomycin,
2) Neomycin, and
3) Kanamycin.

2.1.9.1. Streptomycin

Streptomycin is an antibiotic **produced by *Streptomyces griseus*** (a soil **actinomycete). It is an aminoglycoside antibacterial and anti-mycobacterial.**

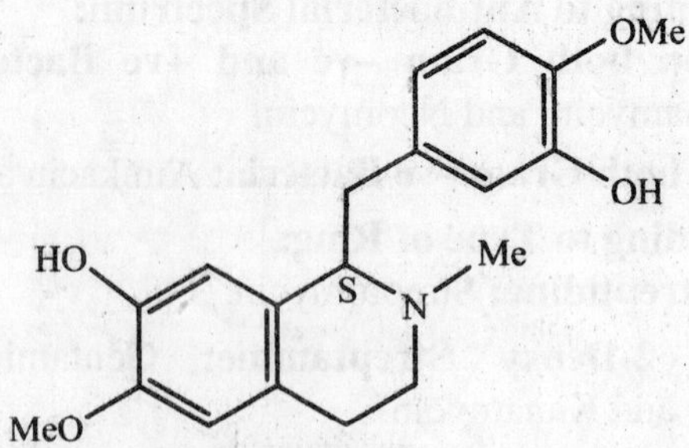

Streptomycin

Mechanism of Action

Streptomycin irreversibly binds to specific 30S-subunit proteins and 16S rRNA. It specifically binds to four nucleotides of 16S rRNA and a single amino acid of protein S12. This interferes with the decoding site in the surrounding area of nucleotide 1400 in 16S rRNA of 30S subunit. This region interacts with the wobble base in the anticodon of tRNA. This causes interference with the initiation complex, misreading of mRNA; due to this incorrect amino acids are inserted into the polypeptide to produce non-functional or toxic peptides and the breakup of polysomes into non-functional monosomes.

Uses

1) Streptomycin is used for treating tuberculosis.
2) In combination with other drugs, it is used for treating tularemia (caused by *Francisella tularensis*), plague (caused by *Yersinia pestis*), severe *M. avium* complex, brucellosis, and Enterococcal endocarditis (caused by *E. faecalis* and *E. faecium*).

Adverse Effects

Nausea, vomiting, stomach upset, loss of appetite, vertigo, injection site reactions (pain, irritation, and redness), tingling or prickling sensation in the face, rash, fever, hives, and oedema.

2.1.9.2. Neomycin

Neomycin is derived from *Streptomyces fradiae*. It is a bactericidal aminoglycoside antibiotic that binds to the 30S ribosome of susceptible organisms. This binding interferes with mRNA binding and acceptor tRNA sites and produces non-functional or toxic peptides.

Mechanism of Action

Neomycin irreversibly binds to specific 30S-subunit proteins and 16S rRNA. It specifically binds to four nucleotides of 16S rRNA and a single amino acid of protein S12. This interferes with the decoding site in the surrounding area of nucleotide 1400 in 16S rRNA of 30S subunit. This region interacts with the wobble base in the anticodon of tRNA. This causes interference with the initiation complex, misreading of mRNA; due to this incorrect amino acids are inserted into the polypeptide to produce non-functional or toxic peptides and the breakup of polysomes into non-functional monosomes.

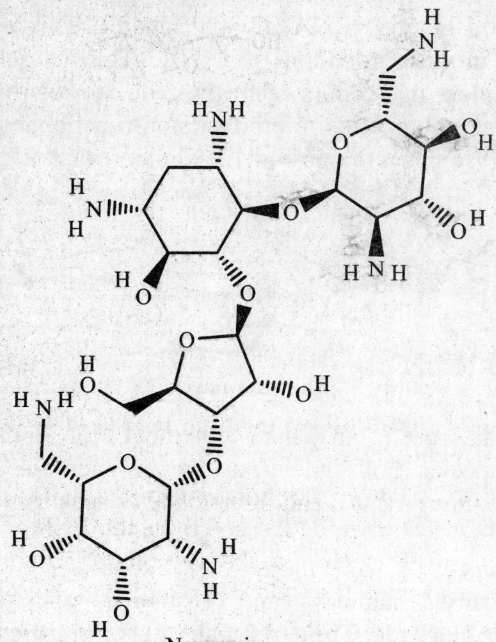

Neomycin

Uses

1) Neomycin is used topically in combination with other anti-infectives in superficial eye infections caused by susceptible bacteria, otitis externa caused by susceptible bacteria, and bacterial infections in skin lesions.
2) It is used as a continuous short-term irrigant or rinse to prevent bacteriuria and gram-negative rod bacteraemia in a bacteriuric patients with indwelling catheters.
3) It is administered orally in hepatic encephalopathy, as a perioperative prophylactic agent, and as an adjunct to fluid and electrolyte replacement in the treatment of diarrhoea caused to Enteropathogenic *E. coli* (EPEC).

Adverse Effects

Common side effects of neomycin include nausea, vomiting, or diarrhoea. Its serious side effects include drowsiness, confusion, mood changes, increased thirst, loss of appetite, weight gain, breathlessness, shallow breathing, hearing problems, vertigo, loss of balance or coordination, trouble in walking, numbness or tingly feeling under skin, muscle twitching, seizures, urinating less or not at all, swelling, severe stomach cramps, and watery or bloody diarrhoea.

2.1.9.3. Kanamycin

Kanamycin (or kanamycin A) is an aminoglycoside bacteriocidal antibiotic that is isolated from *Streptomyces kanamyceticus*. It is most commonly used in the form of kanamycin sulphate. It may be administered orally, intravenously, and intramuscularly. It is used to treat various infections.

Mechanism of Action

Kanamycin irreversibly binds to specific 30S-subunit proteins and 16S rRNA. It specifically binds to four nucleotides of 16S rRNA and a single amino acid of protein S12. This interferes with the decoding site in the surrounding area of nucleotide 1400 in 16S rRNA of 30S subunit. This region interacts with the wobble base in the anticodon of tRNA. This causes interference with the initiation complex, misreading of mRNA; due to this incorrect amino acids are inserted into the polypeptide to produce non-functional or toxic peptides and the breakup of polysomes into non-functional monosomes.

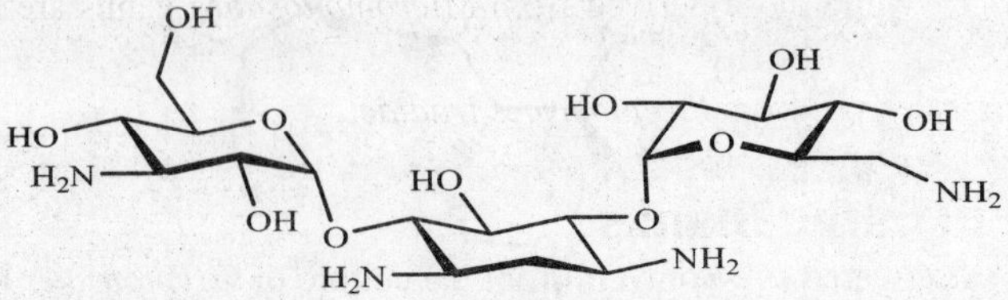

Kanamycin

Uses

Kanamycin is used in the treatment of infections caused by *E. coli*, *Proteus* species (both indole-positive and indole-negative), *E. aerogenes*, *K. pneumoniae*, *S. marcescens*, and *Acinetobacter* species.

Adverse Effects

Kanamycin causes auditory and vestibular toxicity, renal toxicity, and neuromuscular blockade. These risks are higher in patients with a present or past history of undergoing haemodialysis due to renal impairment, in patients undergoing concomitant or sequential treatment with other ototoxic or nephrotoxic drugs or rapid acting diuretic agents given intravenously (ethacrynic acid, furosemide, and mannitol), and in patients who have been treated for longer periods and/or with higher doses than recommended.

2.2. SUMMARY

The details given in the chapter can be summarised as follows:

1) **Aminoglycoside** is a molecule or a portion of a molecule composed of amino-modified sugars.
2) Waksman discovered streptomycin from the culture of *Streptomyces griseus.*
3) **Streptomycin** was the first aminoglycoside-amincyclitol antibiotic and was effective in the treatment of tuberculosis.
4) In 1949, Waksman introduced the second aminoglycoside antibiotic, i.e., **neomycin**.
5) Aminoglycosides derived from bacteria of *Streptomyces* genus are named with the suffix *-mycin*, while those derived from *Micromonospora* genus are named with the suffix *-micin*.
6) Aminoglycosides comprise of two or more amino sugars joined to a highly substituted 1,3-diaminocyclohexane (aminocyclitol) centrally placed ring via glycoside linkage.
7) **Streptomycin** is an antibiotic produced by *Streptomyces griseus* (a soil actinomycete).
8) **Neomycin** is derived from *Streptomyces fradiae*.
9) **Kanamycin** (or kanamycin A) is an aminoglycoside bacteriocidal antibiotic **that is isolated from *Streptomyces kanamyceticus*.**

2.3. EXERCISE

2.3.1. True or False

1) Neomycin is the second aminoglycoside antibiotic.
2) Aminoglycosides derived from bacteria of *Streptomyces* genus are named with the suffix *-micin*, while those derived from *Micromonospora* genus are named with the suffix *-mycin*.
3) Neomycin is derived from *Streptomyces fradiae*.

2.3.2. Fill in the Blanks

4) ________ discovered streptomycin from the culture of *Streptomyces griseus*.
5) Streptomycin is an antibiotic produced by ________.
6) Kanamycin is an aminoglycoside bacteriocidal antibiotic that is isolated from ____.

Answers

1) True	2) False	3) True
4) Waksman	5) *Streptomyces griseus*	6) *Streptomyces kanamyceticus*

2.3.3. Very Short Answer Type Questions

1) What are aminoglycosides?
2) Draw the chemical structure of streptomycin.
3) Give the mechanism of action of kanamycin.
4) Give the uses of neomycin.

2.3.4. Short Answer Type Questions

1) Give the historical background of aminoglycosides.
2) Give the mechanism of action and uses of any two aminoglycosides.
3) Enlist few uses of aminoglycosides. Also give its mechanism of action.

2.3.5. Long Answer Type Question

1) Write an exhaustive note on aminoglycosides.
2) Discuss the complete classification and SAR of aminoglycosides.

CHAPTER 3

Antibiotics-Tetracyclines

3.1. TETRACYCLINES

3.1.1. Introduction

Tetracycline is a potent, broad-spectrum antibacterial agent with activity against a host of gram-positive and gram-negative aerobic and anaerobic bacteria. Therefore, they are the drugs of choice or well-accepted alternatives for various infectious diseases. They are also used in the treatment of sexually transmitted and *Gonococcal* diseases, urinary tract infections, bronchitis, and sinusitis.

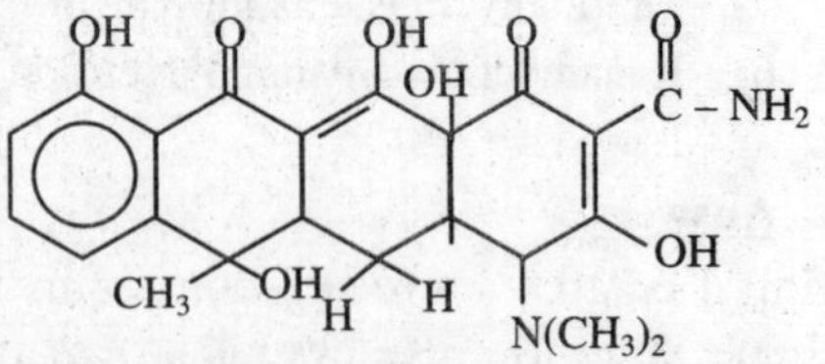

Tetracycline

Most of the marketed tetracyclines (tetracycline, chlortetracycline, oxytetracycline, and demeclocycline) occur naturally and are obtained by the fermentation of *Streptomyces spp.* broths. The duration of antibacterial action of semi-synthetic tetracyclines (methacycline, doxycycline, and minocycline) is longer. They also have a similar profile in terms of antibacterial potency. The activity encompasses many strains of gram-negative organisms (*E. coli*, *Proteus*, *Klebsiella*, *Enterobacter*, *Neisseria*, and *Serratia spp.*) and gram-negative organisms (*Streptococci* and *Staphylococci*). The potency of tetracyclines against *Haemophilus*, *Legionella*, *Chlamydia*, and *Mycoplasma* is of great importance.

3.1.2. Historical Background

Benjamin Minge Duggar discovered the first tetracycline antibiotic, i.e., **chlortetracycline** in **1945** and endorsed it in **1948**.

In 1950, **Robert Burns Woodward** (a Harvard University teacher) decided the compound structure of **oxytetracycline**; the patent security for its fermentation and generation was initially issued in 1950. An examination group of eight researchers (**K.J. Burnings**, **Francis A. Hochstein**, **Frederick J. Pioneer**, **C.R. Stephens**, **Lloyd Hillyard Conover**, **Abraham Bailey**, **Richard Pasternack**, and **Peter P. Regna**) at Pfizer took an interest in the two-year examination prompting the discovery.

3.1.3. Nomenclature

Oxytetracycline is chemically designated as 4-dimethylamino-1,4,4a,5,5a,6,11,12a-octahydro-3,6,10,12,12a-penta-hydroxy-6-methyl-1,11-dioxo-2-naphthacenecarboxamide based on the conventional numbering of various carbon atoms and subsequent labelling of the four aromatic rings in the tetracycline nucleus.

Some other tetracyclines are named as follows:
Methacycline: 6-Methylene-5-oxytetracycline,
Doxycycline: α-6-Deoxy-5-oxytetracycline, and
Rolitetracycline: N-(Pyrrolidinomethyl)-tetracycline.

3.1.4. Stereochemistry

Tetracyclines are a family of broad-spectrum antibiotics used for treating bacterial infections. The parent member of this family is tetracycline itself:

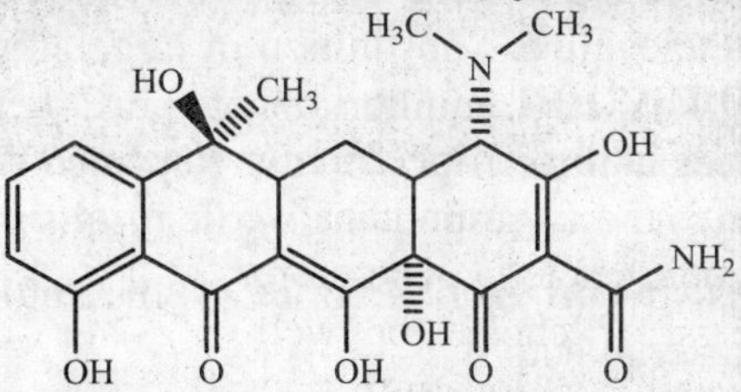

Chiral centres are the carbon atoms with four different groups attached to them. Since there are no internal mirror images, every carbon atom is different. The numbering system for the ring carbon atoms in tetracycline is shown below.

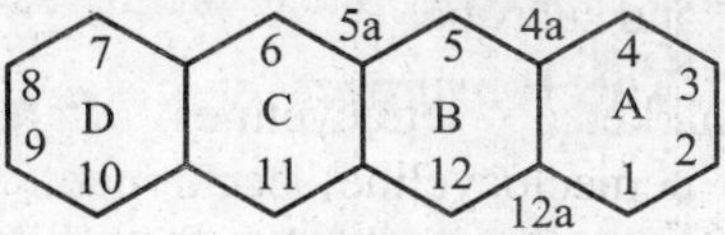

The chiral centres in tetracycline and the groups attached to them are:
C4: N, C3, C4a, H
C4a: C12a, C4, C5,H
C5a: C11a, C5, C6, H
C6: O, 6a, 5a, CH_3
C12a: O, C1, C12, C4a

Thus, total **five** chiral centers are present in tetracycline.

3.1.5. Structure-Activity Relationship

The main structural feature of tetracycline is a linearly fused tetracyclic nucleus and each ring should be six-membered and carbocyclic. The D-ring should be aromatic and the A-ring should be substituted at each of its carbon atoms for remarkable activity. The B-ring and C-ring should tolerate certain substituent changes till the keto-enol system (at C-11, C-12, C-12a) remains intact and conjugated to the phenolic D-ring. Aromatisation of D-ring or C-ring leads to negative effects. The D-, C-, B-ring phenol-, keto-enol system is vital, and the A-ring should contain a conjugated keto-enol system.

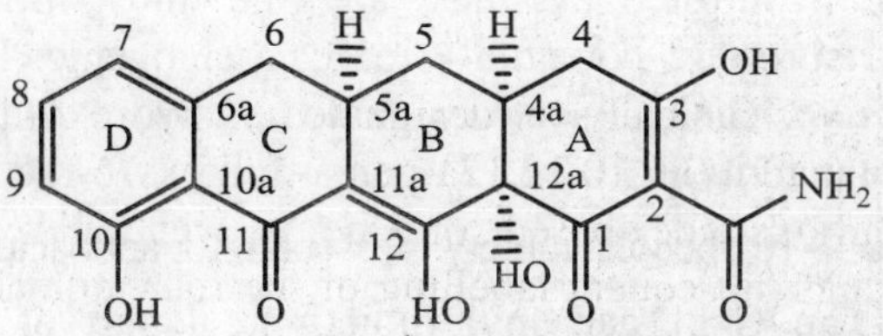

The A-ring contains a tricarbonyl derived keto-enol array at C-1, C-2, and C-3. A basic amine function at C-4 of A-ring is another structural requirement for good antibacterial activity.

1) **C-1 Substituents:** The keto-enol system of the A-ring is essential for antibacterial activity. All the variations at C-l have failed.
2) **C-2 Substituents:** Carboxamide moiety present in all naturally occurring tetracyclines is vital for antibacterial activity. The amide is left unsubstituted or is monosubstituted in the form of activated alkylaminomethyl amide (Mannich bases), **e.g.,** rolitetracycline. Substitution of large alkyl group on carboxamide alters the normal keto-enol equilibrium of the C-1, C-2 and C-3 conjugated system and reduces antibacterial activity. Replacement of carboxamide group or its dehydration to the corresponding nitrile results in the loss of activity.
3) **C-3 Substituents:** In conjugation with C-1, the keto-enol conjugated system is vital for antibacterial activity.
4) **C-4 Substituents:** Naturally occurring tetracyclines contain α-C-4 dimethylamino substituent that favours the keto-enolic character of the A-ring. Replacement of dimethylamino group with a hydrazone, oxime or hydroxyl group results in the loss of activity due to the increase in heteroatom basicity.
5) **C-4a Substituents:** The α-hydrogen at C-4a of tetracyclines is vital for antibacterial activity.
6) **C-5 Substituents:** Naturally occurring antibacterial tetracyclines have an unsubstituted methylene moiety at C-5. Oxytetracycline contains C-5 α-hydroxyl group, is potent, and has been chemically modified to semi-synthetic tetracyclines. Alkylation of the hydroxyl group at C-5 results in the loss of activity. Ester formation is acceptable if the free oxytetracycline can be liberated *in vivo*; only small alkyl esters are useful.
7) **C-5a Substituents:** Configuration of the naturally occurring tetracyclines places the C-5a hydrogen atom in an α-configuration. Epimerisation diminishes the antibacterial activity.
8) **C-6 Substituents:** C-6 position can tolerate various substituents. Most of the tetracyclines have α-methyl group and α,β-hydroxyl group at C-6. Demeclocycline is a naturally occurring C-6 demethylated chlortetracycline with excellent antibacterial activity. This C-6 methyl group and also C-6 hydroxyl group contributes little to the tetracycline activity. Removal of this group forms doxycycline which shows remarkable antibacterial activity.
9) **C-7 and C-9 Substituents:** Nature of the aromatic D-ring influences the C-7 position to electrophilic substitution, and nitro and halogen groups have been introduced. Some C-7 nitrotetracyclines are the most potent of all tetracyclines *in vitro*, but were potentially toxic/carcinogenic. Halogenated derivatives are less active. The C-7 acetoxy, azido and hydroxyl tetracyclines show less antibacterial activity.
10) **C-10 Substituents:** The C-10 phenolic moiety is essential for antibacterial activity.
11) **C-11 Substituents:** The C-11 carbonyl moiety is a part of one of the conjugated keto-enol system that is vital for antibacterial activity.

12) **C-11a Substituents:** Few modifications at C-11a of tetracycline have been done due to the harmful effects on the keto-enol system, which is essential for magnesium cation binding and tetracycline uptake by the bacterial cell.

13) **C-12 Substituents:** The C-12 position of tetracycline is a part of keto-enol system that is essential for drug uptake, binding and antibacterial activity.

14) **C-12a Substituents:** The C-12a hydroxyl group is vital for antibacterial activity, although it can be esterified to provide tetracycline with increased lipophilicity. If the alkyl ester is small in size and undergoes rapid hydrolysis to liberate free tetracycline, antibacterial properties are retained.

3.1.6. Chemical Degradation

Tetracyclines undergo epimerisation at C-4 solutions of intermediate pH range; the obtained isomers are called **epitetracyclines**. Under acidic conditions, equilibrium is established in about one day consisting of equal amount of isomers. Epitetracylines show less activity than the natural isomers.

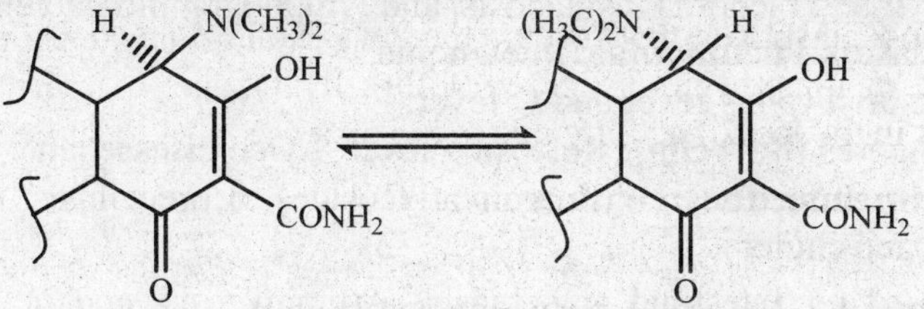

Epi Natural

Strong acid and bases are detrimental to the tetracyclines having a hydroxyl group at C-6, thereby causing an activity loss through modification of C-ring.

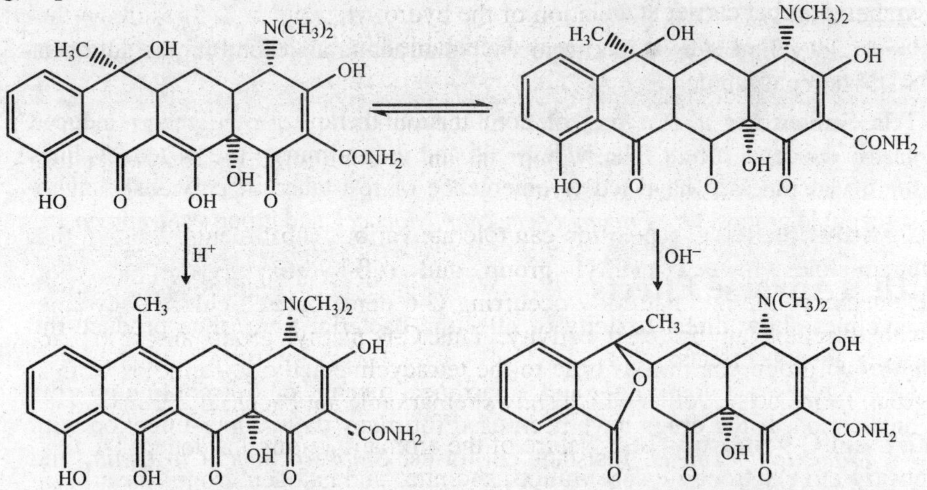

5, 6 -anhydrotetracycline Isotetracycline

Strong acids cause dehydration through a reaction involving the C-6 hydroxyl group and C-5a hydrogen. The double bond formed between C-5a and C-6 induces the double bond between C-11a and C-12 to shift between C-11 and C-11a, thus forming a more energetically favoured resonance of the naphthalene group found in the inactive anhydrotetracylines. Strong bases induce a reaction between the C-6 hydroxyl group and the ketone group at C-11, thus cleaving the bond between C-11 and C-11a and forming the lactone ring found in the inactive isotetracycline.

3.1.7. Mechanism of Action

Tetracyclines are bacteriostatic in nature. They inhibit protein synthesis by binding to 30S ribosomes in susceptible organisms. After this binding, the attachment of aminoacyl-t-RNA to the mRNA-ribosome complex is hindered, and thus the peptide chain fails to grow.

3.1.8. Classification

Tetracyclines are classified as follows:

1) **Short Acting (Half-Life 6 Hours):** Chlortetracycline and Oxytetracycline.
2) **Intermediate Acting (Half-Life 16 Hours):** Demeclocycline and Methacycline.
3) **Long Acting (Half-Life 18-24 Hours):** Doxycycline and Minocycline.

3.1.9. Uses

Tetracyclines have the following uses:

1) Tetracyclines are drugs of choice for:
   i) **Chlamydia:** Trachoma, psittacosis, and lymphogranuloma venereum,
   ii) **Mycoplasma Pneumoniae:** Pneumonia,
   iii) **Rickettsia:** Typhus fever and Q fever,
   iv) **Spirochaetes (Borrelia):** Relapsing fever, Lyme disease, and
   v) **Gram (–) Infections:** With aminoglycosides in brucellosis, tularaemia, plague, and cholera.
2) They are used for intestinal amoebiasis, actinomycosis, and *P. falciparum* malaria.
3) Minocycline (200mg of oral dose taken daily for 5 days) is used to treat meningococcal carrier state.
4) Demeclocycline is used in chronic hyponatraemia as it inhibits the action of ADH in renal tubules.
5) Tetracyclines are also a part of combination therapy for *H. pylori* induced gastric/duodenal ulcers. The widespread and indiscriminate use of tetracyclines for trivial illnesses have led to emergence of resistance in previously highly susceptible groups, *viz.*, *Pneumococci*, *Staphylococci*, and group A *Streptococci*.

3.1.10. Adverse Effects

Tetracyclines show direct toxicity or alter the bacterial flora, thus produce the following adverse effects:

1) **GIT:** Nausea, vomiting, and diarrhoea occur on discontinuing the medication. If the drugs have been used for many days, super-infection with *Pseudomonas*, *Proteus*, resistant coliforms, *Staphylococci*, *Clostridia*, and *Candida* occurs.
2) **Bone and Teeth:** Tetracyclines chelates with calcium and deposits on the newly formed bones and teeth; however in adults, they do not affect teeth and also deposit in bones in negligible amount. Tetracyclines during pregnancy (especially during the last 2 trimesters) can deposit in foetal teeth and produce yellow or brown discolouration and enamel dysplasia of milk teeth.
3) **Hepatotoxicity:** In high doses, they can impair hepatic function in pregnant women.

4) **Renal Toxicity:** They can cause renal tubular necrosis. Only doxycycline, and no other tetracyclines, should be given to patients with renal dysfunction.
5) **Photosensitisation:** Demeclocycline can induce sensitisation of skin to sunlight and UV light.
6) **Vestibular Disturbances:** Minocycline and doxycycline (in high doses) cause dizziness, vertigo, nausea, and vomiting.

3.1.11. Important Products

The following drugs are studied in detail:

1) Oxytetracycline,
2) Chlortetracycline,
3) Minocycline, and
4) Doxycycline.

3.1.11.1. Oxytetracycline

Oxytetracycline is a tetracycline analogue isolated from the *Streptomyces rimosus*, and used for treating various clinical conditions.

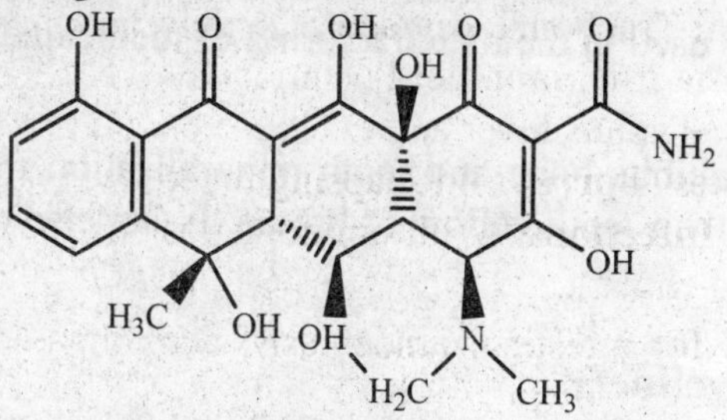

Oxytetracycline

Mechanism of Action

Oxytetracycline inhibits translation, thus inhibiting cell growth. It reversibly binds to the 30S ribosomal subunit and prevents the binding of amino-acyl tRNA to the A site of bacterial ribosome. Oxytetracycline being lipophilic in nature can easily cross the cell membrane or undergo passive diffusion through porin channels in the bacterial membrane.

Uses

Oxytetracycline is used in infections caused by various gram-positive and gram-negative microorganisms including *Mycoplasma pneumoniae, Pasteurella pestis, Escherichia coli, Haemophilus influenzae*, and *Diplococcus pneumoniae*.

Adverse Effects

Common side effects of oxytetracycline include irritation at the injection site, nausea, stomach upset, vomiting, diarrhoea, sensitivity to sunlight, swelling, rashes, hives, loss of appetite, swollen tongue, difficulty in swallowing, serious allergic reactions (anaphylaxis), and anaemia.

3.1.11.2. Chlortetracycline

Chlortetracycline is the first member of the tetracycline family. It was discovered in **1945** by **Benjamin Minge Duggar**, who observed that this antibiotic was the product of an actinomycete strain he cultured and obtained from a soil sample. The organism was named *Streptomyces aureofaciens* due to its gold-hued colour.

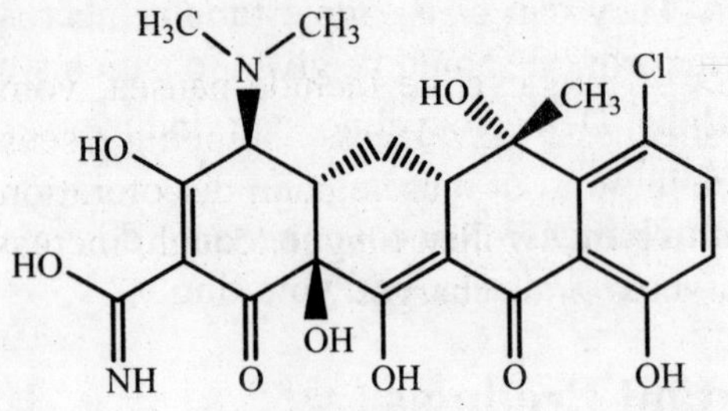

Chlortetracycline

Mechanism of Action

Chlortetracycline competes for the A site of the bacterial ribosome with tRNA carrying amino acids, thus prevents the addition of more amino acids to the peptide chain. This inhibition of protein synthesis in turn inhibits bacterial cell growth and reproduction as the required proteins are not synthesised.

Uses

Chlortetracycline is used in the manufacturing of medicated animal feeds.

Adverse Effects

Chlortetracycline inhibits bone and tooth mineralisation in growing and unborn animals, and turns their teeth yellow or brown. It can also cause liver and kidney impairment.

3.1.11.3. Minocycline

Minocycline is a tetracycline analogue, 7-dimethylamino but lacking 5-methyl and hydroxyl groups. It is effective against tetracycline-resistant *Staphylococcus* infections.

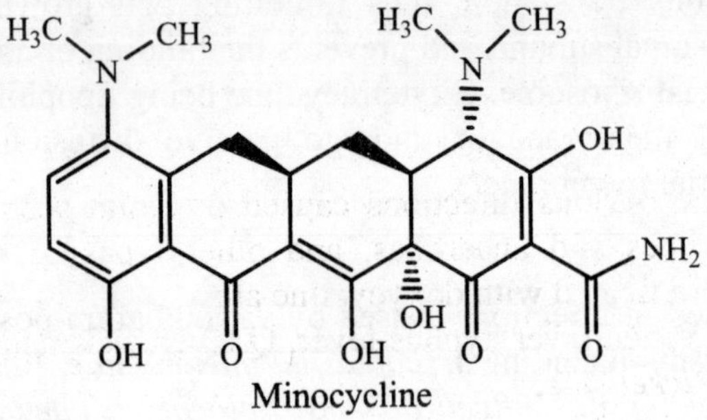

Minocycline

Mechanism of Action

Minocycline crosses the lipid bilayer or undergoes passive diffusion through porin channels in the bacterial membrane. It binds to the 30S ribosomal subunit, prevents the binding of tRNA to the mRNA-ribosome complex, and interferes with protein synthesis.

Uses

Minocycline is used in infections caused by susceptible strains of microorganisms, such as Rocky Mountain spotted fever, typhus fever, Q fever, rickettsial pox and tick fevers caused by *Rickettsiae*, upper respiratory tract infections caused by *Streptococcus pneumonia* and asymptomatic carriers of *Neisseria meningitidis*.

Adverse Effects

Common side effects of minocycline include nausea, vomiting, upset stomach, diarrhoea, light-headedness, dizziness, spinning sensation, unsteadiness, drowsiness, tired feeling, joint or muscle pain, discoloration of skin or nails, skin rash or itching, mouth sores, swollen tongue, cough, increased skin sensitivity to sunlight, or vaginal itching or discharge.

3.1.11.4. Doxycycline

Doxycycline is a broad-spectrum antibiotic and a synthetic derivative of oxytetracycline. It is a second-generation tetracycline with lesser toxicity than first-generation tetracyclines. It may be used for treating various bacterial infections, depending on the results of antibiotic susceptibility testing.

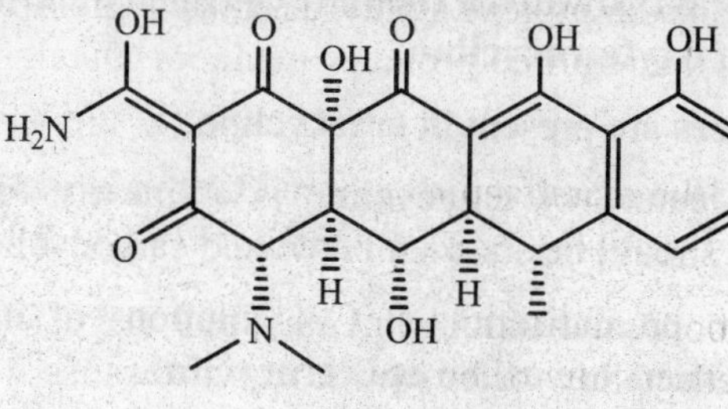

Doxycycline

Mechanism of Action

Doxycycline binds to the 16S rRNA portion of the bacterial ribosome and inhibits translation, thus prevents tRNA from binding to the RNA-30S bacterial ribosomal subunit, which is required for delivering amino acids for protein synthesis. Therefore, initiation of protein synthesis by polyribosome formation is obstructed, and this in turn stops bacterial replication and produces a bacteriostatic effect.

Uses

Doxycycline is used in various infections caused by gram-positive and gram-negative bacteria, aerobes and anaerobes, and other types of bacteria. Some major infections that are treated with doxycycline are:

1) Rocky mountain spotted fever, typhus fever, Q fever, rickettsial pox, and tick fevers caused by *Rickettsiae*,
2) Respiratory tract infections caused by *Mycoplasma pneumonia*,
3) Lymphogranuloma Venereum (LGV), trachoma, inclusion conjunctivitis, and uncomplicated urethral, endocervical or rectal infections (in adults) caused by *Chlamydia trachomatis*,
4) Psittacosis (ornithosis) caused by *Chlamydia psittaci*,
5) Non-gonococcal urethritis caused by *Ureaplasma urealyticum*, and
6) Relapsing fever due to *Borrelia recurrentis*.

Adverse Effects

Common side effects of doxycycline include loss of appetite, nausea, vomiting, diarrhoea, rash, photosensitivity, hives, and haemolytic anaemia.

3.2. SUMMARY

The details given in the chapter can be summarised as follows:

1) **Tetracycline** is a potent, broad-spectrum antibacterial agent with activity against a host of gram-positive and gram-negative aerobic and anaerobic bacteria.
2) Most of the marketed tetracyclines (tetracycline, chlortetracycline, oxytetracycline, and demeclocycline) occur naturally and are obtained by the fermentation of *Streptomyces spp.* broths.
3) **Benjamin Minge Duggar** discovered the first tetracycline antibiotic, i.e., chlortetracycline in **1945** and endorsed it in **1948**.
4) In 1950, Robert Burns Woodward (a Harvard University teacher) decided the compound structure of **oxytetracycline**.
5) Total **five chiral centers** are present in tetracycline.
6) The main structural feature of tetracycline is a linearly fused tetracyclic nucleus and each ring should be six-membered and carbocyclic.
7) Tetracyclines undergo epimerisation at C-4 solutions of intermediate pH range; the obtained isomers are called **epitetracyclines.**
8) **Oxytetracycline** is a tetracycline analogue isolated from the *Streptomyces rimosus*, and used for treating various clinical conditions.
9) **Chlortetracycline** was discovered in 1945 by Benjamin Minge Duggar, who observed that this antibiotic was the product of an actinomycete strain he cultured and obtained from a soil sample. The organism was named *Streptomyces aureofaciens* due to its gold-hued colour.
10) Minocycline is a tetracycline analogue, 7-dimethylamino but lacking 5-methyl and hydroxyl groups.
11) Doxycycline is a broad-spectrum antibiotic and a synthetic derivative of oxytetracycline. It is a second-generation tetracycline with lesser toxicity than first-generation tetracyclines.

3.3. EXERCISE

3.3.1. True or False

1) In 1950, Robert Burns Woodward decided the compound structure of tetracycline.
2) Total six chiral centers are present in tetracycline.
3) Oxytetracycline is a tetracycline analogue isolated from the *Streptomyces rimosus.*
4) Doxycycline is a broad-spectrum antibiotic and a synthetic derivative of minocycline.

3.3.1. Fill in the Blanks

5) _______ discovered chlortetracycline, the first tetracycline antibiotic, in 1945.
6) Tetracyclines undergo epimerisation at C-4 solutions of intermediate pH range; the obtained isomers are called _______.

7) Minocycline is a tetracycline analogue, _____ but lacking 5-methyl and hydroxyl groups.
8) ________is a second-generation tetracycline with lesser toxicity than first-generation tetracyclines.

Answers

1) **False**	2) **False**	3) **True**
4) **False**	5) **Benjamin Minge Duggar**	6) **Epitetracyclin**
7) **7-dimethylamino**	8) **Doxycycline**	

3.3.2. Very Short Answer Type Questions

1) Draw the chemical structure of tetracycline.
2) Classify tetracycline.
3) Draw the chemical structure of oxytetracycline.
4) Give the mechanism of action of chlortetracycline.
5) Give the uses of doxycycline.

3.3.3. Short Answer Type Questions

1) Give the historical background and nomenclature of tetracycline.
2) Give the chemical degradation of tetracycline.
3) Enlist the uses and adverse effects of tetracycline.

3.3.4. Long Answer Type Questions

1) Write an exhaustive note on tetracycline.
2) Discuss the SAR of tetracycline.

CHAPTER 4 Antibiotics-Macrolides

4.1. MACROLIDES

4.1.1. Introduction

Macrolides are compounds with a macrocyclic lactone ring (containing 14 or 16 atoms) with attached deoxy sugars. Erythromycin is the prototype drug which was obtained in **1952** from *Streptomyces erythreus.* It consists of two sugar moieties attached to a 14-atom lactone ring. Clarithromycin and azithromycin are semi-synthetic derivatives of erythromycin.

Macrolides are orally administered, but can be taken via parenteral route. They are used to treat pharyngitis and pneumonia caused by *Streptococcus* in individuals allergic to penicillin. They are used in pneumonia caused by *Mycoplasma* species or *Legionella pneumophila* (organism causing Legionnaire disease). They are also used in pharyngeal carriers of *Corynebacterium diphtheriae* (bacillus causing diphtheria).

4.1.2. Historical Background

Macrolide antibiotics are an old and well-established class of antimicrobial agents having a significant role in the chemotherapy of infectious diseases. Some important characteristics of macrolides are their moderate broad spectrum of antimicrobial activity, orally effective administration route, and a high margin of safety (high therapeutic index). Macrolides are the primary antibiotic of choice in a few cases. They are also vital as an alternative drug of choice to penicillins. In past two decades, macrolides have undergone a remarkable resurgence that is characterised by:

1) Discovery and commercial development of some important new semi-synthetic derivatives possessing various modified characteristics, and
2) Clinical efficacy in the treatment of several infectious diseases, which were initially not associated with macrolide therapy.

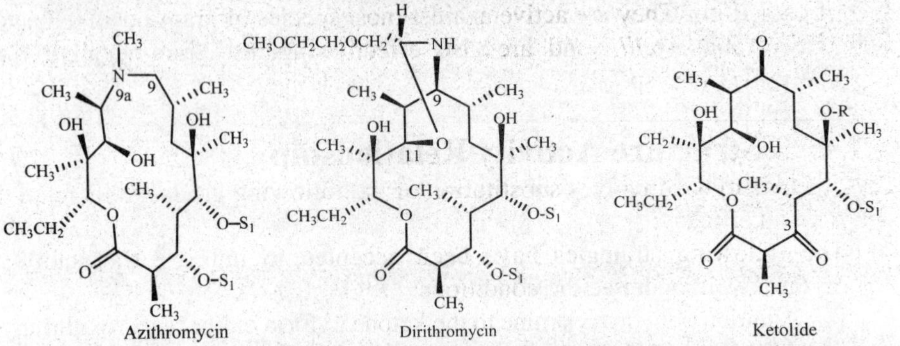

Figure 4.1: Structures of Semi-Synthetic Derivatives of Erythromycin A

Erythromycin is the prototype for macrolide class. It is a structurally complex secondary metabolite that was isolated from the culture broth of *Saccharopolyspora erythraea* (originally named *Streptomyces erythreus*, a microorganism isolated from soil sample) in **1952. Erythromycin A**, obtained by fermentation, is the principal component of erythromycin antibiotic. Its structure comprises of a highly substituted 14-membered lactone (named erythronolide A), to which the following substituents are attached:

1) An amino sugar (D-desosamine) via β-glycosidic linkage to the 5-hydroxyl group, and
2) A neutral sugar (L-cladinose) via α-glycosidic bond to the 3-hydroxyl group.

Erythromycin remains the most important macrolide antibiotic that has been used in respiratory tract, skin and many other infections. Several **limitations of erythromycin** that were identified early include its chemical instability under acidic conditions, low degree of oral bioavailability, bitter taste, low antibiotic concentrations in serum, short *in vivo* half-life, high inter- and intra-patient variability, and gastrointestinal pain and discomfort.

These interrelated problems and limitations were overcome by introducing erythromycin as enteric-coated, acid-resistant tablets and granules to prevent its degradation in the acidic environment of the stomach so that it reaches the alkaline upper intestine for absorption.

4.1.3. Nomenclature

Macrolide antibiotics are produced by *Streptomyces* species. They have the following common chemical features:

1) A macrocyclic lactone having 12 to 17 atoms, hence named macrolide,
2) A ketone group,
3) One or two amino sugars linked to the nucleus via glycosidic linkage,
4) A neutral sugar linked to the amine sugar or to the nucleus, and
5) Presence of the dimethyl amino moiety on the sugar residue; this explains the basicity of macrolides and thus the formation of salts.

The antibacterial spectrum of activity of the more potent macrolides is similar to that of penicillins. They are active against most species of gram-positive bacteria, both *Cocci* and *Bacilli*, and are also effective against gram-negative *Cocci*, especially *Neisseria* sp.

4.1.4. Structure-Activity Relationship

SAR of macrolides involves substitution of the following groups to increase their activity and efficacy:

1) The following strategies have been accepted to improve the stability of erythromycin under acidic conditions:
   i) Addition of hydroxylamine to the ketone to form oxime, **e.g.,** roxithromycin.
   ii) Alteration of C-6 hydroxyl group, **which is the nucleophilic functionality that initiates erythromycin degradation. Removal of** the nucleophilic

nature of this hydroxyl group retains the antibacterial properties, provided that the size of the group is small enough to not affect ribosomal binding, **e.g.,** clarithromycin.

2) The azalides (**e.g.,** azithromycin) are semi-synthetic 15-membered congeners in which a nitrogen atom has been introduced to expand a 14-membered precursor. This expands the activity spectrum of macrolides.

The two most important semi-synthetic 16-membered macrolides are miocamycin and rokitamycin (**figure 4.2**).

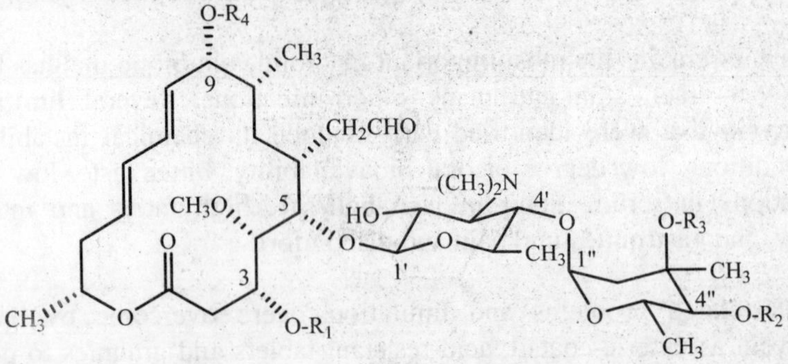

Drug Names	R_1	R_2	R_3	R_4
Josamycin (Leucomycin A_3)	Acetyl	Isovaleryl	H	H
Leucomycin A_5	H	n-Butyryl	H	H
Rokitamycin	H	n-Butyryl	Propionyl	H
Midecamycin A_1	Propionyl	Propionyl	H	H
Miocamycin	Propionyl	Propionyl	Acetyl	Acetyl

Figure 4.2: Structures of 16-Membered Clinical Macrolides

Miocamycin is the 9,3"-di-O-acetyl derivative of midecamycin A_1, which is a naturally occurring component produced in the fermentation of *Streptomyces aureofaciens*. **Rokitamycin** is the 3"-O-propionyl derivative of leucomycin A_5, which is a component of leucomycin complex (kitasamycin) produced in the fermentation of *Streptomyces kitasatoensis*.

Both these compounds possess favourable features similar to other macrolides such as efficacy against susceptible microorganisms, good tissue concentrations, oral bioavailability, and patient tolerability.

4.1.5. Chemical Degradation

Erythromycin becomes unstable under acidic conditions. The C-6 hydroxyl group reversibly attacks the C-9 ketone to form a hemi-ketal intermediate. Dehydration prevents regeneration of the parent erythromycin and the C-12 hydroxyl group can add to produce a spiro-ketal species. The cladinose group is cleaved from the macrocycle and desosamine is released under more harsh conditions. Useful antibacterial activity lasts upon dehydration of the hemi-ketal and the spiro-ketal is also weakly active.

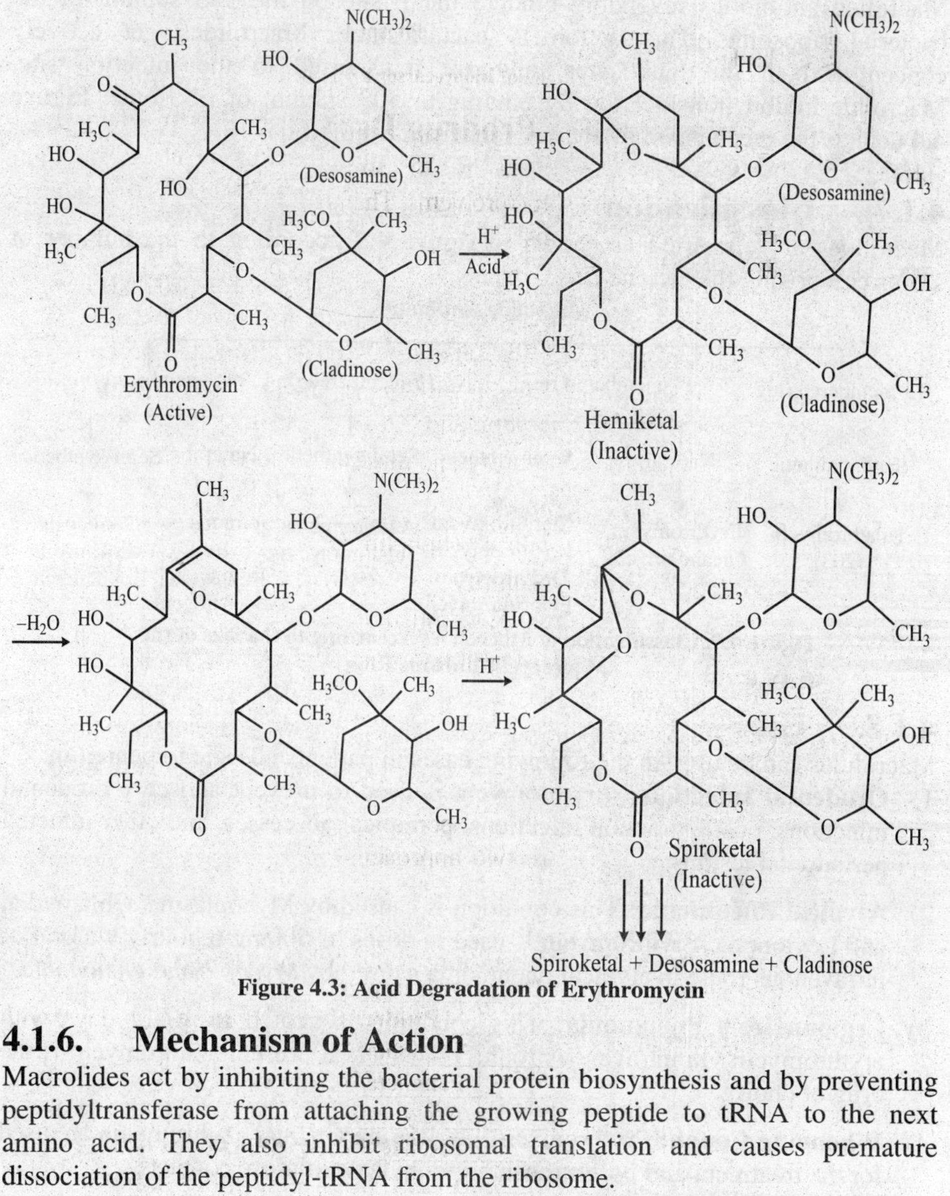

Figure 4.3: Acid Degradation of Erythromycin

4.1.6. Mechanism of Action

Macrolides act by inhibiting the bacterial protein biosynthesis and by preventing peptidyltransferase from attaching the growing peptide to tRNA to the next amino acid. They also inhibit ribosomal translation and causes premature dissociation of the peptidyl-tRNA from the ribosome.

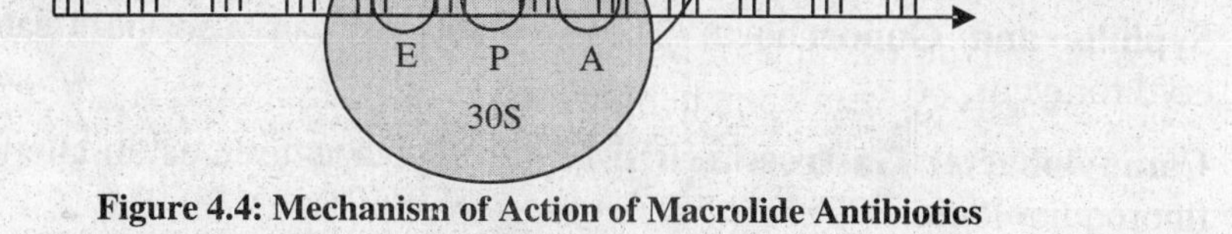

Figure 4.4: Mechanism of Action of Macrolide Antibiotics

Macrolide antibiotics reversibly bind to the P site on the 50S subunit of the bacterial ribosome. This action is bacteriostatic. Macrolides get actively concentrated in the leukocytes, and are transported to the infection site. Macrolide inhibit translocation by binding to 50S subunit of ribosome. **Figure 4.4** depicts the mechanism of action of macrolide antibiotics.

4.1.7. Classification

Macrolides are classified as shown in **figure 4.5** according to the number of atoms comprising the lactone ring.

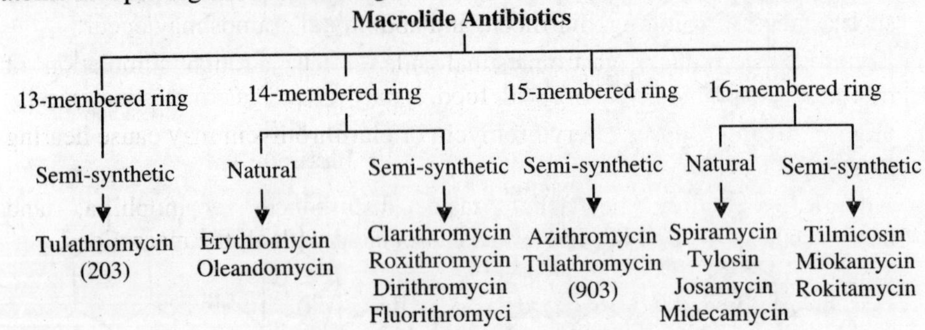

Figure 4.5: Classification of Macrolides According to the Size of the Macrocyclic Lactone Ring

4.1.8. Uses

Macrolides can be used in the following cases in patients allergic to penicillin:

1) **Orodental Infections:** Erythromycin is used to prevent and cure orodental infections, post-extraction infections, periapical abscesses, and other infected periodontal lesions.
2) **Atypical Pneumonia:** This condition is caused by Mycoplasma, Chlamydia, and Legionella. Erythromycin is used in doses of 500mg 6 hourly via oral or intravenous route in atypical pneumonia caused by *Mycoplasma pneumonia*.
3) **Legionnaire's Pneumonia:** This condition is treated in 10-14 days with erythromycin via intravenous route. However, at present azithromycin is the drug of choice.
4) **Whooping Cough:** Erythromycin, clarithromycin, and azithromycin are used for the treatment and post-exposure prophylaxis of close contacts.
5) **Streptococcal Infections:** Erythromycin is used for pharyngitis, tonsillitis, and scarlet fever.
6) **Staphylococcal Infections:** Erythromycin is used for minor infections.
7) **Diphtheria:** Erythromycin is used in acute stage as well as in the carrier stage of diphtheria.
8) **Syphilis and Gonorrhoea:** These conditions can also be treated with erythromycin.
9) **Campylobacter Gastroenteritis:** Erythromycin is used as an alternative to fluoroquinolones.

10) **Tetanus:** Erythromycin eradicates the carrier state.
11) **Anthrax:** Erythromycin is used as an alternative to penicillin.
12) Erythromycin ointment is used for skin infections and boils; while the lotion is used for acne vulgaris.

4.1.9. Adverse Effects

Macrolides show the following adverse effects:

1) They do not produce serious toxic effects although gastrointestinal symptoms such as nausea, vomiting, diarrhoea, and abdominal cramps may occur.
2) Erythromycin induces gastrointestinal side effects through stimulation of motility. If administered along with food, it may reduce gastrointestinal upset.
3) High intravenous doses of erythromycin or clarithromycin may cause hearing loss and QT prolongation.
4) Allergic reactions, headache, taste disturbance, eosinophilia, and hepatotoxicity are rare adverse effects associated with all the macrolides.

4.1.10. Important Products

The following drugs are studied in detail:

1) Erythromycin, 2) Clarithromycin, and 3) Azithromycin.

4.1.10.1. Erythromycin

Erythromycin is a bacteriostatic macrolide antibiotic produced by a strain of *Saccharopolyspora erythraea* in **1952**. It is widely used in various infections caused by gram-positive and gram-negative bacteria. It can be administered in various forms, like intravenous, topical preparations, and eye drops.

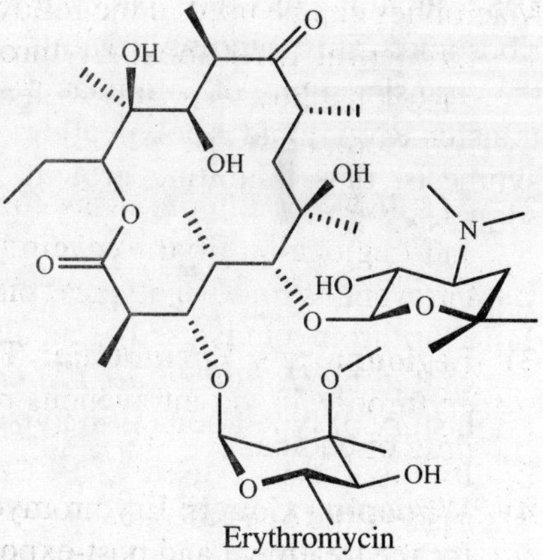

Erythromycin

Mechanism of Action

Erythromycin binds to the 23S ribosomal RNA molecule in the 50S subunit of ribosomes in susceptible bacterial organisms and inhibits protein synthesis. It also blocks protein synthesis by inhibiting the transpeptidation/translocation step of protein synthesis and by inhibiting the assembly of 50S bacterial ribosomal subunit. This controls various bacterial infections.

Uses

1) Erythromycin is used in infections of respiratory tract, including bronchitis, pneumonia, Legionnaires' disease (a type of lung infection), pertussis (whooping cough), and diphtheria (a serious infection in the throat).
2) It is also used in STDs, like syphilis.
3) It is used to treat ear, intestine, gynaecologic, urinary tract, and skin infections.
4) It prevents recurrent rheumatic fever.

Adverse Effects

Some common side effects of erythromycin are nausea, vomiting, diarrhoea, stomach pain, and loss of appetite. The adverse effects of erythromycin include signs of liver disease (such as persistent nausea/vomiting, jaundice, dark urine, severe stomach/abdominal pain), unusual tiredness, muscle weakness, slurred speech, blurred vision, drooping eyelids, and hearing loss.

4.1.10.2. Clarithromycin

Clarithromycin is a semi-synthetic macrolide antibiotic, which is derived from erythromycin. It binds to the bacterial 50S ribosomal subunit and inhibits protein synthesis. Clarithromycin may be bacteriostatic or bactericidal depending on the organism and drug concentration.

Mechanism of Action

Clarithromycin is first metabolised to an active metabolite, i.e., 14-OH clarithromycin that works synergistically with its parent compound. Then it passes through the bacterial cell wall and reversibly binds to domain V of the 23S ribosomal RNA of the 50S subunit of the bacterial ribosome. This binding inhibits the translocation of aminoacyl transfer-RNA and polypeptide synthesis, thus inhibiting protein synthesis.

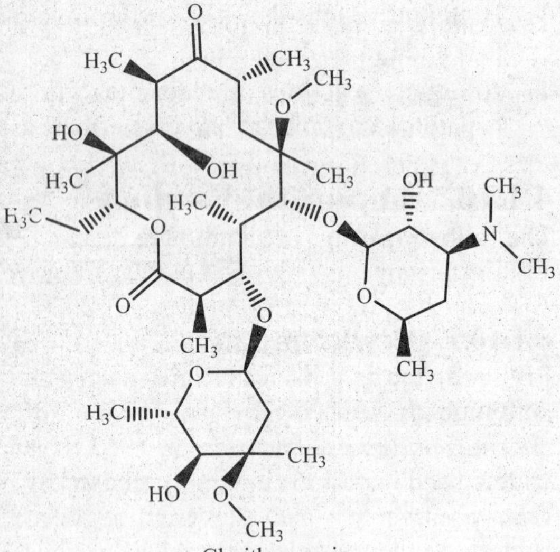

Clarithromycin

Uses

1) Clarithromycin is used as an alternative in the treatment of acute otitis media caused by *H. influenzae*, *M. catarrhalis*, or *S. pneumoniae* in patients with a history of type I penicillin hypersensitivity.
2) It is also used in pharyngitis and tonsillitis caused by susceptible *Streptococcus pyogenes*, and respiratory tract infections, including acute maxillary sinusitis, acute bacterial exacerbations of chronic bronchitis, mild to moderate community-acquired pneumonia, Legionnaires' disease, and pertussis.
3) It is useful in the treatment of uncomplicated skin or skin-structure infections, *Helicobacter pylori* infection, duodenal ulcer disease, bartonella infections, early Lyme disease, and encephalitis caused by *Toxoplasma gondii* (in HIV infected patients in conjunction with pyrimethamine).
4) Clarithromycin may also decrease the occurrence of cryptosporidiosis, prevent the occurrence of α-haemolytic *Streptococcal endocarditis*, and serve as a primary prevention for Mycobacterium Avium Complex (MAC) bacteraemia or disseminated infections (in adults, adolescents, and children with advanced HIV infection).

Adverse Effects

The adverse effects of clarithromycin include gastrointestinal effects, general abnormal taste, diarrhoea, nausea, vomiting, elevated blood urea nitrogen, abdominal pain, rash, indigestion, heartburn, headache, longer time for blood clotting, severe allergic reaction, loss of appetite, anxiety, dizziness, breathlessness, elevated liver function tests, swelling in tongue, hallucinations, liver dysfunction, hepatitis, hypoglycaemia, increased blood levels of alkaline phosphatase, aspartate aminotransferase, bilirubin, and creatinine, jaundice, leukopenia, manic behaviour, neuromuscular blockage, neutropenia, pancreatitis, psychosis, heart rhythm disorder, seizures, Stevens-Johnson syndrome, thrombocytopenia, and flatulence.

4.1.10.3. Azithromycin

Azithromycin is a broad-spectrum macrolide antibiotic with a long half-life and a high degree of tissue penetration. It is a part of the *azalide* sub-class of macrolides, and has a 15-membered ring with a methyl-substituted nitrogen (and not a carbonyl group) at C-9a on the aglycone ring to prevent its metabolism.

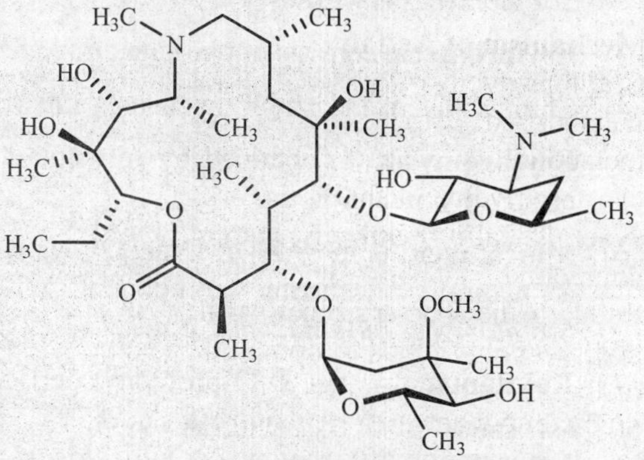

Azithromycin

Mechanism of Action

Azithromycin binds to the 23S rRNA of the bacterial 50S ribosomal subunit. This binding blocks the transpeptidation/translocation step of protein synthesis, thus inhibiting bacterial protein synthesis. This controls various bacterial infections. The strong affinity of azithromycin for bacterial ribosomes is consistent with its broad-spectrum antibacterial activity.

Uses

Azithromycin is used in the treatment of the following bacterial infections:

1) Sinus infections related to *Moraxella catarrhalis* or *Streptococcus pneumonia*,
2) Community-acquired pneumonia caused by *Chlamydia pneumonia*, *Haemophilus influenzae*, or *S. pneumonia*,
3) Chronic obstructive pulmonary disease complications related to *M. catarrhalis* or *S. pneumonia*,
4) Skin infections related to *Staphylococcus aureus*, *Streptococcus pyogenes*, or *Streptococcus agalactiae*,
5) Tonsillitis caused by *S. pyogenes*,
6) Urethritis and cervicitis caused by *Chlamydia trachomatis*,
7) Chancroid genital ulcers (in males) caused by *Haemophilus ducreyi*, and
8) **Ear infections (in children of 6 months and above) caused by** ***M. catarrhalis*****.**

Adverse Effects

Common adverse effects of azithromycin include diarrhoea, nausea, abdominal pain, stomach upset, vomiting, constipation, dizziness, tiredness, headache, vaginal itching or discharge, nervousness, insomnia, skin rash or itching, ringing in ears, hearing problems, or decreased sense of taste or smell.

4.2. SUMMARY

The details given in the chapter can be summarised as follows:

1) **Macrolides** are compounds with a macrocyclic lactone ring (containing 14 or 16 atoms) with attached deoxy sugars.
2) **Erythromycin** is the prototype drug which was obtained in 1952 from *Streptomyces erythreus.*
3) **Erythromycin** consists of two sugar moieties attached to a 14-atom lactone ring.
4) Clarithromycin and azithromycin are semi-synthetic derivatives of erythromycin.
5) **Erythromycin A**, obtained by fermentation, is the principal component of erythromycin antibiotic.
6) **Miocamycin** is the 9,3"-di-O-acetyl derivative of midecamycin A_1, which is a naturally occurring component produced in the fermentation of *Streptomyces aureofaciens.*
7) **Rokitamycin** is the 3"-O-propionyl derivative of leucomycin A_5, which is a component of leucomycin complex (kitasamycin) produced in the fermentation of *Streptomyces kitasatoensis.*
8) **Clarithromycin** is a semi-synthetic macrolide antibiotic, which is derived from erythromycin.
9) **Azithromycin** is a broad-spectrum macrolide antibiotic with a long half-life and a high degree of tissue penetration.
10) **Azithromycin** is a part of the *azalide* sub-class of macrolides, and has a 15-membered ring with a methyl-substituted nitrogen (and not a carbonyl group) at C-9a on the aglycone ring to prevent its metabolism.

4.3. EXERCISE

4.3.1. True or False

1) Erythromycin consists of three sugar moieties attached to a 14-atom lactone ring.
2) Miocamycin is the 3"-O-propionyl derivative of leucomycin A_5 produced in the fermentation of *Streptomyces kitasatoensis.*
3) Azithromycin is a part of the *azalide* sub-class of macrolides.
4) Clarithromycin is a semi-synthetic macrolide antibiotic, which is derived from azithromycin.

4.3.2. Fill in the Blanks

5) Macrolides are compounds with a macrocyclic lactone ring with attached _____.

6) Erythromycin is the prototype drug which was obtained in 1952 from _____.
7) ________ is a broad-spectrum macrolide antibiotic with a long half-life and a high degree of tissue penetration.
8) ________ is the principal component of erythromycin antibiotic.

Answers

1) False	2) False	3) True
4) False	5) Deoxy sugars	6) *Streptomyces erythreus*
7) Azithromycin	8) Erythromycin A	

4.3.3. Very Short Answer Type Questions

1) What are macrolides?
2) Classify macrolides.
3) Draw the chemical structure of erythromycin.
4) Give the mechanism of action of clarithromycin.
5) Give the uses of azithromycin.

4.3.4. Short Answer Type Questions

1) Give the historical background and nomenclature of macrolides.
2) Give the chemical degradation of macrolides.
3) Discuss the SAR of macrolides.
4) Enlist the uses and adverse effects of macrolides.

4.3.5. Long Answer Type Question

1) Write an exhaustive note on macrolides.

CHAPTER 5 Antibiotics-Miscellaneous

5.1. MISCELLANEOUS ANTIBIOTICS

5.1.1. Introduction

Some other antibiotics commonly in use are:

1) Chloramphenicol, and
2) Clindamycin.

5.1.2. Chloramphenicol

Chloramphenicol is bacteriostatic in nature, and is a prototypical broad-spectrum antibiotic along with the tetracyclines. Chloramphenicol is active against many gram-positive and gram-negative organisms. It occurs as fine, white to greyish, white or yellowish white needle-like crystals or elongated plates. It is slightly soluble in water; and freely soluble in acetone, alcohol, ethyl acetate, and propylene glycol.

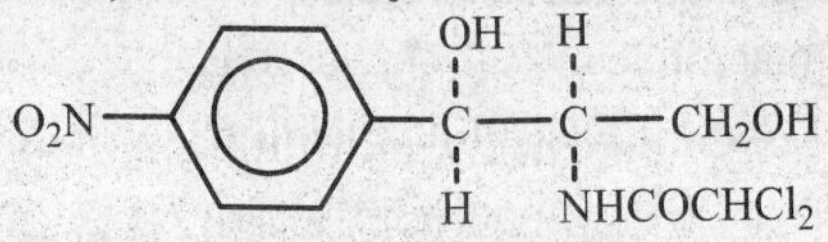

Chloramphenicol

Chloramphenicol palmitate obtained from *Streptomyces venezuelae*, is a fine, white, unctuous, crystalline powder, with a faint odour and bland, mild taste. It is insoluble in water; freely soluble in acetone and chloroform; soluble in ether; sparingly soluble in alcohol; and very slightly soluble in hexane solvent.

5.1.2.1. Historical Background

Chloramphenicol was isolated by **Ehrlich** in **1947** from *Streptomyces venezuelae*. **Gargye and Dutta** reported in **1959** that systemic administration of chloramphenicol causes ototoxicity. They reported a case of irreversible sudden onset of nerve deafness after taking high doses of chloramphenicol intravenously.

A chemical feature of this antibiotic was the presence of a nitrobenzene moiety that was a derivative of dichloroacetic acid. Synthesis of the natural product was reported in **1949**, and chloramphenicol became the first completely synthetic antibiotic to be marketed.

5.1.2.2. Structure-Activity Relationship

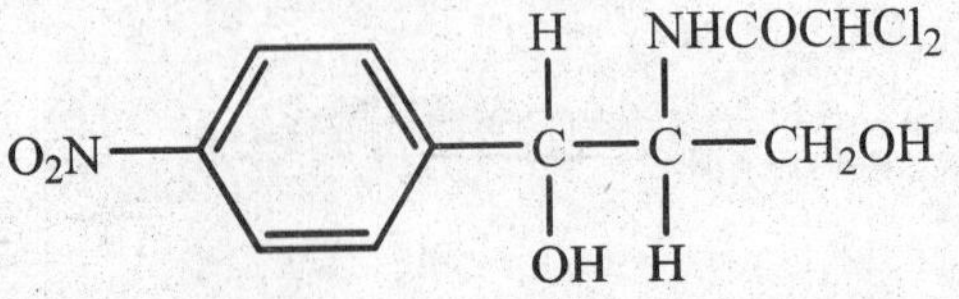

SAR of chloramphenicol can be studied as follows:

1) **Effect on *p*-Nitrophenyl Group**
   i) Replacement of the nitro group by other substituents reduces its antibacterial activity.
   ii) Shifting the nitro group from *para* position also reduces its antibacterial activity.
   iii) Replacing the phenyl groups with alicyclic moieties forms less potent compounds.
   iv) Replacing the *p*-nitrophenyl group with other aryl structures do not result in any loss of activity.
2) **Effect on Dichloracetamido Side Chain**
   i) Other dihaloderivatives of the side chain are less potent, though major activities are retained.
   ii) In case of trihalo derivatives, **Hansch *et al.*** in the light of QSAR calculations claimed that $NHCOCF_3$ derivatives would be 1.7 times as active as the chloramphenicol.
3) **SAR of 1,3-Propanediol:** Modification of the primary alcoholic group on C-1 reduces the activity, and hence the alcoholic group is considered essential for activity.

The antibacterial activity of chloramphenicol resides only in the D-threo compound because its other three isomers are inactive compounds.

Chloramphenicol is a broad-spectrum antibiotic. Due to serious haematological abnormalities that led to aplastic anaemia, the drug was re-audited to establish its clinical position. Nitrobenzene moiety of chloramphenicol depresses the bone marrow and affects the blood elements, thus leading to a fatal outcome.

Chloramphenicol offers three reaction sites open for microbial inactivating enzymes, resulting into:

1) Reduction of nitro group, and
2) Hydrolysis of amide linkage and acetylation (by chloramphenicol acetyltransferase) of the hydroxyl groups in 1,3-propanediol portion to produce 3-acetoxy chloramphenicol and 1,3-diacetoxychloramphenicol metabolites that lack antibacterial activity.

5.1.2.3. Synthesis

Chloramphenicol can be synthesised as follows:

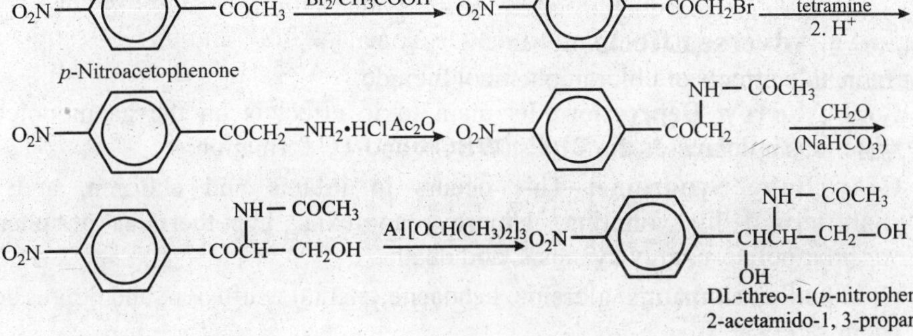

DL-threo-1-(*p*-nitrophenyl)-2-acetamido-1, 3-propanediol

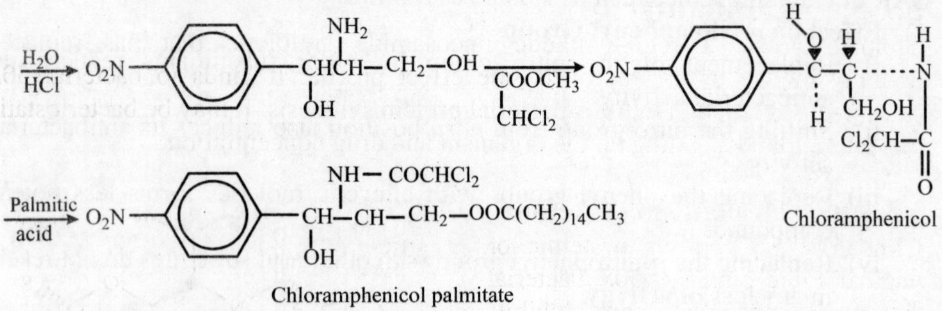

5.1.2.4. Mechanism of Action

Chloramphenicol inhibits protein synthesis at the peptidyl transferase reaction by binding to the bacterial 50S ribosomal subunit. Protein synthesis in these organelles is inhibited at high circulating chloramphenicol levels (resulting in bone marrow toxicity) as the bacterial and mammalian mitochondrial ribosomes are quite similar.

5.1.2.5. Uses

Chloramphenicol has a wide antimicrobial spectrum including gram-positive and gram-negative bacteria (also salmonella), mycoplasma, and rickettsia. It acts as a bacteriostatic agent for most organisms, but for *Haemophilus*, *Neisseria*, and some strains of bacteroides it acts as a bactericidal.

Chloramphenicol is not in use any longer because of its ADR, bacterial resistance, and also the availability of better alternatives. However, it is an alternative drug for the following diseases:

1) **Enteric Fever:** It was the drug of choice for enteric fever originally; but is now on the reserve list as safer drugs (cotrimoxazole, ampicillin, and ciprofloxacin) have been introduced.
2) **Meningitis:** It shows activity against *H. influenzae* meningitis. It is also used in brain abscess. It can be used as an alternative to β-lactams in sensitive patients or in diseases caused by penicillin-resistant organisms.
3) **Topical Uses:** It has a wide antimicrobial spectrum. It is used in eye and ear infections as drops and ointments. It has a good penetration into ocular tissues and aqueous humour.
4) **Other Uses:** It is also used in severe rickettsial infections, infections by anaerobic organisms (sepsis), and pneumonia or laryngotracheitis caused by *Haemophilus*.

5.1.2.6. Adverse Effects

Common side effects of chloramphenicol include:

1) **Bone Marrow Depression:** Its main toxic effect is on the haemopoietic system as it depresses the RBCs, WBCs, and TC formation.
2) **Gray Baby Syndrome:** This occurs in infants and children, and is characterised by vomiting, lethargy, anorexia, hypothermia, peripheral vascular collapse, grey cyanosis, and death.
3) GI irritation, stomatitis, glossitis, headache, mental confusion, and depression occur rarely.

5.1.3. Clindamycin

Clindamycin is a semi-synthetic lincosamide antibiotic that has replaced lincomycin due to its improved side effect profile. It binds to bacterial 50S ribosomal subunit and inhibits bacterial protein synthesis. It may be bacteriostatic or bactericidal depending on the organism and drug concentration.

5.1.3.1. Mechanism of Action

Clindamycin given via systemic or vaginal route binds to 50S bacterial ribosomal subunits and inhibits bacterial protein synthesis. It mainly binds to the 23S RNA subunit. Clindamycin given via topical route reduces free fatty acid concentrations on skin and suppresses the growth of *Propionibacterium acnes* (*Corynebacterium acnes*, an anaerobe present in sebaceous glands and follicles).

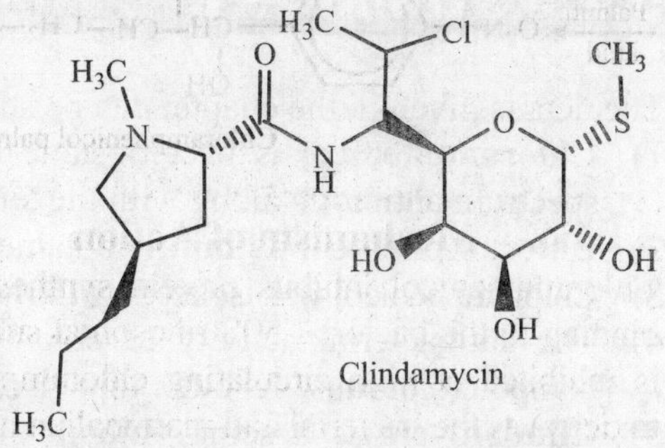

Clindamycin

5.1.3.2. Uses

Clindamycin has the following uses:

1) It is used in infections caused by susceptible anaerobic bacteria, including *Bacteroides* spp., *Peptostreptococcus*, anaerobic streptococci, *Clostridium* spp., and microaerophilic streptococci.
2) It is useful in polymicrobial infections, like intra-abdominal or pelvic infections, osteomyelitis, diabetic foot ulcers, aspiration pneumonia, and dental infections.
3) It is also used in the treatment of MSSA and respiratory infections caused by *S. pneumoniae* and *S. pyogenes* in patients intolerant to other indicated antibiotics or infected with resistant organisms.
4) It can be used vaginally to treat vaginosis caused by *Gardnerella vaginosis*.
5) It reduces the toxin-producing effects of *S. aureus* and *S. pyogenes,* and thus is used in necrotizing fasciitis.
6) It is topically used to treat acne.

5.1.3.3. Adverse Effects

Clindamycin causes the following adverse effects:

1) Skin problems, such as hives, rash, red, shedding, or peeling skin,
2) Jaundice,
3) Vomiting, severe stomach pain, or diarrhoea,
4) Signs of low blood pressure, ranging from dizziness to fainting,
5) Pain or difficulty in swallowing, pain behind the breastbone, heartburn or acid regurgitation (signs of inflammation in oesophagus),
6) Vein irritation in patients receiving injections of clindamycin,
7) Fever or body aches,
8) Blisters or swelling in lips, mouth, eyes, ears, nose, or genital areas,

9) Signs of abnormal bleeding caused by low blood-clotting cells (thrombocytopenia), such as easy bruising, red pin-prick spots on the skin, gums bleeding while brushing teeth, and
10) Abnormally high or low levels of eosinophils and granulocytes.

5.2. SUMMARY

The details given in the chapter can be summarised as follows:

1) **Chloramphenicol** is bacteriostatic in nature, and is a prototypical broad-spectrum antibiotic along with the tetracyclines.
2) **Chloramphenicol palmitate** obtained from *Streptomyces venezuelae*.
3) Chloramphenicol was isolated by Ehrlich in 1947 from *Streptomyces venezuelae.*
4) The antibacterial activity of chloramphenicol resides only in the D-threo compound because its other three isomers are inactive compounds.
5) **Clindamycin** is a semi-synthetic lincosamide antibiotic that has replaced lincomycin due to its improved side effect profile.

5.3. EXERCISE

5.3.1. True or False

1) Chloramphenicol was isolated by Ehrlich in 1947 from *Streptomyces venezuelae*.
2) Clindamycin is a semi-synthetic lincosamide antibiotic that has replaced lincomycin due to its improved side effect profile.

5.3.2. Fill in the Blanks

3) Chloramphenicol palmitate obtained from ________.
4) The antibacterial activity of chloramphenicol resides only in the ________ because its other three isomers are inactive compounds.

<u>Answers</u>

1) True 2) True 3) *Streptomyces venezuelae* 4) D-threo compound

5.3.3. Very Short Answer Type Questions

1) Draw the chemical structure of chloramphenicol.
2) Give the mechanism of action of chloramphenicol.
3) Draw the chemical structure of clindamycin.
4) Give the mechanism of action of clindamycin.

5.3.4. Short Answer Type Questions

1) Discuss the SAR of chloramphenicol.
2) Give the synthesis of chloramphenicol.
3) Enlist the uses and adverse effects of chloramphenicol.
4) Give the uses and adverse effects of clindamycin.

5.3.5. Long Answer Type Question

1) Write an exhaustive note on chloramphenicol.
2) Give a brief review of clindamycin.

CHAPTER 6
Pro-drugs

6.1. PRODRUGS

6.1.1. Introduction

Albert in the late 1950s used the term **prodrug** to indicate pharmacologically inactive compounds that can be used to modify the physical and chemical properties of a drug to increase its use and/or to decrease its toxicity. Prodrug is a covalently bonded chemically modified inactive drug precursor. It has a weak linkage between drug and inert chemical that can be broken by enzymatic or non-enzymatic process in the body to let the drug exert its therapeutic effect.

Prodrugs can also be termed as **proagent**, **congeners**, **latentiated** and **reversible** or **bioreversible derivatives**. The design approach is referred to as drug latentiation or latentiation. Prodrug is made up of an active drug and promoiety. The latter is not required for pharmacological action but is selected carefully so that it offers a desirable property to the drug; thus, the compound exhibits a desirable pharmacological property. The promoiety should be safe and excreted from the body at the earliest possible time.

6.1.2. Basic Concept of Prodrug

There are many therapeutic drugs with unwanted properties that may become pharmacological, pharmaceutical, or pharmacokinetic barriers in clinical drug application. There are various approaches of diminishing the undesirable drug properties and maintaining the desirable therapeutic activity; however, the chemical approach using drug derivatisation offers the highest flexibility and is an important way by which drug efficacy can be improved. The prodrug approach using reversible derivatives is used for optimising the clinical application of drug. This approach gained interest in early 1970s for improving drug therapy. Since then many prodrugs have been designed and developed to overcome pharmaceutical and pharmacokinetic barriers in clinical drug applicaiton, such as low oral drug absorption, lack of site specificity, chemical instability, toxicity, and poor patient compliance (bad taste, odour, pain at injection site, etc.). Once the barrier to the use of the parent compound has been overcome, these temporary forms are converted to the free parent compound to exert its pharmacological activity. The prodrug approach has been illustrated in **figure 6.1**:

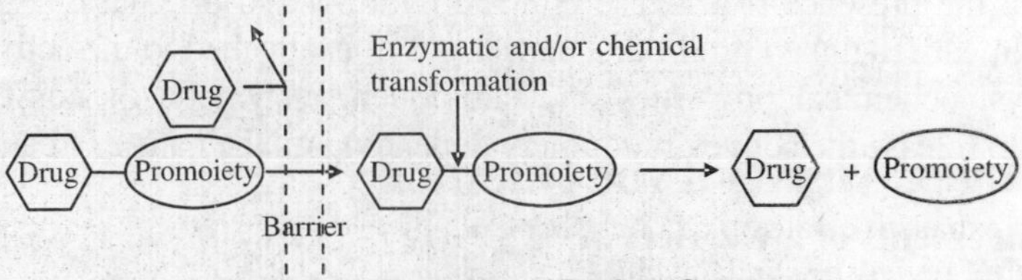

Figure 6.1: Illustration of Prodrug Concept

Drug-promoiety complex is the pharmacologically inactive prodrug. The barrier is any liability or limitation of a parent drug that prevents optimal biopharmaceutical or pharmacokinetic performance, and thus should be overcome so that a marketable drug can be developed. Drug and promoiety are covalently linked via bioreversible groups that are chemically or enzymatically labile. Ideal prodrug yields the parent drug with high recovery ratios and non-toxic promoiety.

Ideal Requirements of a Prodrug

1) It should not have any intrinsic pharmacological action.
2) It should undergo rapid metabolism chemically or enzymatically into active form where desired.
3) The metabolic fragments apart from the active drug should be non-toxic.

6.1.3. Objectives of Prodrug Design

Prodrug designing has the following objectives:

1) It brings the active drugs to their respective active sites.
2) It provides the desired pharmacological effects and minimises the adverse metabolic and/or toxicological effects.
3) It improves the clinical and therapeutic effectiveness of drugs exhibiting some undesirable properties that may hinder their clinical efficacy.
4) It avoids clinical co-administration of two drugs to enhance pharmacological activity or prevent clinical side effects. Simultaneous administration may not lead to equivalent absorption or transportation to site of action. Hence, mutual prodrug concept is employed when two synergistic drugs are to be co-administered at the same site. Mutual prodrugs are synthesised with the pharmacological objective to improve each drug's efficacy, optimise delivery, and lower toxicity.

6.1.4. Classification of Prodrugs

Depending on the constitution lipophilicity method of bioactivation and catalyst involved, prodrugs are classified in the following two groups:

1) Carrier-linked prodrugs, and
2) Bioprecursor prodrugs.

6.1.4.1. Carrier-Linked Prodrugs

In carrier-linked prodrugs, the active drug and an inert carrier are covalently linked. These prodrugs are ester or amide. They have modified lipophilicity due to the attached carrier. The active drug is released by chemical or enzymatical hydrolytic cleavage. **For example**, ditrimethylethanoate groups of dipivaloyl adrenaline in the presence of esterase enzyme hydrolyse to original OH groups on adrenaline. In carrier-linked prodrug, a carrier group is attached to the active drug to alter its physicochemical properties and subsequent enzymatic or non-enzymatic mechanism to release the active drug moiety depending on the nature of carrier used.

Ideal Requirements of a Carrier

1) It should be biologically inactive, non-toxic, and non-immunogenic.
2) It should reduce the drug activity.

3) It should reduce the toxicity of host drug.
4) It should carry and release the drug at specific site of action.
5) It should release the drug chemically or enzymatically.
6) It should easily biotransform and excrete after drug release.
7) It should be easy to prepare.
8) It should easily combine with the drug.

Types of Carrier-Linked Prodrugs

1) **Double or Cascade-Latentiated Prodrugs:** A prodrug is derivatised such that only enzymatic conversion to prodrug is possible before the latter can cleave to release the active drug.

2) **Macromolecular Prodrugs:** In these, macromolecules like polysaccharides, dextrans, cyclodextrins, proteins, peptides and polymers, are used as carriers.

3) **Site-Specific Prodrugs:** In these, a carrier transports the active drug to a specific site of target.

4) **Mutual Prodrugs:** In these, an inert molecule is not used as a carrier, but it is a biologically active drug. A mutual prodrug has two pharmacologically active agents that are coupled together so that each acts as a promoiety for the other agent and *vice versa*. Since the selected carrier's biological action is similar to that of the parent drug, it may show synergistic action or have some additional biological actions (that the parent drug does not have).

   The carrier can also be a drug that helps in targeting the parent drug to a specific site or organ or cells or may improve site specificity of a drug. The carrier drug can also overcome some side effects of the parent drug.

Advantages of carrier-Linked Prodrugs

1) It increases drug absorption,
2) It reliefs the pain at the site of injection,
3) It masks the unpleasant taste of some drugs,
4) It reduces drug toxicity,
5) It reduces metabolic inactivation of the drug, and
6) It increases chemical stability of the drug.

6.1.4.2. Bioprecursor Prodrugs

The bioprecursor prodrugs do not contain carriers but ready up on metabolism to induce the functionally active species. These prodrugs rely on oxidative or reductive activation reactions (unlike the hydrolytic activation of carrier-linked prodrugs). They metabolise into a new compound that is active, and if not it further metabolises to an active metabolite (**e.g.** amine to aldehyde to carboxylic acid).

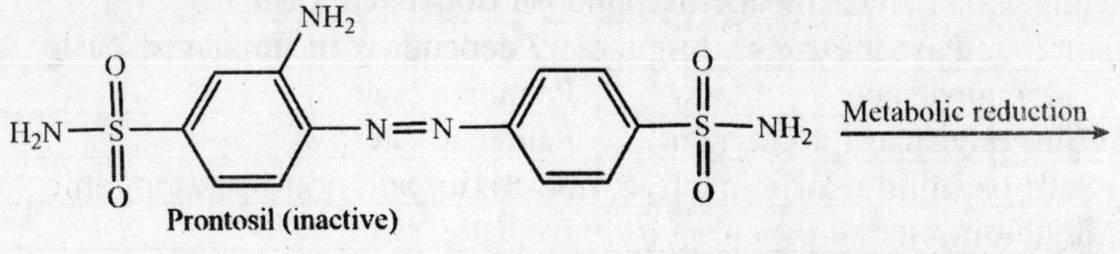

Prontosil (inactive)

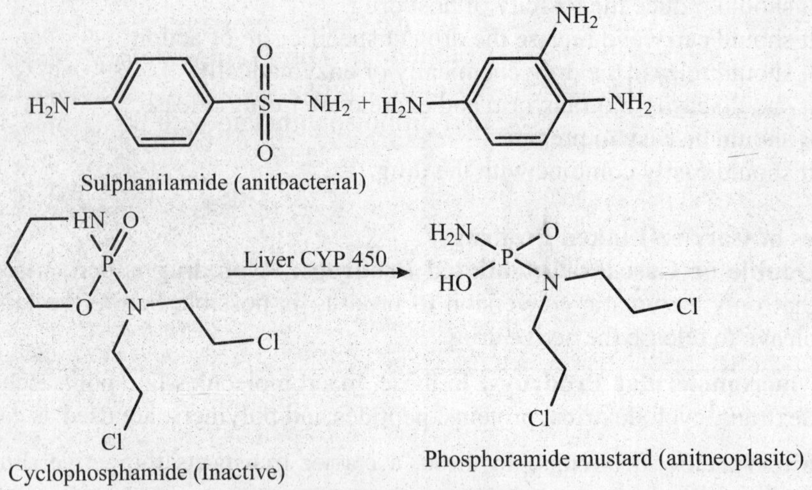

Figure 6.2: Examples of Bioprecursor Prodrugs

6.1.5. Applications of Prodrug Design

The aim of prodrug development is to solve specific pharmaceutical or pharmacological and pharmacokinetic problems. The main objectives of prodrugs are:

1) **Pharmaceutical Applications**
   i) Improvement of taste,
   ii) Improvement of odour,
   iii) Change of physical form for preparation of solid dosage forms,
   iv) Reduction of gastrointestinal irritation,
   v) Reduction of pain on injection, and
   vi) Enhancement of drug solubility and dissolution rate.

2) **Pharmacokinetic Applications**
   i) Enhancement of bioavailability (lipophilicity),
   ii) Improved stability and solubility,
   iii) Prevention of pre-systemic metabolism,
   iv) Prolongation of duration of action,
   v) Reduction of toxicity, and
   vi) Site-specific drug delivery.

6.1.5.1. Improvement of Taste

Poor patient compliance in children occurs due to the bitterness, acidity, or causticity of the drugs. There are two approaches to overcome the bad taste of drug. First is reduction of drug solubility in saliva and the other is to lower the affinity of drug towards taste receptors, thus, masking the bitter taste. Some **examples** of drugs with improved taste are given in **table 6.1**:

Table 6.1: Drugs with Improved Taste

Parent Drugs	Prodrugs with Improved Taste
Chloramphenicol	Palmitate ester
Clindamycin	Palmitate ester
Sulfisoxazole	Acetyl ester
Erythromycin	Estolate

6.1.5.2. Improvement of Odour

A compound's odour depends on its vapour pressure. A liquid with high vapour pressure will have a strong odour. **For example,** ethyl mercaptan is a foul smelling liquid and is used in leprosy treatment. It is converted to phthalate ester, which is a diethyl dithioisophthalate with higher boiling point and no odour.

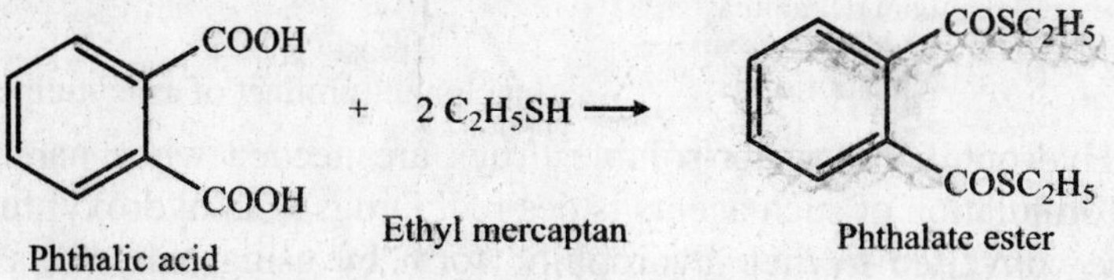

6.1.5.3. Change of Physical Form for Preparation of Solid Dosage Forms

Drugs which are in liquid form cannot be formulated as a tablet, especially if their dose is high. Such liquid drugs are converted into solid prodrugs by the formation of symmetrical molecule with higher tendency to crystallise. An **example** of such a drug is ester of ethyl mercapto and trichloroethanol.

6.1.5.4. Reduction in Gastrointestinal Irritation

Several drugs irritate and damage the gastric mucosa through direct contact increased stimulation of acid secretion or through interference with protective mucosal layer. The NSAID's (especially salicylates) have such a tendency. They lower gastric PH and induce ulceration. **Examples** of prodrug design to overcome such problems of gastric distress are given below:

Parent Drugs	Prodrugs with Enhanced Hydrophilicity
Tocophenols	Sodium succinate ester
Metronidazole	Amino acid esters

6.1.5.5. Reduction of Pain on Injection

Intramuscular injections are painful if the injected drug precipitates in the surrounding cell or if the injected solutions are strongly acidic, alkaline, or alcoholic. **For example**, low aqueous solubility of clindamycin hydrochloride and alkaline solution of phenytoin are the causes of pain on injection. This can be overcome if more water-soluble prodrug of such agent (like 2-phosphate ester of clindamycin) is used.

6.1.5.6. Enhancement of Bioavailability (Lipophilicity)

A big advantage of increased bioavailability through increased lipophilicity is the reduction in new dosage. **For example,** bacampicillin is as effective as ampicillin in $1/3^{rd}$ of the dose of latter.

6.1.5.7. Improved Stability and Solubility

Stability: Use of prodrugs for improving drug stability is a good approach. Several oral drugs may decompose in their shelf-life or in the GIT. **For example,** azacytidine (antineoplastic) undergoes rapid hydrolysis in acidic pH, but its **bisulphite prodrug is more stable.**

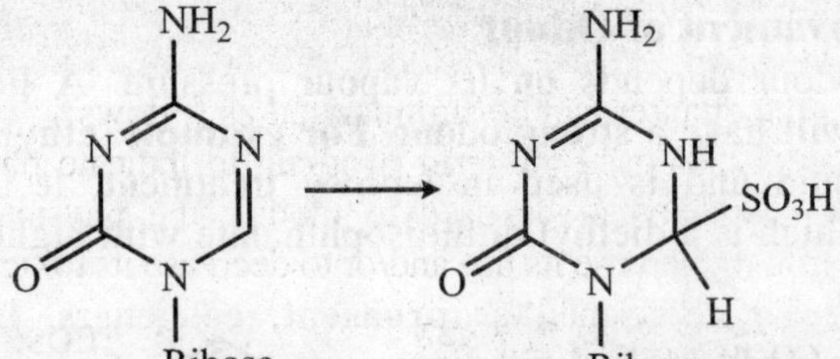

azacytidine bisulphite (product of azacytidine)

Solubility: Hydrophilic or water-soluble drugs are needed when parenteral or ophthalmic formulation of such agents is desired. Drugs with hydroxyl functional group can be converted to their hydrophilic form by using half esters such as hemi-glutarate or hemi-phthalates, the other half of this acid carries sodium, potassium, or amine salts, and renders the moiety more soluble.

Parent Drugs	Prodrugs Causing Little/No Gastric Distress
Salicylic acid	Aspirin
Kanamycin	Kanamycin pamoate

6.1.5.8. Prevention of Pre-Systemic Metabolism

Some corticosteroids, **e.g.,** triamcin, undergo first-pass hepatic metabolism, and this can be prevented by using their esters or either prodrugs. Frequent dosing is required for drugs with short biological half-lives. This can be overcome by using controlled release and prodrug approaches.

6.1.5.9. Prolongation of Duration of Action

The **rate controlling steps** in enhancement of duration of action of drug are:

1) The release rate of prodrug from the site of application or administration in the systemic circulation, and
2) The conversion rate of prodrug into the active drug in blood.

6.1.5.10. Reduction of Toxicity

An important objective of drug design is to develop a drug with high activity and low toxicity. **For example**, NSAID's meant for systemic use have a local side effect of gastric distress, which can be overcome by using prodrugs. Another **example** is sulindac bioprecursor, which is converted into its sulfoxide as it does not cause any gastric distress and undergoes better absorption in blood.

6.1.5.11. Site-Specific Drug Delivery

A drug after its systemic absorption gets distributed to various body parts, including the target site and non-targeted tissues. A distribution pattern has the following **disadvantages**:

1) The drug may cause undesirable toxic effect on non-targeting tissues.
2) Due to dilution a smaller fraction of drug reaches the target site.
3) If the target site has a long distribution time, the drug is eliminated without even reaching the site.

These problems can be overcome by targeting the drug to its site of action by altering its deposition characteristics.

6.2. SUMMARY

The details given in the chapter can be summarised as follows:

1) **Albert** in the late 1950s used the term **prodrug** to indicate pharmacologically inactive compounds that can be used to modify the physical and chemical properties of a drug to increase its use and/or to decrease its toxicity.
2) Prodrugs can also be termed as **proagent**, **congeners**, **latentiated** and **reversible** or **bioreversible derivatives**.
3) In **carrier-linked prodrugs**, the active drug and an inert carrier are covalently linked.
4) **Double or cascade-latentiated prodrugs** are derivatised such that only enzymatic conversion to prodrug is possible before the latter can cleave to release the active drug.
5) In **macromolecular prodrugs**, macromolecules like polysaccharides, dextrans, cyclodextrins, proteins, peptides and polymers, are used as carriers.
6) In **site-specific prodrugs**, a carrier transports the active drug to a specific site of target.
7) In **mutual prodrugs**, an inert molecule is not used as a carrier, but it is a biologically active drug.
8) The **bioprecursor prodrugs** do not contain carriers but ready up on metabolism to induce the functionally active species.

6.3. EXERCISE

6.3.1. True or False

1) In macromolecular prodrugs, the active drug and an inert carrier are covalently linked.
2) In carrier-linked prodrugs, a carrier transports the active drug to a specific site of target.

6.3.2. Fill in the Blanks

3) In _____, an inert molecule is not used as a carrier, but it is a biologically active drug.
4) The ________ do not contain carriers but ready up on metabolism to induce the functionally active species.

Answers

1) False 2) False 3) Mutual prodrugs 4) Bioprecursor prodrugs

6.3.3. Very Short Answer Type Questions

1) What are prodrugs?
2) Give the ideal requirements of prodrugs.
3) Give the objectives of prodrug designing.
4) What are the advantages of carrier-linked prodrugs?
5) How pain on injection can be reduced by prodrugs?

6.3.4. Short Answer Type Questions

1) Discuss the basic concept of prodrugs.
2) Give the classification of prodrugs.
3) How taste, odour, stability and solubility of drugs can be improved by prodrugs?

6.3.5. Long Answer Type Question

1) **Write an exhaustive note on pharmacokinetic applications of prodrugs.**

CHAPTER 7 Antimalarials

7.1. ANTIMALARIALS

7.1.1. Introduction

Malaria is an infectious disease affecting humans and other animals. It is a mosquito-borne infectious disease caused by parasitic protozoans (group of single-celled microorganisms) of *Plasmodium* type. The symptoms of this disease include fever, vomiting, fatigue, and headache. The symptoms usually begin 10-15 days after being bitten by mosquitoes. In severe cases, the skin becomes yellow, the patient experiences seizures, goes to coma, or finally dies. Malaria is **transmitted by an infected female Anopheles mosquito**, which introduces the parasites from its saliva into the person's blood. The parasites reach the liver to mature and reproduce there. Five species of *Plasmodium* can infect humans. *P. falciparum* causes most of the deaths; while *P. vivax, P. ovale*, and *P. malariae* cause milder forms of malaria; *P. knowlesi* rarely cause a disease in humans.

The risks can be reduced by the prevention of mosquito bites by using mosquito nets, repellents, spraying insecticides, and draining standing water. Many medicines are available to prevent malaria. Sulfadoxine or pyrimethamine is the drugs indicated in infants and after the first trimester of pregnancy in areas having high rate of malaria. Mefloquine, lumefantrine, sulfadoxine, or pyrimethamine is also given. If artemisinin is not available, quinine can be used along with doxycycline.

7.1.2. Etiology of Malaria

Malaria is a life-threatening disease, transmitted through the bite of an infected female *Anopheles* mosquito, carrying the *Plasmodium* parasite. The infected mosquito releases the parasite in the blood by biting an individual.

Causative Agent

The causative agent of malaria is a protozoan parasite of the genus *Plasmodium*. The species of plasmodium responsible for malaria in human beings are ***P. falciparum*** and ***P. vivax*** causing about 80% of recognised cases of malaria and approximately 90% of deaths. Malaria is also caused by other species such as ***P. ovale***, ***P. malariae***, ***P. knowesli***, and ***P. semiovale***. The female **Anopheles mosquito** acts as a **vector** for human beings.

Mode of Transmission

Malaria is caused by a microscopic parasite which transmits by mosquito bites. The transmission cycle involves:

1) **Uninfected Mosquito:** A mosquito becomes infected by feeding on a malaria-infected person.
2) **Transmission of Parasite:** If the infected mosquito now bites health individuals, the malarial parasites are transmitted to them.

3) **In the Liver:** Parasites then reach the liver, where some types of them remain dormant for even a year.
4) **Into the Bloodstream:** The parasites on maturing leave the liver and infect the RBCs. At this point, the symptoms of malaria are observed.
5) **On to the Next Person:** If at this point an uninfected mosquito bites an infected person, it will become infected with the malarial parasite and will transmit the infection to another healthy person it will bite.

As the malarial parasites infect RBCs, individuals may also suffer from malaria on coming in contact with the infected blood as follows:
1) From mother to unborn child,
2) Through blood transfusions, and
3) By sharing needles used for injecting drugs.

Life Cycle of Malarial Parasite

The life cycle (**figure 7.1**) for all the five species of malarial parasite is almost similar and involves the following **three stages**:
1) Infecting an individual with sporozoites,
2) Asexual reproduction, and
3) Sexual reproduction.

The first two stages occur within the human body, while the third stage begins in the human body and completes within the mosquito body.

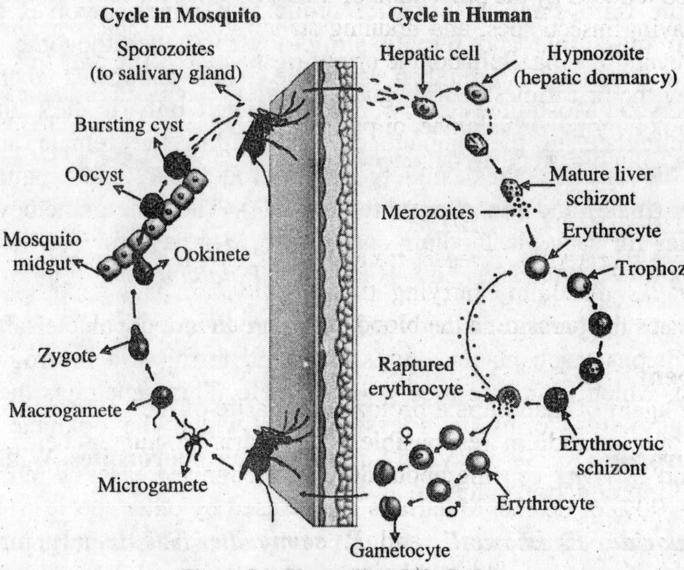

Figure 7.1: Plasmodium Life Cycle

In humans, infection occurs when an infected female Anopheles mosquito bites and injects saliva infected with **sporozoites** into the **bloodstream**. It is the first life stage of plasmodium, and is known as **stage of infection**.

The next stage is **asexual reproduction**, which is divided into the **pre-erythrocytic** (or **exoerythrocytic**) and the **erythrocytic phases**. In about 30-60 minutes after the parasites have been injected in the humans, sporozoites reach the **liver cells** (first target) through blood circulation, and start dividing and producing **schizonts** within

6-7 days. Each schizont further produces numerous **merozoites** (**exoerythrocytic schizogony**) which are released into the bloodstream. With this the pre-erythrocytic phase of the asexual reproductive stage comes to an end.

In ***P. vivax*** and ***P. ovale***, the sporozoites may not follow the reproduction step and remain dormant in the liver cells; such dormant sporozoites are called **hypnozoites**, which may become activated after weeks, months, or even years causing relapses and entering the bloodstream (as merozoites). The pre-erythrocytic phase is non-pathogenic, does not give any symptoms or signs of the disease, and duration is different for all species of parasite.

Merozoites in the blood stream now invade the **red blood cells** (second target), to begin the erythrocytic phase within. The first stage within the RBCs is the **ring stage** that develops into a **trophozoite**, which cannot digest the haem so converts it into **haemozoin** and digest the globin protein which provides amino acids for their reproduction. The **erythrocytic schizont** (initially immature and then mature into schizont) forms the next cellular stage in which a **new generation merozoites** (**erythrocytic schizogony**) are produced. When the RBCs rupture, these merozoites are released in the bloodstream to invade other RBCs. At this point parasitaemia and other clinical signs appear. The liver phase occurs only once, whereas the erythrocytic phase occurs in multiple cycles. The merozoites released after each cycle form the febrile waves.

Now occurs the third stage of sexual reproduction which involves **parasite differentiation** into **male** and **female gametocytes** (non-pathogenic form of parasite). These gametocytes are taken up by the female anopheles when it bites an infected person. Mosquitoes can become infected only if they bite when gametocytes circulate in the human's blood. Within the female anopheles mosquitoes, the gametocytes undergo **gametogenesis** and mature into **microgametes** (male) and **macrogametes** (female). The time gametocytes take to mature varies for each plasmodium species, i.e., 3-4 days for *P. vivax* and *P. ovale*, 6-8 days for *P. malariae*, and 8-10 days for *P. falciparum*.

The microgamete nucleus in the mosquito gut, produce eight nuclei after three successive divisions; each nucleus fuses with and fertilises a macrogamete to form a **zygote**, which is transformed into **ookinete**. This penetrates the midgut wall of mosquito and forms an **oocyst**, within which the ookinete nucleus undergoes **sporogony** for 8-15 days to form numerous **sporozoites**. With this the stage of sexual reproduction comes to an end.

The sporozoites are released in the mosquito cavity after the oocyst ruptures. Only a few hundreds of released sporozoites reach the salivary glands of mosquitoes. Now when these infected mosquitoes bite another healthy individual (host), they inject the infected saliva into the host and a new cycle starts all over again.

Symptoms

The infected person suffers from **high fever** (which comes and goes); the pattern of fever depends on the species of malarial parasite. At the initial stage, malaria infection seems to be like flu with **high fever**, **fatigue**, and **body aches**, with **hot and cold stages**. Signs and symptoms in children are not specific, thus their diagnosis is delayed. The infected person also suffers from **headache**, **nausea**, **shaking chills** (rigors), **sweating**, and **weakness**. **Anaemia** is a common symptom of malarial infection due to the attack of the *Plasmodium* parasite on the RBCs.

Most severe form of malaria is caused by *P. falciparum*. Along with fever, the infected person also suffers from other complications like **haemolytic anaemia** (due to destroyed RBCs), **yellow skin discoloration**, **kidney failure**, **pulmonary oedema** (fluid in the lungs), **cerebral malaria**, **convulsions**, **coma**, or **death**.

Prevention

Malaria can be prevented and controlled by the following measures:

1) By an early diagnosis using blood smears,
2) By consulting to the health authorities without delaying,
3) By properly maintaining the drainage system, as the stagnant water is a perfect breeding place for mosquitoes.
4) By using DDT or kerosene for destroying the mosquitoes.
5) By using mosquito nets and/or repellents for preventing mosquito bites.
6) By treating the infected person with anti-malarial drugs, **e.g.,** quinine and chloroquine.
7) By conducting seminars on sanitary measures and proper drainage system.

7.1.3. Historical Background

Malaria has even contributed to the decline of Greek civilisation. It widely occurred in colonial India and in China South of Yangtze River. In traditional Chinese medicine, roots of ***Dichroa febrifuga*** (Saxifragaceae) (Changshan) were used. **Febrifugine** (an alkaloid) was extracted for malarial treatment but it was too emetic to be acceptable. Another herb for antimalarial activity that came 2000 years ago is **quinqho**. The plant ***Artemisia annua*** (Asteraceae) gave artemisinine (qinghaosu). The indigenous people of South America used the bark of ***Cinchona pubescens*** (Rubiaceae) (Jesuite's bark) to control malarial fever. **Pelletier and Caventou** isolated quinine (the active principle of cinchona), and **Woodward and Doering** synthesised it.

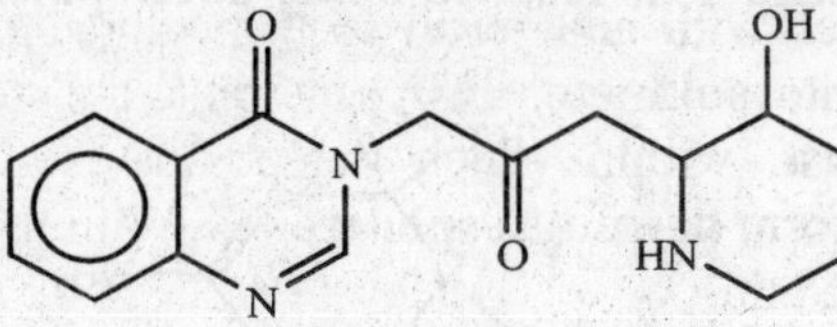

Febrifugine

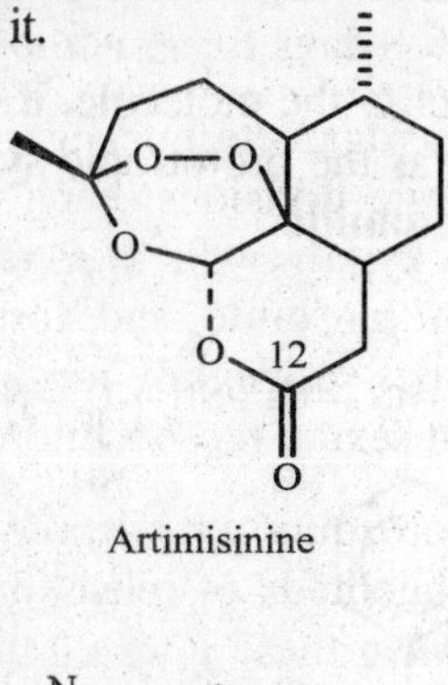

Artimisinine

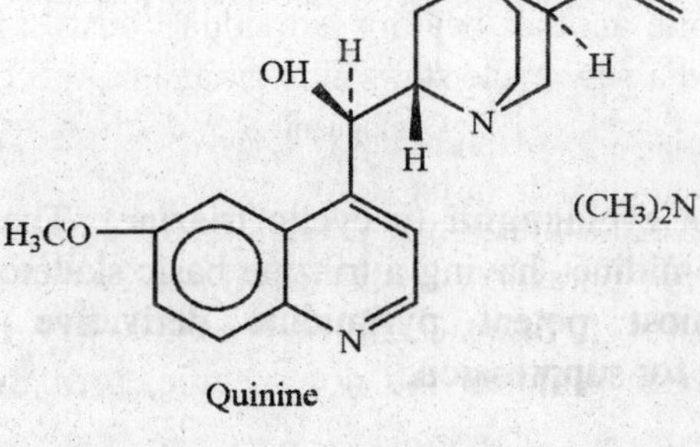

Quinine

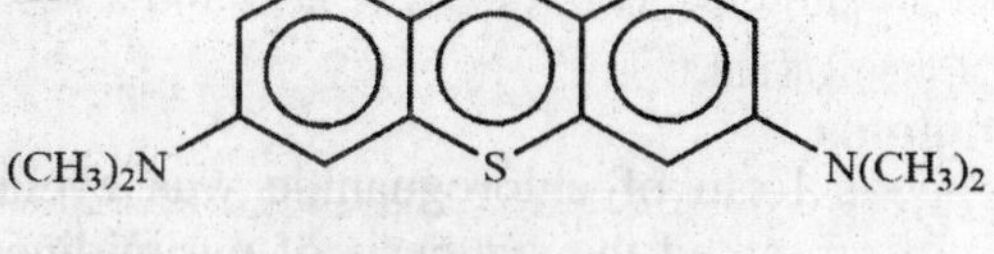

Methylene blue

Quinine was the only anti-parasitic agent that was also effective against malaria. During World War II, the supply of cinchona bark was cut off to Germans and Japanese. At that time, the first synthetic compound was **methylene blue** (dye). Consequently, chemists designed potential antimalarial agents based on the modifications that resulted in the synthesis of compounds having 6-methoxy quinoline moiety and the diethylamino alkylamino type of side chain.

This concluded the discovery of **pamaquine**. However, it was toxic and chemists made further research to obtain **quinacrine** (an acidalkylaminoalkylamino acridine). It was also toxic and was not effective against *vivax* malaria.

The 4-aminoquinolines are central for investigation and French and German synthesised **sontoquine**. Through this process, **chloroquine** was developed as a very effective and the most widely used antimalarial drug. Another drug that is structurally closely related to pamaquine and is the drug of choice against relapsing *vivax* malaria is **primaquine**.

Afterwards, **prontosil** also presented antimalarial activity against *P. falciparum* and *P. vivax*. Its metabolite, **sulfanilamide**, also exhibit a significant antimalarial activity. Next conclusion was to combine the structural features of sulphanilamido-pyrimidine and quinacrine. The pyrimidine ring was selected as the attachment site for the basic alkylaminoalkyl side chain, because it was found to be having tautomeric forms, that are essential for antimalarial activity.

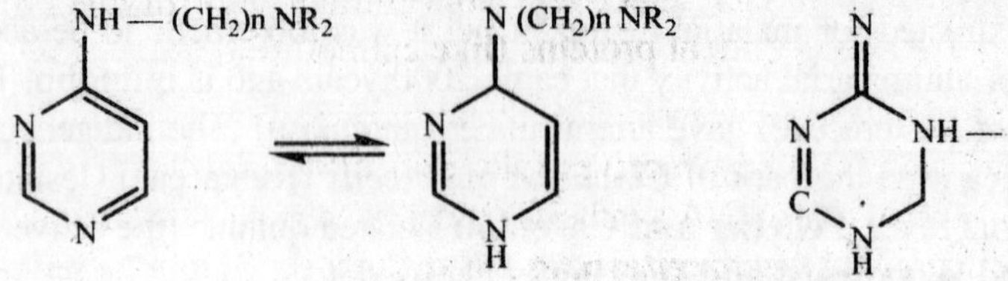

To simplify the molecule, it was logical that the pyrimidine may not be necessary as long as the prototropic system is present. This resulted in the development of **chloroguanide**.

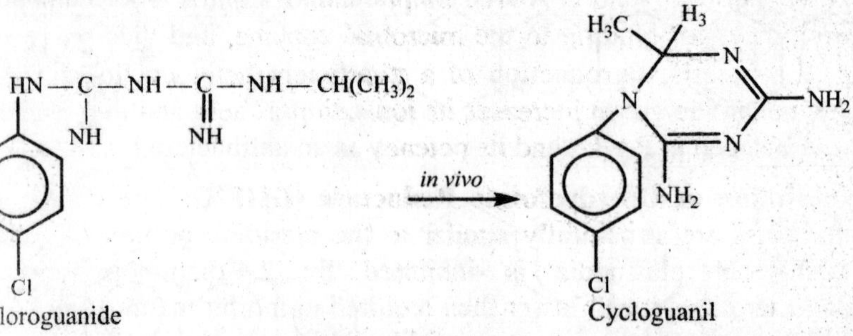

Chloroguanide Cycloguanil

The active form of chloroguanide was **cycloguanil** (a cyclic triazine). These findings prompted the synthesis of pyrimidines having a triazine basic skeleton, like 2,4-diaminopyrimidines. **The most potent pyrimidine derivative is pyrimethamine, which by itself is used for suppression.**

7.1.4. Mechanism of Action

The anti-malarial drugs act in the following ways:

1) **Intercalation with DNA:** The agents containing quinoline ring are attached to DNA. The flat ring system intercalates between base pairs in double helical DNA and the side chains in their charged tertiary amino group bind ionically to negatively charged phosphate group of the deoxyribose phosphate back bone. The other interactions include alcoholic hydroxyl groups of quinolone methanols form hydrogen bonds with any one DNA base, and the 7-chloro atom in chloroquinine and analogs is electrostatically attracted to the guanine-2-amino group (guanidine specificity). These bindings inhibit the separation of complementary strands of the parent double-helical DNA (**figure 7.2**).

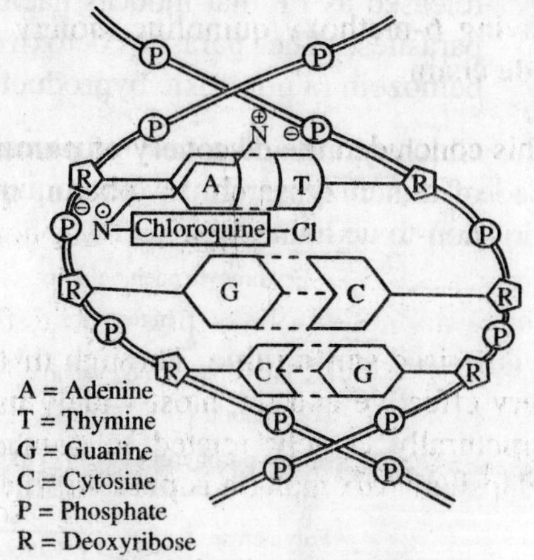

Figure 7.2: A Possible Mechanism of Action of Chloroquine at the Molecular Level

The antimalarial alkaloid concentrates in blood schizontocides and increases the pH of acidic vesicles in sensitive malarial parasites. Thereafter, they interfere with lysosomal degradation of haemoglobin and results in clumping of pigments. The plasmodia selectively concentrate these drugs. However, the functions of Ca^{2+}-dependent proteins (like calmodulin) are also inhibited.

2) **Inhibition of Folic Acid Synthesis:** The compounds in this class are structurally similar to folic acid. The host receives folic acid from food, while the parasite (that requires folic acid for DNA synthesis) is deprived of this vital compound.

   i) **Inhibition of Dihydropteroate Synthase:** Sulphonamides and sulphones act as antimetabolites and inhibit dihydropteroate synthase enzyme that catalyses the condensation of pyrophosphate ester of 2-amino-4-oxo-6-hydroxymethyl dihydropteridine with *Para*-Aminobenzoic Acid (PABA). Sulphonamides and PABA compete with each other for binding to the microbial enzyme, and thus prevents folic acid synthesis. Introduction of a π-deficient heterocyclic ring into the sulphonamide group increases its ionisation as acid and this increases its resemblance to PABA and its potency as an antibacterial.

   ii) **Inhibition of Dihydrofolate Reductase (DHFR):** The compounds in this class are structurally similar to the pteridine portion of folic acid. DHFR of plasmodia is inhibited by 2,4-diaminopyrimidines at concentrations much lower than required to inhibit mammalian enzymes. DHFR catalyses the reduction of dihydrofolate to tetrahydrofolate, which is required for biosynthesising purines, pyrimidines, and DNA. These agents tightly bind to DHFR of plasmodia. Inhibition of DHFR by **pyrimethamine in malarial parasite can be seen by failure** of nuclear **division at the time of schizont formation in erythrocytes** and liver.

3) **Inhibition of Polymerase Enzyme:** In **figure 7.3**, a recent mechanism of action of chloroquine, amodiaquine, and other 4-aminoquinolines is shown. This mode of action involves interaction of chloroquine with ferriprotoporphyrin IX (FP). On digestion of haemoglobin, its heme part is released as FP that induces haemolysis of erythrocytes and lysis of malarial parasites. The parasite detoxifies the released FP by converting it to hemozoin (a non-toxic byproduct).

Chloroquine and a few structurally related anti-malarials inhibit the activity of this enzyme. Thus, chloroquine prevents the conversion of toxic FP to a non-toxic hemozoin.

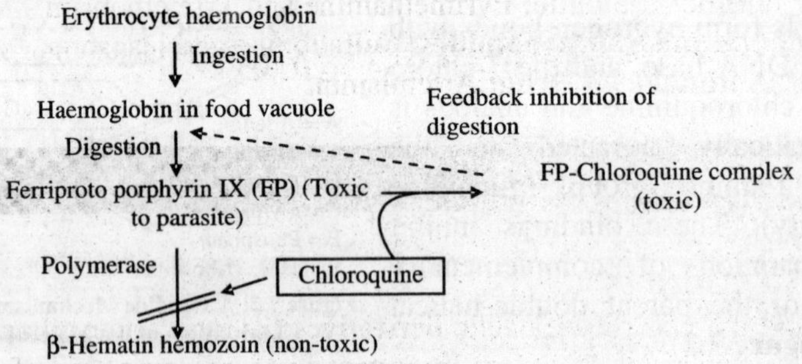

Figure 7.3: Polymerase Inhibition by Chloroquine

4) **Oxidant Drugs:** Malarial parasite inhibits the host cell's ability to prevent and/or repair oxidative damage through a number of mechanisms. Malarial parasites are destroyed by reactive oxygen intermediates produced by activated macrophages. Many oxidant drugs damage the parasitised red cells. Artemisinin is a novel endoperoxide that acts by this mechanism. Some quinones catalyse the production of oxidants in the infected erythrocytes. They undergo cyclic one-electron oxidation-reductions. The enzyme-deficient erythrocytes have reduced ability to survive oxidant stress, thus are prone to premature lysis before parasite maturation. As a result, the host cells die before the infection spreads. The oxidant drugs (**e.g.,** artemisinin) and quinones induce oxidative damage to infected cells and destroy them early.

7.1.5. Classification

Antimalarial drugs are classified as follows:

1) **Based on the Affected Plasmodial Stage**
   i) **Primary Tissue Schizonticides:** They destroy the primary tissue schizonts in the liver immediately after the infection, **e.g.,** Primaquine.
   ii) **Blood Schizonticides:** They suppress the symptoms by destroying the schizonts and merozoites in the erythrocytes, **e.g.,** Chloroquine, Amodiaquine, Mefloquine, and Quinine.
   iii) **Gametocides:** They prevent the spread of infection by destroying the gametocytes in the blood, **e.g.,** Primaquine for *P. falciparum*, and Chloroquine for *P. vivax*, *P. malariae*, and *P. ovale*.
   iv) **Sporonticides:** They eradicate malaria by preventing sporogony in the mosquito, **e.g.,** Chloroguanide and Pyrimethamine.

v) **Secondary Tissue Schizonticides:** They cure chronic relapsing fevers due to infection by *P. vivax*, *P. malariae*, and *P. ovale*. They do so by destroying the secondary exoerythrocytic tissue schizonts developing in the liver (**e.g.,** Primaquine).

2) **Based on their Chemical Structure**
   i) **Quinoline Derivatives:** Cinchona alkaloids, 4-Amino quinolines, 8-Amino quinolines, and Mefloquine.
   ii) **9-Amino Acridines:** Quinacrine and Acriquine
   iii) **2,4-Diaminopyrimidines:** Pyrimethamine.
   iv) **Biguanides:** Proguanil and Chlorproguanil.
   v) **Pyrimidine Analogue:** Pyrimethamine and Trimethoprim.
   vi) **Suphone and Sulphonamides:** Sulfadoxine and Dapsone.
   vii) **New Antimalarial Drug:** Artemisinin.

7.2. QUINOLINES

7.2.1. Introduction

Quinoline and its fused heterocyclic derivatives having various pharmacological activity functional groups form an important class of compounds for new drug development. Therefore, many researchers have synthesised these compounds as target structures and evaluated their biological activities.

7.2.2. Classification

Quinoline is classified as follows:

1) **Cinchona Alkaloids:** The bark of cinchona comprises of a mixture of more than 20 alkaloids. Four major alkaloids are isolated from cinchona:
   i) **Quinine:** $R_1 = OCH_3$; $R_2 = -CH = CH_2$ (–) isomer,
   ii) **Quinidine:** $R_1 = OCH_3$; $R_2 = -CH = CH_2$ (+) isomer,
   iii) **Cinchonine:** $R_1 = H$; $R_2 = -CH = CH_2$ (+) isomer, and
   iv) **Cinchonidine:** $R_1 = H$; $R_2 = -CH = CH_2$ (–) isomer.

These alkaloids are effective against erythrocytic merozoites and are used in the suppressive treatment of malaria. The four alkaloids are derivatives of 4-quinolinemethanol linked with a substituted quinuclidine moiety.

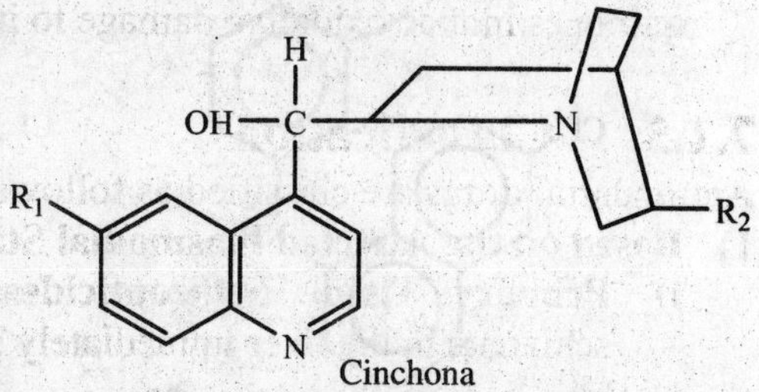

Cinchona

The sulfate salt of quinine is orally active, and its dihydrochloride salt is used intravenously. Its levorotatory form shows antimalarial activity. It may cause local tissue damage, thus is not suitable for subcutaneous or intramuscular administration.

Quinine is used in chloroquine-resistant *P. falciparum* infections. At high doses, it may produce a depressant effect on the heart (like quinidine). It causes vasodilation and hypotension. It exerts curare-like effect and antagonises the actions of physostigmine on the skeletal muscles. Due to this reason, quinine may be used in the symptomatic relief of nocturnal muscle cramps or myotonia congenital. It has analgesic, antipyretic, and local anaesthetic properties. Its toxic doses may lead to abortion.

2) 4-Amino Quinolines

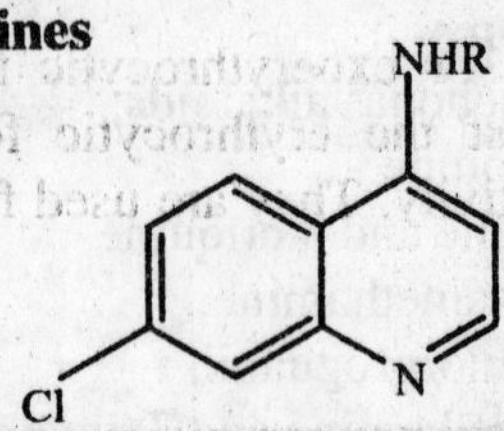

Drugs	R
Chloroquine	— $CH(CH_3)$ — $(CH_2)_3$ — $N(C_2H_5)_2$
Hydroxy chloroquine	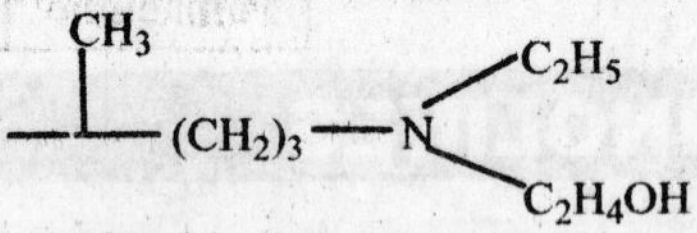
Amodiaquine	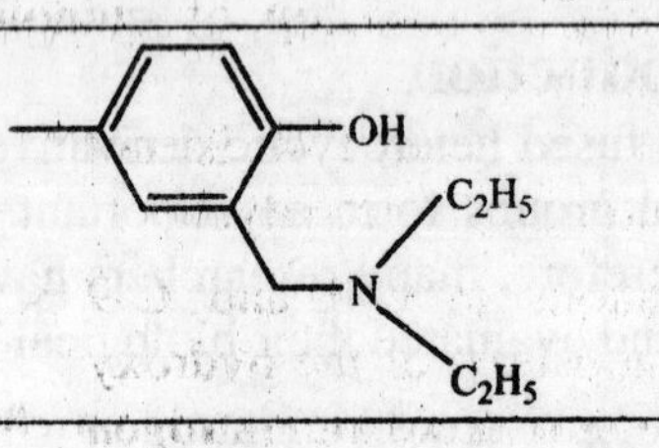

Amodiaquine hydrochloride, amopyroquine, bispyroquine, chloroquine, chloroquine hydrochloride, chloroquine phosphate, cycloquine, hydroxychloroquine sulphate, hydroxypiperaquine phosphate, tebuquine, and tripiperaquine are the drugs that belong to this class (**figure 7.4**).

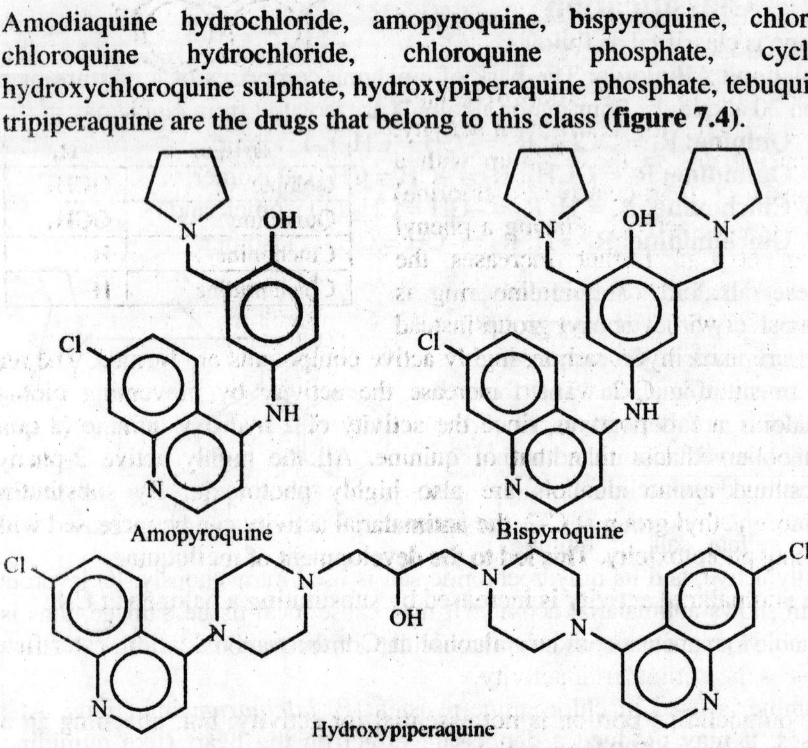

Amopyroquine Bispyroquine

Hydroxypiperaquine

Figure 7.4: Examples of 4-Aminoquinolines

3) **8-Amino Quinolines:** These structural analogues offer a more significant derivative from the basic quinine moiety. From structural aspect, these drugs are optimally substituted by a side chain having 4-6 carbon atoms and a methoxy group at C-6. The 8-aminoquinoline analogues are more toxic than the 4-aminoquinolines.

   They are active against the pre- or exoerythrocytic form of the malarial parasite, but lack activity against the erythrocytic forms. The 8-aminoquinolines exhibit gametocidal activity. They are used for the radical cure of relapsing *vivax* malaria.

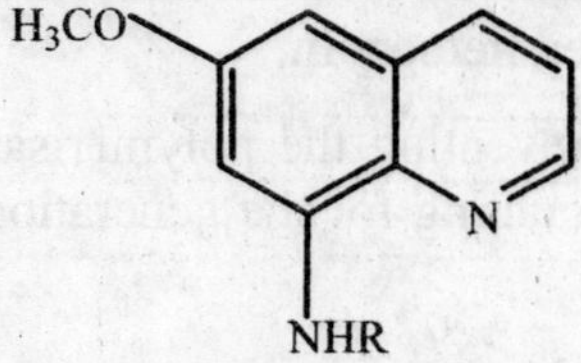

Drugs	R
Primaquine	$—CH(CH_3)—(CH_2)_3—NH_2$
Pamaquine	$—CH(CH_3)—(CH_2)_3—N(C_2H_5)_2$

7.2.3. SAR

The structure-activity relationship of quinolines involves substitution of the following functional groups:

1) Asymmetry at C-3 and C-4 is not essential for antimalarial activity.
2) The configurations at C-8 and C-9 affect the juxtaposition of the hydroxy group and the non-aromatic nitrogen atom; this relationship is associated with antimalarial activity.

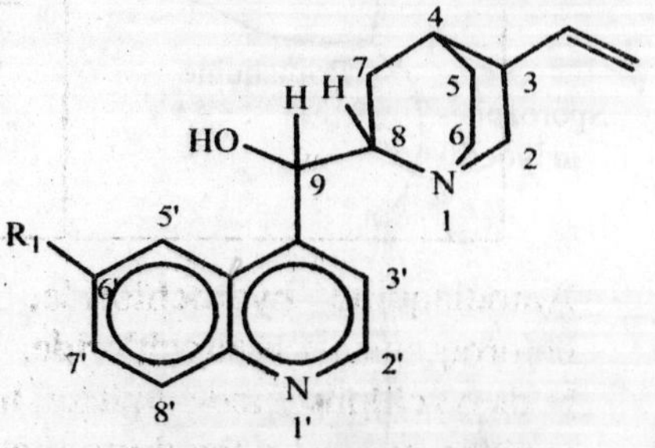

Drugs	R_1
Quinine	OCH_3
Quinidine	OCH_3
Cinchonine	H
Cinchonidine	H

3) Presence of methoxy group in quinine is not essential for antimalarial activity. Replacing this methoxy group with a halogen (particularly chlorine) enhances the activity. Placing a phenyl group at C-2 further increases the activity. If C-2 of quinoline ring is substituted with a phenyl group instead of an aliphatic hydrocarbon, highly active compounds are formed. The reason for substituting C-2 was to increase the activity by preventing biological oxidation at this position, since the activity of 2-hydroxy quinine (a quinine metabolite) is less than that of quinine. All the highly active 2-phenyl-4-quinolinyl amino alcohols are also highly phototoxic. By substituting a trifluoromethyl group at C-2, the antimalarial activity can be increased without causing phototoxicity. This led to the development of mefloquine.
4) The antimalarial activity is increased by substituting a halogen at C-8.
5) By modifying the secondary alcohol at C-9 through oxidation, esterification reduces the antimalarial activity.
6) The quinuclidine portion is not essential for activity; but, attaching an alkyl tertiary amine at C-9 is essential.

7.2.4. Mechanism of Action

The bite of an infected female *Anopheles* mosquito causes malarial infection in humans. Plasmodium parasites first accumulate in the hepatocytes and then enter the erythrocytes for the next stage of their maturation. After a few days, the infected erythrocytes burst and release the merozoites giving rise to periodic fevers of malaria. These merozoites infect the new erythrocytes and the cycle within the erythrocytes start again. The parasite in the erythrocytes of the host degrades haemoglobin and digests 30% or more of the protein moiety and uses it as a source of amino acids for synthesising its own protein. The free and toxic heme (ferriprotoporphyrin IX) left after digestion is polymerised to a microcrystalline, non-toxic, redox inactive iron (III) heme pigment called **hemozoin**.

The anti-malarial activity of quinolones involves preventing the polymerisation of toxic heme to non-toxic hemozoin, probably accounting for the generation of toxicity to the parasite.

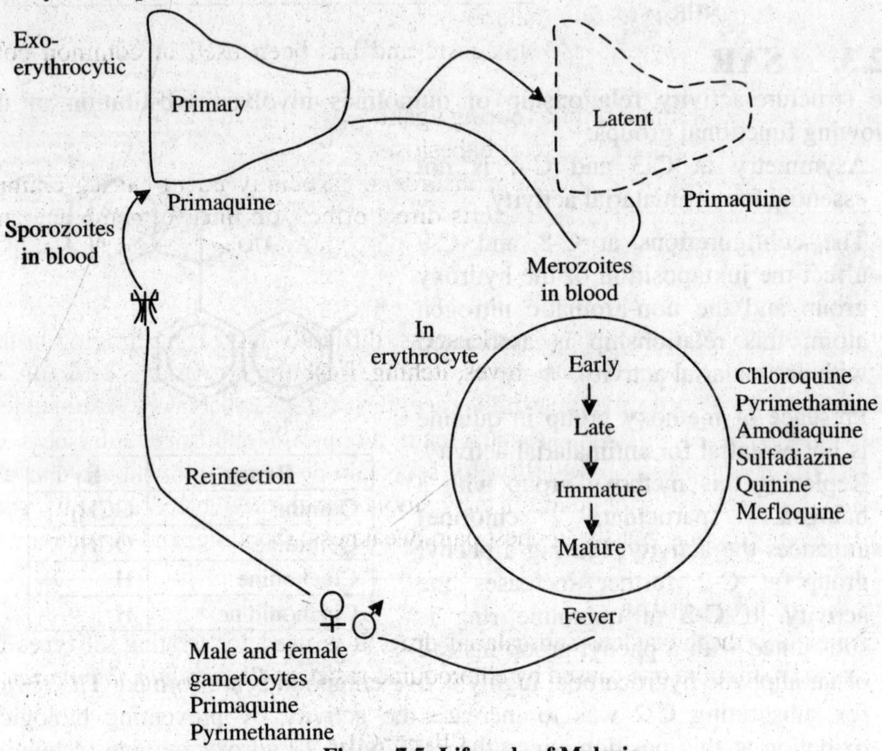

Figure 7.5: Lifecycle of Malaria

7.2.5. Important Products

The following drugs are studied in detail:

1) Quinine sulphate,
2) Chloroquine,
3) Amodiaquine,
4) Primaquine phosphate,
5) Pamaquine,
6) **Quinacrine hydrochloride, and**
7) **Mefloquine.**

7.2.5.1. Quinine Sulphate

Quinine is an alkaloid derived from Cinchona bark. It is an antimalarial agent and an active ingredient in extracts of cinchona used before 1633.

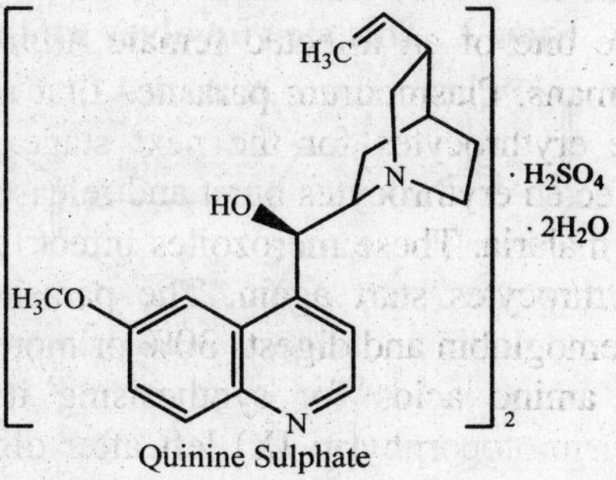

Quinine Sulphate

Mechanism of Action

Quinine and related anti-malarial drugs are toxic to the malarial parasite. They interfere with the parasite's ability to breakdown and digest haemoglobin. As a result, the parasite starves and/or builds up toxic levels of partially degraded haemoglobin within itself.

Uses

1) Quinine is used for treating malaria.
2) It is a mild antipyretic and analgesic and has been used in common cold preparations.
3) It was used as a bitter and flavouring agent.
4) It is still used in the treatment of babesiosis.
5) It is also used in some muscular disorders, especially nocturnal leg cramps and myotonia congenita, as it exerts direct effects on muscle membrane and sodium channels.

Adverse Effects

Quinine may give rise to nausea, restlessness, difficulty in hearing, ringing in the ears, confusion, nervousness, rash, hives, itching, flushing, hoarseness, difficulty in breathing or swallowing, swelling of the face, throat, lips, eyes, hands, feet, ankles, or lower legs, fever, blisters, stomach pain, vomiting, diarrhoea, blurriness or changes in colour vision, inability to see, faintness, easy bruising, unusual bleeding, blood in the urine, dark or tarry stools, nosebleeds, bleeding gums, sore throat, fast or irregular heartbeat, chest pain, weakness, sweating, and dizziness.

7.2.5.2. Chloroquine

Chloroquine is the precedent antimalarial drug. It is used for treating all types of malaria, excluding the one caused by chloroquine-resistant *Plasmodium falciparum.*

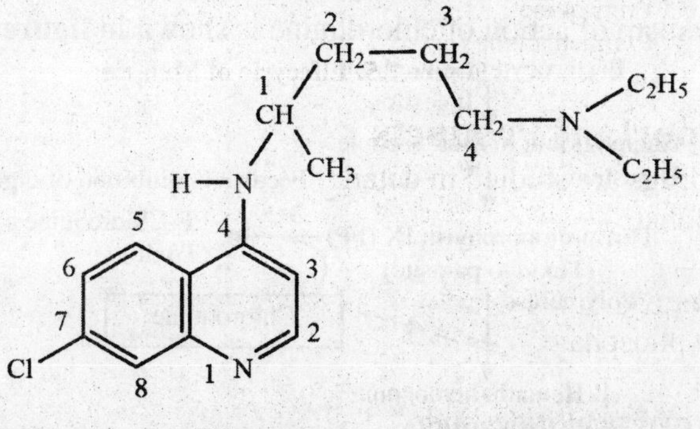

Chloroquine

Synthesis

1) **Step A: This step involves synthesis of quinoline moiety**

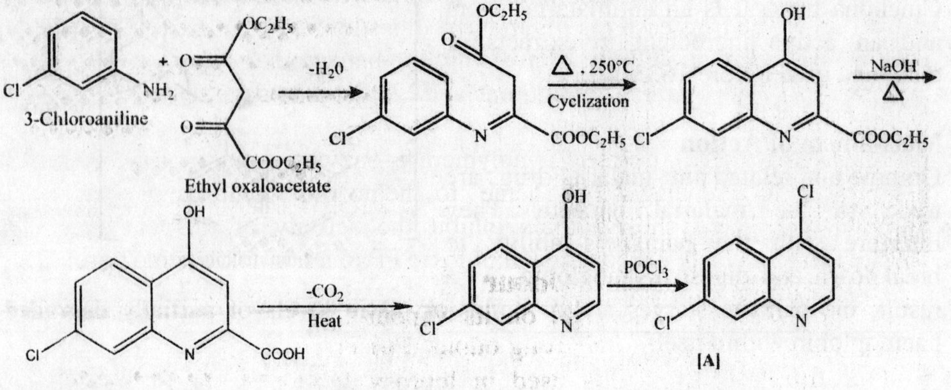

2) **Step B:**

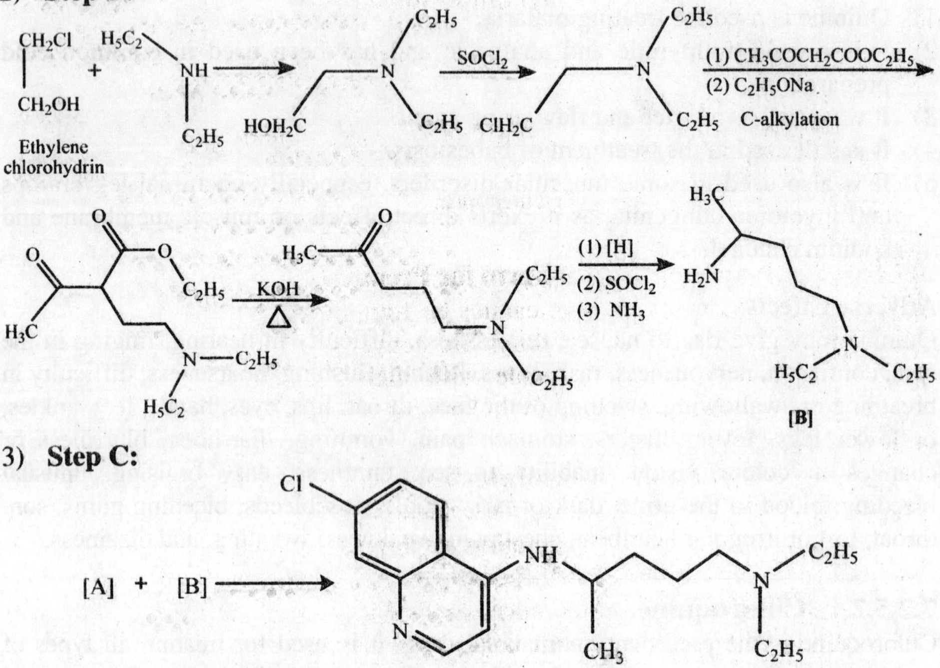

3) **Step C:**

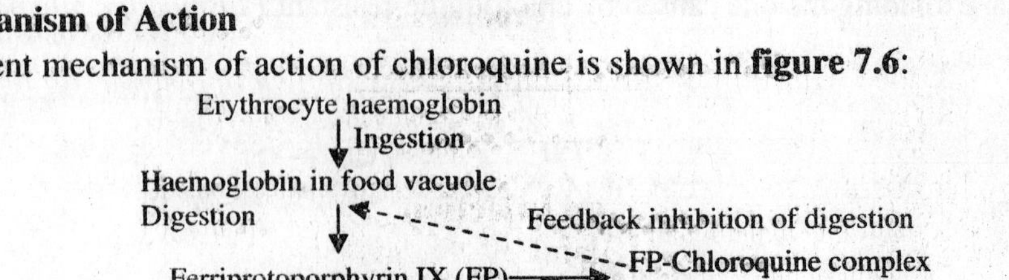

Mechanism of Action

A recent mechanism of action of chloroquine is shown in **figure 7.6**:

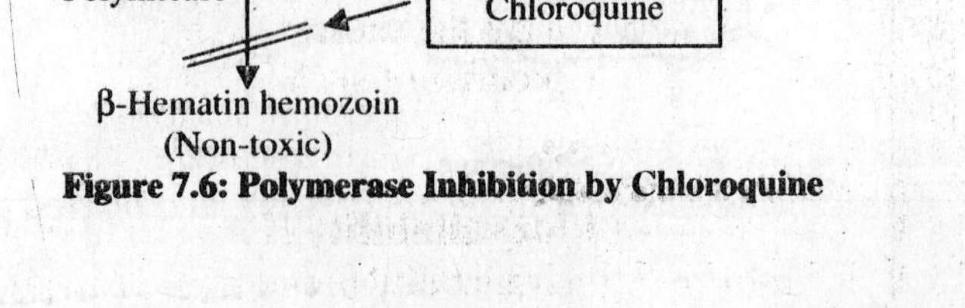

Figure 7.6: Polymerase Inhibition by Chloroquine

The mechanism involves interaction between ferriprotoporphyrin IX (FP) and chloroquine. FP has induces haemolysis of erythrocytes and lysis of malarial parasites. Heme is released as FP after the digestion of haemoglobin. The parasite de-toxifies the released FP by conversing it to hemozoin (a non-toxic byproduct). A complex forms between chloroquine and FP that is toxic to the cell.

Slater *et al.* (1992) isolated a polymerase enzyme from *P. falciparum* that catalyses the conversion of heme to hemozoin. Chloroquine and other structurally related anti-malarials inhibit the activity of this enzyme. Thus, chloroquine prevents the conversion of toxic FP to a non-toxic hemozoin.

Uses

1) Chloroquine is used for acute malarial attacks caused by *P. vivax*, *P.malariae*, *P. ovale*, and susceptible strains of *P. falciparum*.
2) It is also used for suppressive treatment of malaria.

Adverse Effects

Chloroquine at the doses specified for preventing malaria gives rise to gastrointestinal problems, stomach ache, itch, headache, nightmares, and blurred vision.

7.2.5.3. Amodiaquine

Amodiaquine is a 4-aminoquinoquinoline derivative containing anti-inflammatory properties.

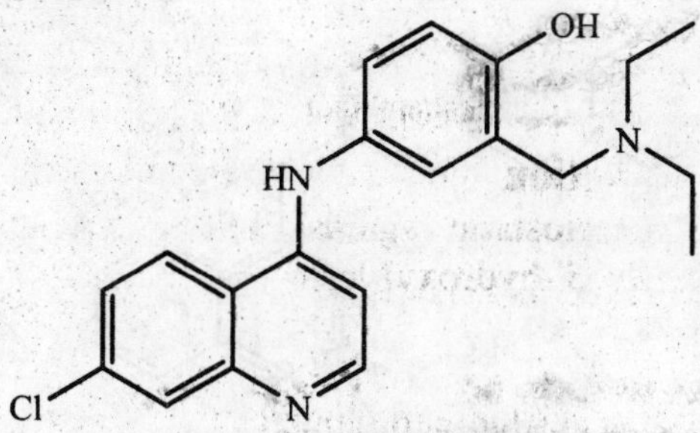

Amodiaquine

Mechanism of Action

The plasmodicidal action of amodiaquine is not completely firm. Like other quinoline derivatives, it is assumed to inhibit heme polymerase activity. This causes the accumulation of free heme that is toxic to the parasites. Amodiaquine binds to the free heme and prevent the parasite from converting it to a less toxic form. This drug-heme complex is toxic and disrupts membrane function.

Uses

Amodiaquine is used for treating acute malarial attacks having symptoms like fever, chills, and sweating.

Adverse Effects

Amodiaquine at doses specified for preventing malaria gives rise to gastrointestinal problems, stomach ache, itch, headache, nightmares, and blurred vision.

7.2.5.4. Primaquine Phosphate

Primaquine is an aminoquinoline which is indicated orally for radically curing and preventing relapse of vivax and ovale malaria after treatment with blood schizontocide.

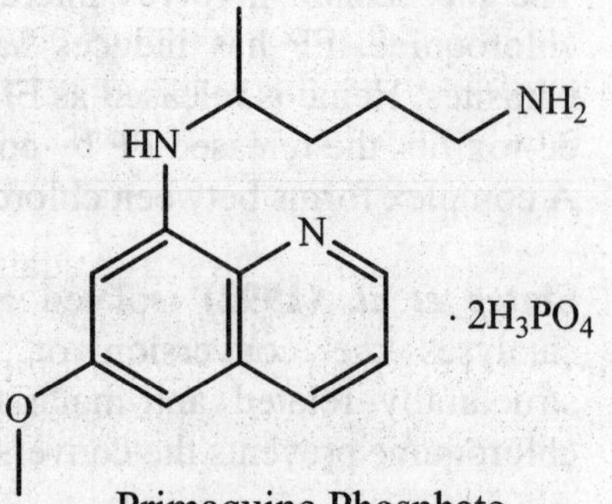

Primaquine Phosphate

Mechanism of Action

The mechanism of action of primaquine is not well understood. It is assumed to generate reactive oxygen species, interfere with the electron transport in the parasite, or bind to and alter the properties of protozoal DNA.

Uses

Primaquine is used for treating malaria caused by *P. ovale* and *P. vivax.*

Adverse Effects

Primaquine causes nausea, vomiting, epigastric distress, abdominal cramps, leukopenia, leukocytosis, agranulocytosis, methaemoglobinemia in NADH methaemoglobin reductase-deficient individuals, haemolytic anaemia (G6PD deficient), thrombocytopaenia, and AV block.

7.2.5.5. Pamaquine

Pamaquine is an 8-aminoquinoline drug that is closely related to primaquine. It was earlier used for the treatment of malaria.

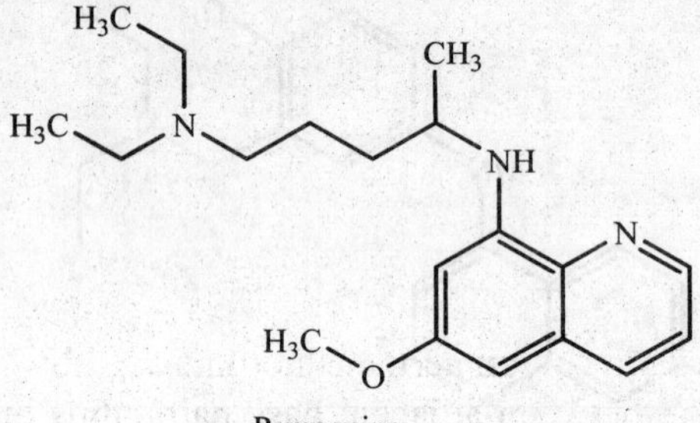

Pamaquine

Synthesis

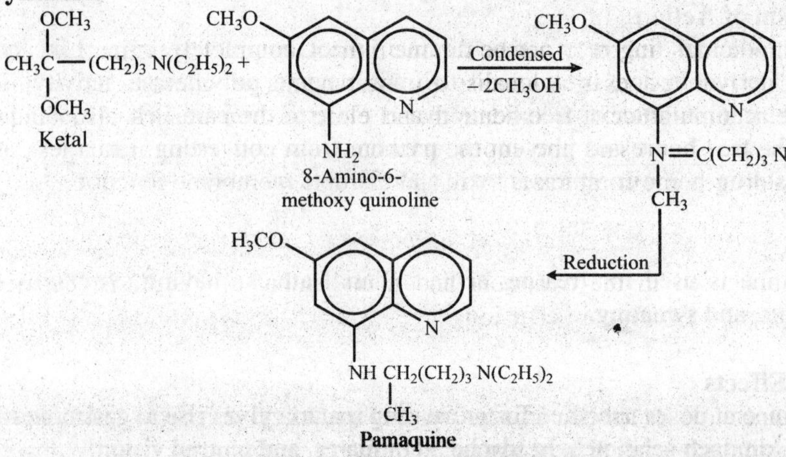

Pamaquine

Mechanism of Action

The mechanism of action of pamaquine is not yet clear. It is assumed to generate reactive oxygen species, interfere with the electron transport in the parasite, or bind to and alter the properties of protozoal DNA.

Uses

1) Pamaquine is effective against the hypnozoites of the relapsing malaria (*P. vivax* and *P. ovale*).
2) It is also effective against the erythrocytic stages of all four human malarias.

Adverse Effects

Pamaquine causes haemolytic anaemia in patients with G6PD deficiency.

7.2.5.6. Quinacrine Hydrochloride

Quinacrine is an acridine derivative that was widely used as an antimalarial but recently has been succeeded by chloroquine. It has also been used as an anthelmintic and in the treatment of giardiasis and malignant effusions.

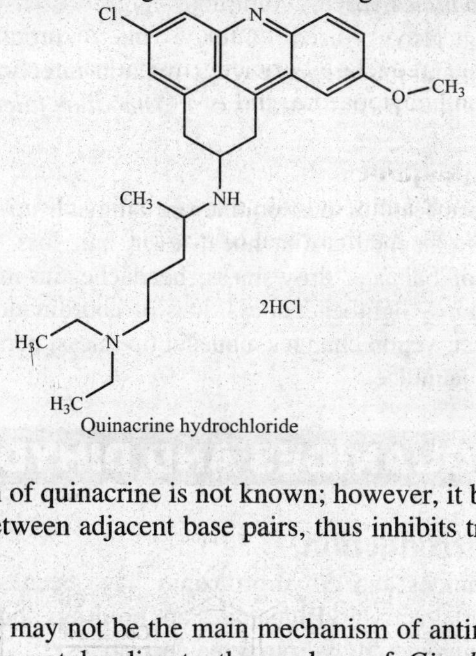

Quinacrine hydrochloride

Mechanism of Action

The anti-parasitic action of quinacrine is not known; however, it binds to DNA *in vitro* by intercalation between adjacent base pairs, thus inhibits transcription and translation to RNA.

However, DNA binding may not be the main mechanism of antimicrobial action of quinacrine as it does not localise to the nucleus of *Giardia trophozoites*. Quinacrine inhibits succinate oxidation and electron transport. It also binds to nucleoproteins, suppresses the lupus erythematous cell factor, and acts as a strong inhibitor of cholinesterase.

Uses

Quinacrine is used in the treatment and management of giardiasis, cutaneous leishmaniasis, and malignant effusions.

Adverse Effects

Quinacrine causes diarrhoea, dizziness, nausea, vomiting, head pain, loss of **appetite, skin discoloration, and stomach cramps.**

7.2.5.7. Mefloquine

Mefloquine is a phospholipid-interacting antimalarial that is very effective against *Plasmodium falciparum* and has very few side effects.

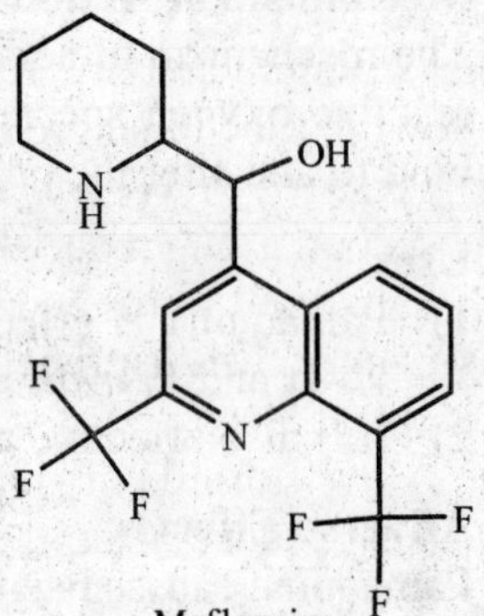

Mefloquine

Mechanism of Action

Mefloquine causes swelling of the *Plasmodium falciparum* food vacuoles. It may form toxic complexes with free heme that damages the membranes and interact with other plasmodial components.

Uses

1) Mefloquine is used in the treatment of mild to moderate acute malaria caused by mefloquine-susceptible strains of *Plasmodium falciparum* or by *Plasmodium vivax*.
2) It is also used for the prophylaxis of *Plasmodium falciparum* and *Plasmodium vivax* malaria infections, including prophylaxis of chloroquine-resistant strains of *Plasmodium falciparum*.

Adverse Effects

Common side effects of mefloquine are stomach upset, stomach pain, nausea, vomiting, loss of appetite, diarrhoea, fever, hair loss, ringing in ears, dizziness, vertigo, loss of balance, drowsiness, headache, insomnia, cough, muscle pain, weakness, itching, lightheadedness, loss of coordination, numbness and tingling of hands or feet, vision changes, unusual tiredness, persistent nausea or vomiting, dark urine, or jaundice.

7.3. BIGUANIDES AND DIHYDROTRIAZINES

7.3.1. Introduction

Several biguanides and dihydrotriazines have been synthesised and tested for their antimalarial activity. Biguanides are prodrugs and are not active till they are metabolised *in vivo* to dihydrotriazine derivatives.

Guanidine analogues remain inactive till they get cyclised metabolically to a dihydro-s-triazine analogue that is somewhat similar to either the pteridine moiety of folic acid or pyrimethamine as shown below:

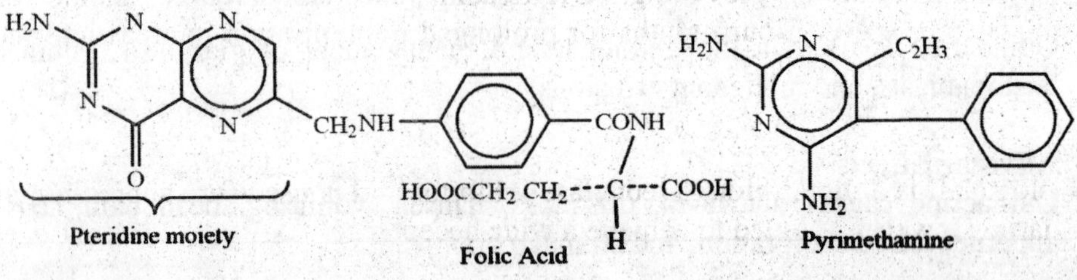

7.3.2. SAR

The structure-activity relationship of biguanides involves substitution of the following functional groups:

1) Presence of N^1-aryl is essential for anti-malarial activity, but introducing a second group reduces the activity.
2) Dihalogen substitution at C-3 and C-4 of the benzene ring yields potent drugs.
3) Alkyl substituents on N^1, N^2, or N^4 reduce the antimalarial activity.
4) Replacing the isopropyl group with a normal propyl group at N^5 gives essentially equal activity.
5) Introducing shorter or longer alkyl chains reduces the antimalarial activity.

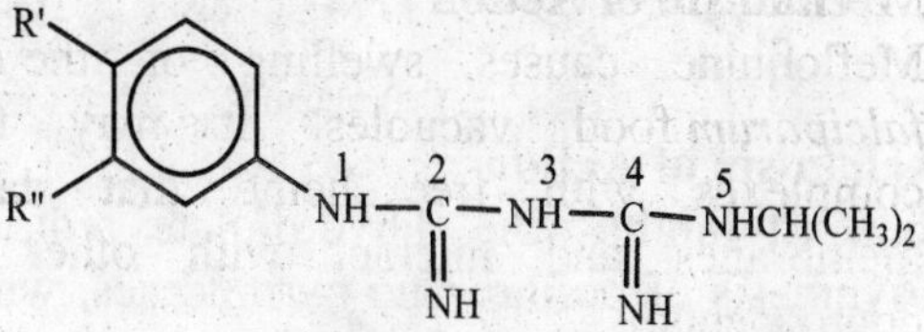

Drugs	R′	R″
Proguanil (chloroguanide)	Cl	H
Chloroproguanil	Cl	Cl
Bromoguanil	Br	H
Nitroguanil	NO_2	H

7.3.3. Important Products

The following drugs are studied in detail:

1) Cycloguanil pamoate, and
2) Proguanil.

7.3.3.1 Cycloguanil Pamoate

Cycloguanil is the active metabolite of proguanil.

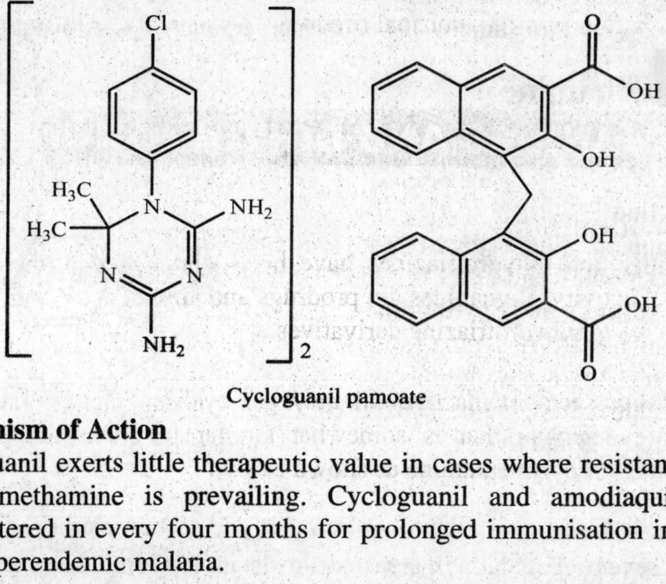

Cycloguanil pamoate

Mechanism of Action

Cycloguanil exerts little therapeutic value in cases where resistance to proguanil or pyrimethamine is prevailing. Cycloguanil and amodiaquine should be administered in every four months for prolonged immunisation in areas infested with hyperendemic malaria.

Uses

Cycloguanil is a dihydrofolate reductase inhibitor and is used for suppression of malaria. However, it failed to achieve a wide acceptance.

7.3.3.2. Proguanil

Proguanil is a biguanide compound which forms cycloguanil (an anti-malarial) by getting metabolised in the body. It is generally indicated with atovaquone.

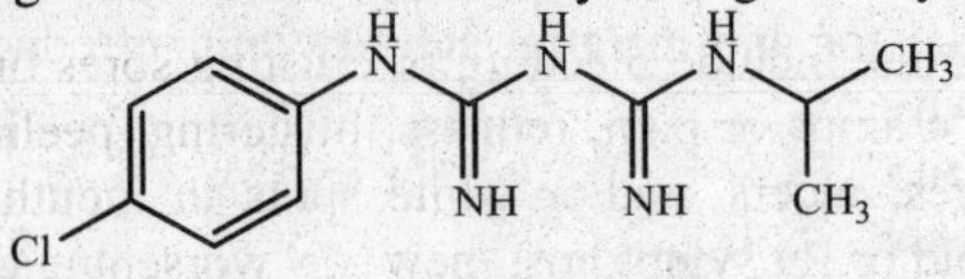

Proguanil

Mechanism of Action

Proguanil inhibits the dihydrofolate reductase of plasmodia and blocks the biosynthesis of purines and pyrimidines, which are essential for DNA synthesis and cell multiplication. As a result, nuclear division fails to occur at the time of schizont formation in erythrocytes and liver.

Uses

Proguanil is used for preventing and suppressing malaria caused by various strains of *P. falciparum* and other species of *Plasmodium*.

Adverse Effects

Proguanil causes nausea, vomiting, abdominal pain, headache, diarrhoea, weakness, loss of appetite, and dizziness.

7.4. MISCELLANEOUS

7.4.1. Introduction

The following drugs are studied in detail:

1) Pyrimethamine, 2) Artesunate, 3) Artemether, and 4) Atovaquone.

7.4.2. Pyrimethamine

Pyrimethamine is a synthetic derivative of ethyl pyrimidine. It has potent antimalarial properties and also inhibits Dihydrofolate Reductase (DHFR).

Mechanism of Action

Pyrimethamine inhibits the dihydrofolate reductase of plasmodia and blocks the biosynthesis of purines and pyrimidines, which are essential for DNA synthesis and cell multiplication. As a result, nuclear division fails to occur at the time of schizont formation in erythrocytes and liver.

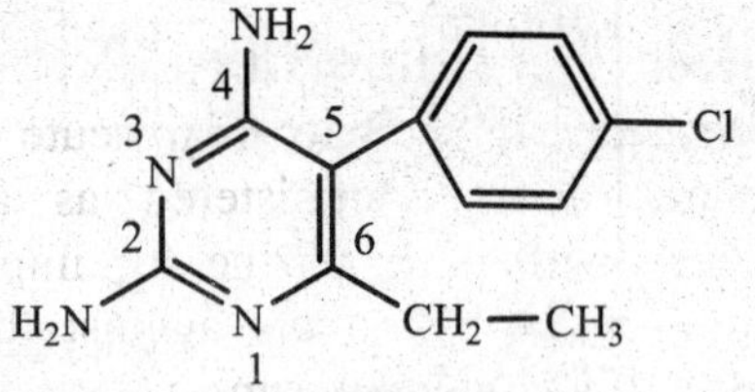

Pyrimethamine

Uses

1) Pyrimethamine is used for treating toxoplasmosis and acute malaria.
2) It is used for preventing malaria in areas non-resistant to pyrimethamine.
3) It is used for treating malaria and prophylaxis as it is a primary tissue schizonticide and slow blood schizonticide.
4) **When used with sulphadiazine, it treats toxoplasmosis (infection due to *Toxoplasma gonadii* which causes eye and brain damage).**

5) Its antimalarial activity enhances when given along with sulphadoxine and dapsone.

Adverse Effects

The adverse effects of pyrimethamine include bleeding or crusting sores on lips, chest pain or discomfort, muscle cramps or pain, redness, blistering, peeling, or loosening of skin, skin rash, sores, ulcers, and/or white spots in mouth, sore throat, blood in urine, fever, cold or flu symptoms, new or worsening cough, fever, trouble in breathing, and irregular heartbeats.

7.4.3. Artesunate

Artesunate is a part of the artemisinin group of drugs used for treating malaria. It is a semi-synthetic derivative of artemisinin that is water-soluble and is thus given by injection.

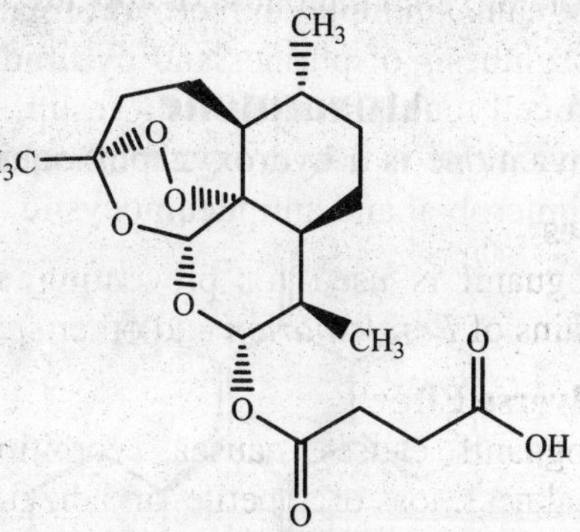

Artesunate

Mechanism of Action

Artesunate involves cleaving the endoperoxide bond through reaction with heme. This generates free radicals that cause alkylation of the parasitic proteins. It inhibits an essential parasite calcium adenosine triphosphatase enzyme. It inhibits malaria proteins EXP1, (a glutathione S-transferase), responsible for breaking down cytotoxic hematin.

Uses

Artesunate is used for the treatment of severe malaria caused by *Plasmodium falciparum* in adults and children.

Adverse Effects

Major and minor side effects for artesunate include dizziness, headache, abdominal pain, diarrhoea, pain at the injection site, fever with body ache, anaemia, low WBC and platelet count, and swelling of the liver.

7.4.4. Artemether

Artemether is used to treat acute uncomplicated malaria. It is administered as a combination therapy with lumefantrine for improved efficacy and to exert its effects against the erythrocytic stages of *Plasmodium spp.*

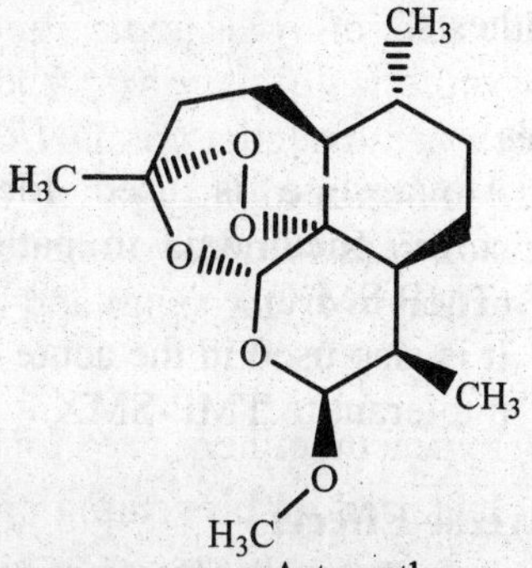

Artemether

Mechanism of Action

Artemether interacts with ferriprotoporphyrin IX (heme) or ferrous ions in the acidic parasite food vacuole, and generates cytotoxic radical species.

The accepted mode of action of the peroxide-containing drug involves its interaction with heme (byproduct of hemoglobin degradation), derived from proteolysis of haemoglobin. This interaction results in the formation of toxic oxygen and carbon-centered radicals.

Uses

1) Artemether and lumefantrine combination therapy is used in the treatment of acute uncomplicated malaria caused by *Plasmodium falciparum*, including malaria acquired in chloroquine-resistant areas.
2) It is also used in uncomplicated malaria when the *Plasmodium* species has not been identified.

Adverse Effects

Chills, dizzy, nausea, vomiting, feeling weak, fever, head pain, heart throbbing or pounding, joint pain, loss of appetite, low energy, muscle pain, and sleep disorder.

7.4.5. Atovaquone

Atovaquone is a hydroxynaphthoquinone or an analog of ubiquinone, that is an antimicrobial and antipneumocystic. It is used in antimalarial protocols.

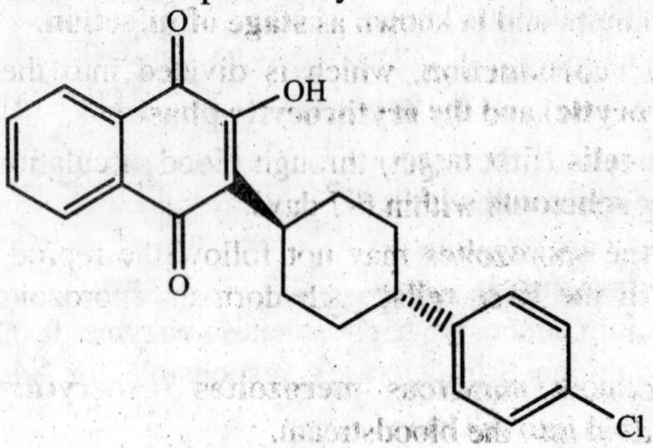

Atovaquone

Mechanism of Action

The mechanism of action of atovaquone against *Pneumocystis carinii* is not fully understood. In *Plasmodium* species, the action site is the cytochrome bc1 complex (Complex III). Several metabolic enzymes are linked to the mitochondrial electron transport chain via ubiquinone. Inhibition of electron transport by atovaquone results in indirect inhibition of these enzymes. The metabolic effects of such blockage include inhibition of nucleic acid and ATP synthesis.

Uses

1) Atovaquone is used for the treatment or prevention of *Pneumocystis carinii* pneumonia in patients intolerant to trimethoprim-sulfamethoxazole (TMP-SMX).
2) It is also used in the acute oral treatment of mild to moderate PCP in patients intolerant to TMP-SMX.

Adverse Effects

The common side effects of atovaquone include nausea, vomiting, stomach pain or upset, diarrhoea, constipation, headache, weakness, dizziness, muscle pain, skin rash, sweating, or insomnia. The serious side effects of atovaquone include easy bruising or bleeding, unusual weakness, fever, or flu symptoms.

7.5. SUMMARY

The details given in the chapter can be summarised as follows:

1) **Malaria** is transmitted by an infected female Anopheles mosquito, which introduces the parasites from its saliva into the person's blood.
2) The species of plasmodium responsible for malaria in human beings are ***P. falciparum*** and ***P. vivax***
3) The female **Anopheles mosquito** acts as a **vector** for human beings.
4) The first two stages of malarial life cycle occur within the human body, while the third stage begins in the human body and completes within the mosquito body.
5) In humans, infection occurs when an infected female Anopheles mosquito bites and injects saliva infected with **sporozoites** into the **bloodstream**. It is the first life stage of plasmodium, and is known as **stage of infection**.
6) The next stage is **asexual reproduction**, which is divided into the **pre-erythrocytic** (or **exoerythrocytic**) and the **erythrocytic phases**.
7) Sporozoites reach the **liver cells** (first target) through blood circulation, and start dividing and producing **schizonts** within 6-7 days.
8) In ***P. vivax*** and ***P. ovale***, the sporozoites may not follow the reproduction step and remain dormant in the **liver cells**; such dormant sporozoites are called **hypnozoites**.
9) Each schizont further produces numerous **merozoites** **(exoerythrocytic schizogony)** which are released into the bloodstream.
10) The first stage within the RBCs is the **ring stage** that develops into a **trophozoite**, which cannot digest the haem so converts it into **haemozoin**.
11) The **erythrocytic schizont** forms the next cellular stage in which a **new generation merozoites** are produced.
12) The third stage of sexual reproduction involves **parasite differentiation** into **male** and **female gametocytes**.
13) Within the female anopheles mosquitoes, the gametocytes undergo **gametogenesis** and mature into **microgametes** and **macrogametes**.
14) The microgamete nucleus in the mosquito gut, produce eight nuclei after three successive divisions; each nucleus fuses with and fertilises a macrogamete to form a **zygote**, which is transformed into **ookinete**.
15) Ookinete penetrates the midgut wall of mosquito and forms an **oocyst**, within which the ookinete nucleus undergoes **sporogony** for 8-15 days to form numerous **sporozoites**.
16) **Quinoline** and its fused heterocyclic derivatives having various pharmacological activity functional groups form an important class of compounds for new drug development.
17) **Cinchona alkaloids** are effective against erythrocytic merozoites and are used in the suppressive treatment of malaria.
18) **Quinine** is an alkaloid derived from Cinchona bark.
19) **Chloroquine is the precedent antimalarial drug.**

20) **Amodiaquine** is a 4-aminoquinoquinoline derivative containing anti-inflammatory properties.

21) **Primaquine** is an aminoquinoline which is indicated orally for radically curing and preventing relapse of vivax and ovale malaria after treatment with blood schizontocide.

22) **Pamaquine** is an 8-aminoquinoline drug that is closely related to primaquine.

23) **Quinacrine** is an acridine derivative that was widely used as an antimalarial but recently has been succeeded by chloroquine.

24) **Mefloquine** is a phospholipid-interacting antimalarial that is very effective against *Plasmodium falciparum* and has very few side effects.

25) **Biguanides** are prodrugs and are not active till they are metabolised *in vivo* to dihydrotriazine derivatives.

26) **Cycloguanil** is the active metabolite of proguanil.

27) **Proguanil** is a biguanide compound which forms cycloguanil by getting metabolised in the body.

28) **Pyrimethamine** is a synthetic derivative of ethyl pyrimidine.

29) **Artesunate** is a part of the artemisinin group of drugs used for treating malaria.

30) **Artemether** is used to treat acute uncomplicated malaria.

31) **Atovaquone** is a hydroxynaphthoquinone or an analog of ubiquinone, that is an antimicrobial and antipneumocystic.

7.6. EXERCISE

7.6.1. True or False

1) The species of plasmodium responsible for malaria in human beings are *P.knowlesi* and *P. malariae.*
2) The asexual reproduction stage is divided into pre-erythrocytic and the erythrocytic phases.
3) Dormant sporozoites are called merozoites.
4) The erythrocytic schizont forms the next cellular stage in which a new generation merozoites are produced.
5) The third stage of sexual reproduction involves parasite differentiation into male and female gametocytes.
6) The microgamete nucleus in the mosquito gut, produce six nuclei after three successive divisions.
7) Ookinete penetrates the midgut wall of mosquito and forms an oocyst.
8) 4-Amino quinolines are effective against erythrocytic merozoites and are used in the suppressive treatment of malaria.
9) Mefloquine is an acridine derivative that was widely used as an antimalarial but recently has been succeeded by chloroquine.
10) Pyrimethamine is a synthetic derivative of ethyl pyrimidine.

7.6.2. Fill in the Blanks

11) The female Anopheles mosquito acts as a ________ for human beings.
12) The first life stage of plasmodium is known as ________.
13) Each schizont produces numerous ______ which are released into the bloodstream.
14) The first stage within the RBCs is the ring stage that develops into a ______, which cannot digest the haem so converts it into ________ .
15) Within the female anopheles mosquitoes, the gametocytes undergo ________ and mature into microgametes and macrogametes.
16) Each nucleus fuses with and fertilises a macrogamete to form a zygote, which is transformed into ________.
17) ________ is an 8-aminoquinoline drug that is closely related to primaquine.
18) Mefloquine is effective against ________.
19) Cycloguanil is the active metabolite of ________.
20) Atovaquone is a ________ or an analog of ________ .

Answers

1) False	2) True	3) False	4) True
5) True	6) False	7) True	8) False
9) False	10) True	11) Vector	12) Stage of infection
13) Merozoites	14) Trophozoite and haemozoin		15) Gametogenesis
16) Ookinete	17) Pamaquine	18) *Plasmodium falciparum*	19) Proguanil
20) Hydroxynaphthoquinone and ubiquinone			

7.6.3. Very Short Answer Type Questions

1) Classify antimalarials based on their chemical structure.
2) Give the chemical structure of primaquine phosphate.
3) Give the mechanism of action of quinacrine hydrochloride.
4) What are the uses of mefloquine?
5) How cycloguanil pamoate acts?
6) Enlist the uses of artesunate and artemether.
7) Draw the structure of atovaquone.

7.6.4. Short Answer Type Questions

1) Discuss the historical background of antimalarials.
2) Give the classification of antimalarials.
3) Write a note on the SAR of quinolones.
4) Give the mechanism of action and uses of quinine sulphate and chloroquine.
5) Write a short note on proguanil and pyrimethamine.

7.6.5. Long Answer Type Question

1) Write an exhaustive note on etiology of malaria.
2) Discuss the mechanism of action of antimalarials.
3) How chloroquine and pamaquine are synthesised?

CHAPTER 8 Anti-Tubercular Agents

8.1. ANTI-TUBERCULAR AGENTS

8.1.1. Introduction

Tuberculosis (TB) is an infective disease, most commonly affecting the lungs, and caused by ***Mycobacterium tuberculosis*** and ***Mycobacterium bovis***. Since TB is an airborne disease, it spreads via air in the form of small droplets. Patients infected with pulmonary TB or laryngeal TB may spread the infection by sneezing, coughing, singing, or even while talking. The infective droplets, once released into the air remain there for a few hours due to their very small size.

Tuberculosis can be treated in a long-term, i.e., 8 months to 3 years. *p*-Aminosalicylic Acid (PAS) was the first discovered chemotherapeutic agent; however, later streptomycin, isoniazid, ethambutol, and rifampin were also discovered. Tuberculosis infection can be cured if proper treatment is given within time. Non-tuberculosis mycobacterial infections are known as ***M. avium* complex (MAC)** as they are caused by *M. avium*, *M. kansaii*, *M. murinum*, and *M. scrofulaceum*. These organisms are resistant to the commonly used anti-tuberculosis drugs; thus along with the standard drugs, some newer agents like fluoroquinolones, amikacin, clarithromycin, azithromycin, or rifabutin are used.

8.1.2. Historical Background

1940 - Development of PAS

The starting point for a history of anti-tubercular drugs is the beginning of Second World War. **Frederick Bernheim** (a biochemist working at Duke University in the United States) believed that this war would result in a massive increase in the suffering and deaths from tuberculosis. He carried out a number of experiments and found that aspirin played a vital role in the life cycle of tuberculosis germ.

In 1943, **Bernheim** proposed to **Ferrosan** (the research director of the firm) the production of two different salicylic acid derivatives. PAS turned out to be the most active among the molecules that were tested. However, its synthesis was very difficult. Until **December 1943**, **Ferrosan** sent 13gm of PAS to **Lehmann**, who on New Year's eve announced to **Ferrosan** that the growth of *M. tuberculosis* was inhibited by PAS.

In 1944, experiments were conducted on rodents and it was found that PAS had negligible toxicity. Due to this reason when the experiments on rodents were not even completed, **Professor Lehmann** wanted to use PAS in humans. The first patient received PAS orally in **October 1944**. At that time a clinical trial was conducted using 20 patients and in **January 1946**, **Lehmann** reported that the most of the patients responded positively with a drop in temperature, weight gain and general improvement.

1943 - Development of Streptomycin

Selman Waksman (a soil microbiologist) was working at the Department of Microbiology at New Jersey Agricultural Experiment Station, at Rutgers University, New Brunswick. In **1939**, he found in his studies of the microbiological effect of the soil that *Actinomycetes* can exert a strange effect on certain soil bacteria and can inhibit their growth. Thereafter, he focused in studying the sensitivity of the TB organism to various *Actinomycetes*.

In **1939**, **Waksman** began a systematic search for soil microbes having the capacity to prevent the growth of disease-producing bacteria. Various preliminary studies of the production of antibiotics by *Actinomycetes* resulted in the isolation of extremely toxic actinomycin in **1940**. After two years, streptothricin was isolated but it also had significant toxicity.

So **Waksman** continued with his study and isolated less toxic **streptomycin** in **September 1943**. He made a public announcement of this isolation in a paper in **January 1944**. On **November 20th, 1944**, streptomycin was first administered to a tuberculosis patient.

1951 - Development of Isoniazid

In **1951**, three pharmaceutical companies (Bayer Chemical in Germany, and Squibb and Hoffmann-LaRoche in the United States) simultaneously discovered the next major drug for tuberculosis treatment, i.e., isonicotinic hydrazide (that was later renamed as isoniazid). Its potency was ten folds than that of the previously tested drugs and it was also non-toxic.

1959 - Development of Rifamycins

In **1957**, rifamycins were discovered at the Lepetit Pharmaceuticals research laboratory in Milan, Italy when a soil sample from a pine forest was analysed. A research group led by **Professor Piero Sensi** and **Dr Maria Teresa Timbal** discovered a new bacterium that was scientifically interesting as it produced a new class of antibiotic molecules. Rifampin was first used clinically in **1966**.

2012 - Development of Delamanid and Bedaquiline

In **2012**, delamanid was made available for the treatment of MDR-TB. A phase 2B trial showed that this drug along with a background regimen resulted in more study subjects becoming non-infectious than those given a placebo with a background regimen. Bedaquiline was made available in **2012** to be used for the treatment of drug-resistant TB when no other treatment is available. However, both these drugs have shown some problems.

8.1.3. Classification

Anti-tubercular drugs are classified as follows:

1) **First Line Drugs**
   i) Isoniazid (H), ii) Rifampin (R), iii) Pyrazinamide (Z), iv) Ethambutol (E), and v) Streptomycin (S).

2) **Second Line Drugs**
   i) Thiacetazone (Tzn), ii) *Para*-aminosalicylic acid (PAS), iii) Ethionamide (Etm), iv) Cycloserine (Cys), v) Kanamycin (Kmc), vi) Amikacin (Am), and vii) Capreomycin(Cpr).

3) **Newer Drugs**
   i) Ciprofloxacin, ii) Ofloxacin, iii) Clarithromycin, iv) Azithromycin, and v) Rifabutin.

8.2. SYNTHETIC ANTI-TUBERCULAR AGENTS

8.2.1. Introduction

The following drugs are studied in detail:
1) Isoniazid,
2) Ethionamide,
3) Ethambutol,
4) Pyrazinamide, and
5) *Para*-amino salicylic acid.

8.2.2. Isoniazid

Isoniazid (or isonicotinylhydrazine, INH) is an organic compound used as the first line drug for preventing and treating tuberculosis.

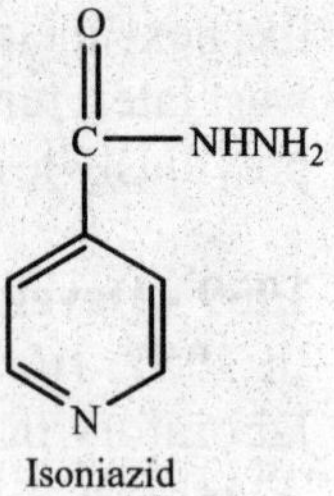

Isoniazid

It was discovered in 1912; however it was found to be effective against tuberculosis in 1951. Isoniazid is not used for treating active tuberculosis because it develops resistance.

8.2.2.1. Mechanism of Action

Isoniazid is a prodrug and should be activated by KatG (a bacterial catalase-peroxidase enzyme). This enzyme catalyses the coupling of isonicotinic acyl with NADH to form isonicotinic acyl-NADH complex. This complex tightly binds to InhA (enoyl-acyl carrier protein reductase) and blocks the natural enoyl-AcpM substrate and the action of fatty acid synthase. This process inhibits the synthesis of mycolic acid that is required for mycobacterial cell wall. Various free radicals are produced by KatG catalysed activation of isoniazid.

8.2.2.2. SAR

The structure-activity relationship of isoniazid involves substitution of the following functional groups:

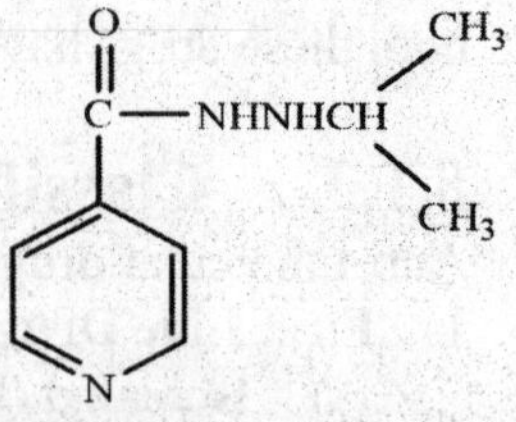

Iproniazid

1) Placement of the hydrazide function to C-2 or C-3 reduced the anti-tubercular activity.
2) Conversion of hydrazide to other carbonyl groups **(e.g., hydroxamic acid or amide) yielded inactive compounds.**

3) Alkyl substitution on hydrazide function produced various effects, like the trialkylated hydrazides were inactive, and the 2,2-dialkyl hydrazides were active.
4) The terminal nitrogen of hydrazide should be basic to retain the anti-tubercular activity.
5) Iproniazid is a substituted hydrazide with good tuberculostatic activity. It has an additional activity as a psychic energizer, thus produced a more symptomatic effect than isoniazid.
6) Reaction of isoniazid with various aldehydes and ketones has resulted in a large number of hydrazones. The activity of these compounds is similar to that of isoniazid because it rapidly hydrolyses to the parent compound.

8.2.2.3. Synthesis

Oxidation of 4-picoline with potassium permanganate produces isonicotinic acid, which reacts with ethanol in the presence of sulphuric acid and converts into ethyl ester. Ester-amide interchange occurs by reaction with hydrazine hydrate and isoniazid is formed.

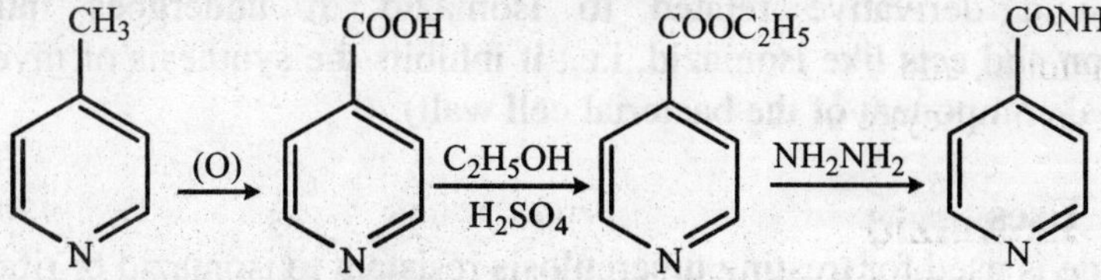

4-Picoline Isonicotinic acid Isoniazid

8.2.2.4. Mechanism of Action

Isoniazid is a prodrug that is activated on the surface of *M. tuberculosis* by katG enzyme to isonicotinic acid, which inhibits synthesis of mycolic acid (required for bacterial cell wall) and makes the bacteria susceptible to reactive oxygen radicals. Isoniazid is either bacteriostatic or bactericidal depending on the drug concentration at the infection site and the susceptibility of the infecting organism.

8.2.2.5. Uses

Isoniazid has the following uses:
1) It is used with other drugs in the treatment of active tuberculosis (TB) infections.
2) It is also used alone to prevent active TB infections in patients infected with the bacteria (people with positive TB skin test).
3) It acts as an antibiotic and treats only bacterial infections (not viral infections).

8.2.2.6. Adverse Effects

Isoniazid gives rise to dose-related side effects. The most common side effect is peripheral neuritis that may be due to competition of the drug with the pyridoxal coenzyme. Allergic reactions are rare but may result in fever, skin eruptions, and hepatitis. Periodic vision tests should be given so that optic neuritis is detected early.

8.2.3. Ethionamide

Ethionamide is a nicotinamide derivative having antibacterial activity, and used for treating tuberculosis.

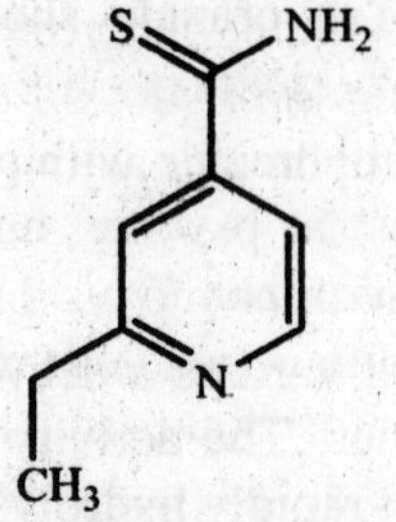

Ethionamide

8.2.3.1. Mechanism of Action

Ethionamide is bacteriostatic or bactericidal depending on the drug concentration at the infection site and the susceptibility of infecting organism. Ethionamide is a nicotinic acid derivative related to isoniazid. It undergoes intracellular modification and acts like isoniazid, i.e., it inhibits the synthesis of mycolic acid (an essential component of the bacterial cell wall).

8.2.3.2. Uses

Ethionamide is used for treating tuberculosis resistant to isoniazid or rifampicin.

8.2.3.3. Adverse Effects

Common side effects of ethionamide include nausea, vomiting, diarrhoea, abdominal or stomach pain, increased saliva, metallic taste in mouth, loss of appetite, sores in mouth, unusual fatigue or weakness, headache, dizziness, tremors (shaking), or rash.

8.2.4. Ethambutol

Ethambutol (EMB or E) is a bacteriostatic anti-mycobacterial drug used for treating tuberculosis. Generally, it is used along with isoniazid, rifampicin and pyrazinamide.

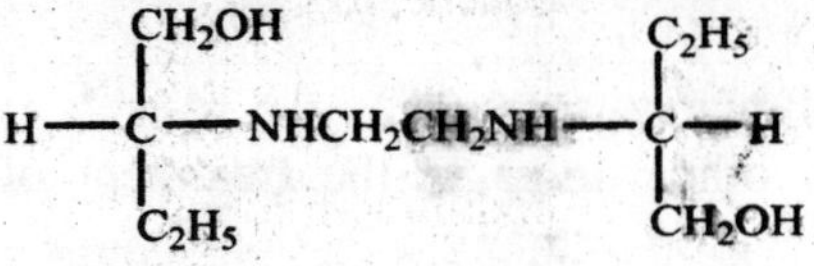

Ethambutol

8.2.4.1. Mechanism of Action

Ethambutol acts as a bacteriostatic against actively growing TB bacilli. Mycolic acids attach to the 5'-hydroxyl groups of D-arabinose residues of arabinogalactan.

As a result, mycolyl-arabinogalactan-peptidoglycan complex forms in the cell wall; this complex inhibits the arabinosyl transferase enzyme and hinders the synthesis of arabinogalactan. Disruption of arabinogalactan synthesis inhibits this complex formation and increases cell wall permeability.

8.2.4.2. SAR

When the distance between nitrogen atoms is altered by inserting a carbon, oxygen, or sulphur atom, the anti-tubercular activity is lost. Replacing the *sec*-butyl group with hydroxy substituted isopropyl or t-butyl groups eliminates the anti-tubercular activity. Moving the hydroxyl group C-3 or C-4 of the *sec*-butyl group also eliminates the anti-tubercular activity.

Replacing the alcohol group with phenoxy, thio, or amino group eliminates the anti-tubercular activity. The methoxy and ethoxy derivatives of ethambutol are as active as the parent compound; however, this activity is due to enzymatic dealkylation and is *in vivo*. The dextrorotary isomer shows greatest activity, since it is 200 to 500 times more active than the levorotatory isomer.

8.2.4.3. Uses

Ethambutol has the following uses:

1) It is used along with other drugs in the treatment of tuberculosis.
2) It is also used to treat MAC (*Mycobacterium avium* complex).

8.2.4.4. Adverse Effects

Ethambutol in daily doses of 15mg/kg produces a very few adverse reactions; while in high doses it causes loss of vision due to retro-bulbar neuritis, and also loss of colour vision.

8.2.5. Pyrazinamide

Pyrazinamide is a synthetic pyrazinoic acid amide derivative having bactericidal properties. It is specifically active against slowly multiplying intracellular bacilli.

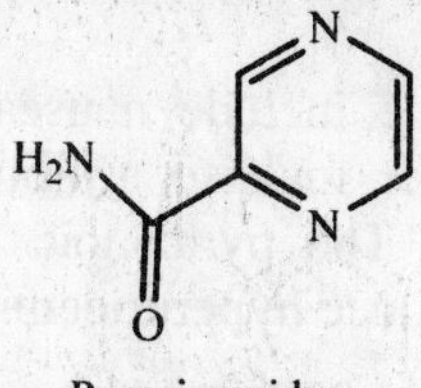

Pyrazinamide

8.2.5.1. Mechanism of Action

Pyrazinamide is a prodrug that inhibits the growth of *Mycobacterium tuberculosis*. This bacterium has pyrazinamidase enzyme that is active under acidic conditions. It converts pyrazinamide to pyrazinoic acid (active form) that accumulates in the bacilli. Accumulation of pyrazinoic acid also disrupts membrane potential and interferes with energy production that is essential for the survival of *M. tuberculosis* at an acidic site of infection.

8.2.5.2. SAR

Previous structural modification of pyrazinamide failed to develop analogues with increased biological activity. Substitution on the pyrazine ring or use of alternate heterocyclic aromatic rings yielded compounds with reduced anti-tubercular activity.

Recently, QSAR was used to prepare a series of analogues having improved biological activity, and the requirements were:

1) Provision for hydrophilicity to allow sufficient plasma concentrations so that the drug can be delivered to the infection site,
2) Lipophilicity to allow the drug to penetrate the mycobacterial cell, and
3) Susceptibility to hydrolysis so that the prodrug is not affected by the extracellular enzymes but undergoes rapid hydrolysis at the action site.

Two compounds, i.e., tert-butyl-5-chloropyrazinamide and 2′-(2′-methyldecyl)-5-chloropyrazinamide meet these criteria.

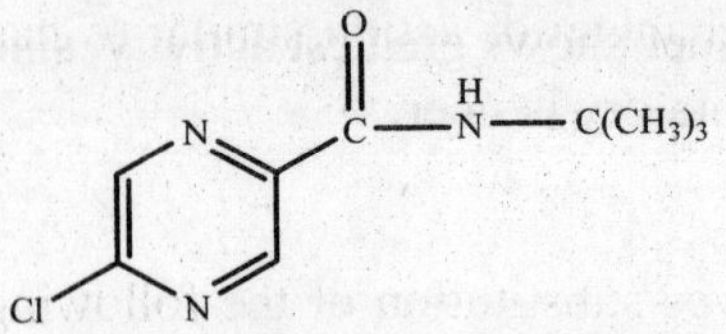

Tert-butyl 5-chloropyrazinoate

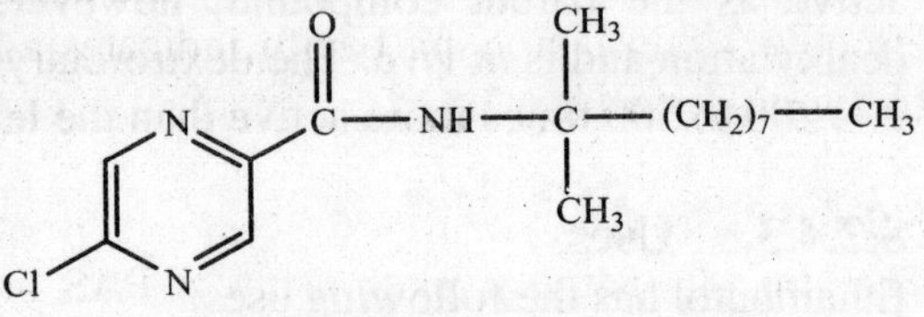

2′-(2′-Methyldecyl) 5-chloropyrazinoate

8.2.5.3. Uses

Pyrazinamide is used alone or along with other drugs for the treatment of the following diseases:

1) It is used along with isoniazid and rifampicin for treating *Mycobacterium tuberculosis.*
2) It is used along with rifampin for treating latent tuberculosis.
3) It is a potent anti-uricosuric drug and is used for diagnosing the causes of hyperuricemia and hyperuricosuria.

8.2.5.4. Adverse Effects

Adverse effects of pyrazinamide include nausea, vomiting, urinary retention, anorexia, dysuria, drug rash, fever, malaise, arthralgia, jaundice, hepatic necrosis, and decreased urate excretion. The pyrazinoic acid metabolites reduce renal tubular excretion of urate and induce hyperuricemia and acute gouty arthritis.

8.2.6. *Para*-Amino Salicylic Acid (PAS)

PAS is an antibiotic which is being used since 1940s for treating inflammatory bowel diseases. It shows greater potency in the treatment of ulcerative colitis and Crohn's disease.

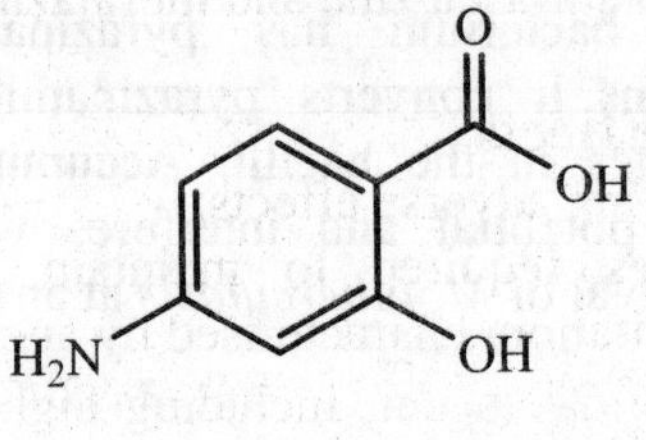

p-Aminosalicyclic acid

8.2.6.1. Synthesis

PAS is synthesised as follows:

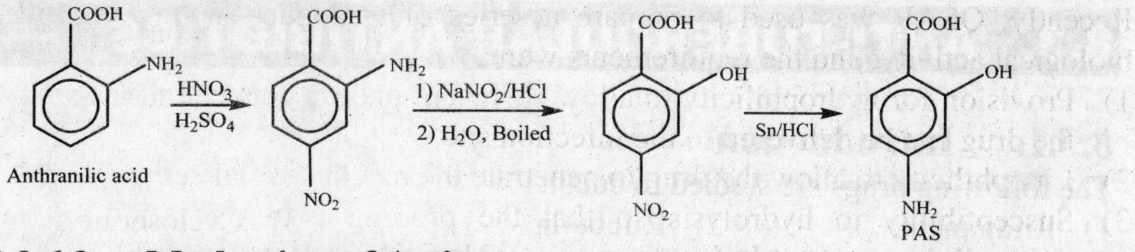

8.2.6.2. Mechanism of Action

PAS slightly affects the respiration of *M. tuberculosis*, indicating that the biochemical rationale leading to its discovery was incorrect. The tuberculostatic activity of PAS can be reversed by the administration of PABA, and this being effective against growing bacilli indicates a mechanism of action similar to that of the sulfonamides.

8.2.6.3. SAR

The structure-activity relationship of PAS involves substitution of the following functional groups:

1) Modifications in the structure of PAS eliminate its anti-tubercular activity unless the parent molecule is readily regenerated.
2) Replacing the primary amino group with hydroxy, alkoxy, tertiary amines, or amides yield inactive compounds.
3) Replacing the hydroxyl group with ether, ester, a thiol, or an amino group also eliminates the anti-tubercular activity.
4) Converting the carboxylic acid group to alkyl esters, amidines, amides, or nitrates also results in loss of activity. However, phenyl esters are active as they can be slowly hydrolysed to the free acid.

8.2.6.4. Uses

PAS has the following uses:

1) After streptomycin, it was the second antibiotic that was effective in tuberculosis treatment. It was a part of the standard treatment for tuberculosis before rifampicin and pyrazinamide were introduced.
2) However its potency is less than that of the five first-line drugs (isoniazid, rifampicin, ethambutol, pyrazinamide, and streptomycin) for treating tuberculosis, still it is used in combination with other anti-TB drugs in multidrug-resistant tuberculosis.
3) It has also been used in the treatment of inflammatory bowel disease, but has been succeeded by sulfasalazine and mesalazine.

8.2.6.5. Adverse Effects

PAS causes the following adverse effects:

1) Its frequent doses required to maintain adequate blood levels cause gastrointestinal irritation, characterised by anorexia and nausea.
2) Allergic reactions may occur, including high fever, malaise, joint pains, or sore throat.
3) Its excretion is associated with loss of cations; therefore, acidosis and hypokalaemia may occur. Acidosis is prevented by using sodium *p*-aminosalicylate.

8.3. ANTI-TUBERCULAR ANTIBIOTICS

8.3.1. Introduction

The following drugs are studied in detail:

1) Rifampicin,
2) Rifabutin,
3) Cycloserine,
4) Streptomycin, and
5) Capreomycin sulphate.

8.3.2. Rifampicin

Rifampicin is a semi-synthetic antibiotic derived from *Streptomyces mediterranei*. It has a broad antibacterial activity, and is also active against several *Mycobacterium*.

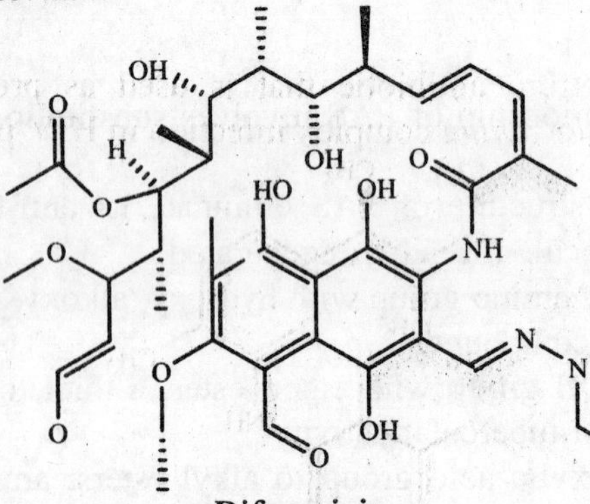

Rifampicin

8.3.2.1. Mechanism of Action

Rifampicin inhibits the DNA-dependent RNA polymerase, and thus suppresses RNA synthesis and cause cell death.

8.3.2.2. SAR

SAR of rifampicin can be summarised as follows:

1) Aliphatic modifications fail to retain the anti-tubercular activity.
2) In naphthalene ring, C-3 and C-4 are bioactive positions. Some derivatives prepared by varying the substituents at these positions show activity nearly as potent as the parent compound on clinical trials.

8.3.2.3. Uses

Rifampicin has the following uses:

1) It is used to treat *Mycobacterium* infections, including tuberculosis and Hansen's disease.
2) With multidrug therapy used as the standard treatment of Hansen's disease, it is used along with dapsone and clofazimine to avoid eliciting drug resistance.
3) Along with fusidic acid, it is useful in Methicillin-Resistant *Staphylococcus aureus* (MRSA).
4) It is used in prophylactic therapy against *Neisseria meningitidis* (meningococcal) infection.
5) It shows some effectiveness against vaccinia virus.

8.3.2.4. Adverse Effects

Rifampicin causes the following adverse effects:

1) **Hepatotoxic:** Hepatitis, jaundice, and liver failure in severe cases.
2) **Respiratory:** Breathlessness.
3) **Cutaneous:** Flushing, pruritus, rash, redness, and watering of eyes.
4) **Abdominal:** Nausea, vomiting, and abdominal cramps with or without diarrhoea.
5) **Flu-like Symptoms:** Chills, fever, headache, arthralgia, and malaise.
6) It also has good penetration into the brain, and thus causes malaise and dysphoria in a minority of users.

8.3.3. Rifabutin

Rifabutin is a broad-spectrum antibiotic that is used as prophylaxis against disseminated *Mycobacterium avium* complex infection in HIV-positive patients.

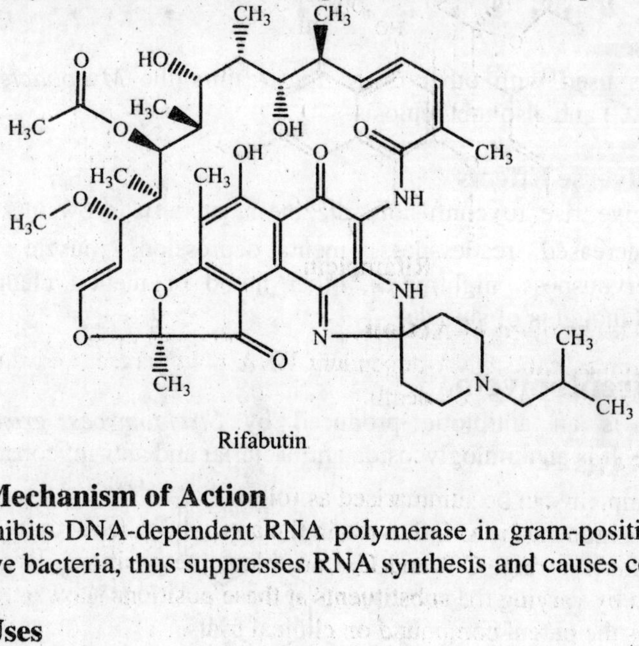

Rifabutin

8.3.3.1. Mechanism of Action

Rifabutin inhibits DNA-dependent RNA polymerase in gram-positive and some gram-negative bacteria, thus suppresses RNA synthesis and causes cell death.

8.3.3.2. Uses

Rifabutin prevents disseminated *Mycobacterium avium* complex (MAC) disease in patients with advanced HIV infection.

8.3.3.3. Adverse Effects

Common side effects of rifabutin include diarrhoea, stomach upset or pain, change in taste, nausea, vomiting, belching, bloating, loss of appetite, headache, skin rash, itching, or red, orange, or brown discoloration of skin, tears, sweat, saliva, urine, or stools.

Rare but serious side effects include easy bleeding or bruising, fever, persistent sore throat/cough, muscle weakness or pain, joint pain or swelling, eye pain or redness, vision problems, chest pain or pressure, persistent nausea or vomiting, unusual weakness or tiredness, or jaundice.

8.3.4. Cycloserine

Cycloserine is a broad spectrum antibiotic which is used along with other anti-tubercular drugs as a second line agent for treating drug-resistant tuberculosis.

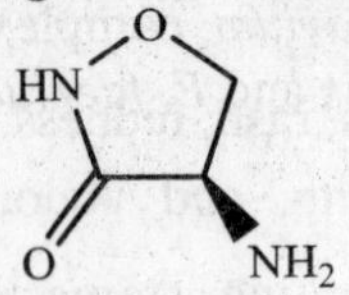

Cycloserine

8.3.4.1. Mechanism of Action

Cycloserine is an analog of D-alanine amino acid. It interferes with an early step in bacterial cell wall synthesis in the cytoplasm by competitive inhibition of L-alanine racemase and D-alanylalanine synthetase enzymes. The fomer forms D-alanine from L-alanine and the latter incorporates D-alanine into the pentapeptide required for peptidoglycan formation and bacterial cell wall synthesis.

8.3.4.2. Use

Cycloserine is used with other drugs for treating the *Mycobacterium avium* Complex (MAC) and also tuberculosis.

8.3.4.3. Adverse Effects

Cycloserine give rise to confusion, dizziness, anxiety, drowsiness, increased irritability, increased restlessness, mental depression, muscle twitching or trembling, nervousness, nightmares, other mood or mental changes, speech problems, and thoughts of suicide.

8.3.5. Streptomycin

Streptomycin is an antibiotic produced by *Streptomyces griseus* (a soil actinomycete). It is an aminoglycoside antibacterial and anti-mycobacterial.

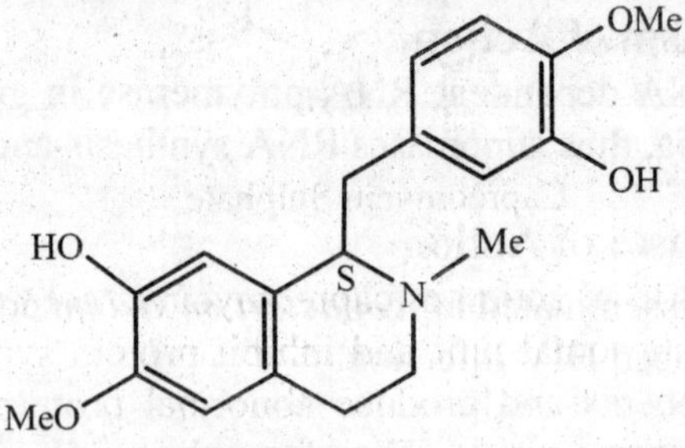

Streptomycin

8.3.5.1. Mechanism of Action

Streptomycin irreversibly binds to specific 30S subunit proteins and 16S rRNA. It specifically binds to four nucleotides of 16S rRNA and a single amino acid of protein S12. This interferes with decoding site near the nucleotide 1400 in 16S rRNA of 30S subunit. This region interacts with the wobble base in the anticodon of tRNA. This interferes with the initiation complex, causing misreading of mRNA so incorrect amino acids are inserted into the polypeptide leading to non-functional or toxic peptides and breakup of polysomes into non-functional monosomes.

8.3.5.2. Uses

Streptomycin is used for treating tuberculosis. In combination with other drugs, it is used for treating tularemia (caused by *Francisella tularensis*), plague (caused by *Yersinia pestis*), severe *M. avium* complex, brucellosis, and Enterococcal endocarditis (caused by *E. faecalis* and *E. faecium*).

8.3.5.3. Adverse Effects

Streptomycin causes nausea, vomiting, stomach upset, loss of appetite, vertigo, injection site reactions (pain, irritation, and redness), tingling or prickling sensation in the face, rash, fever, hives, and oedema.

8.3.6. Capreomycin Sulphate

Capreomycin is a cyclic peptide antibiotic produced by *Streptomyces capreolus*.

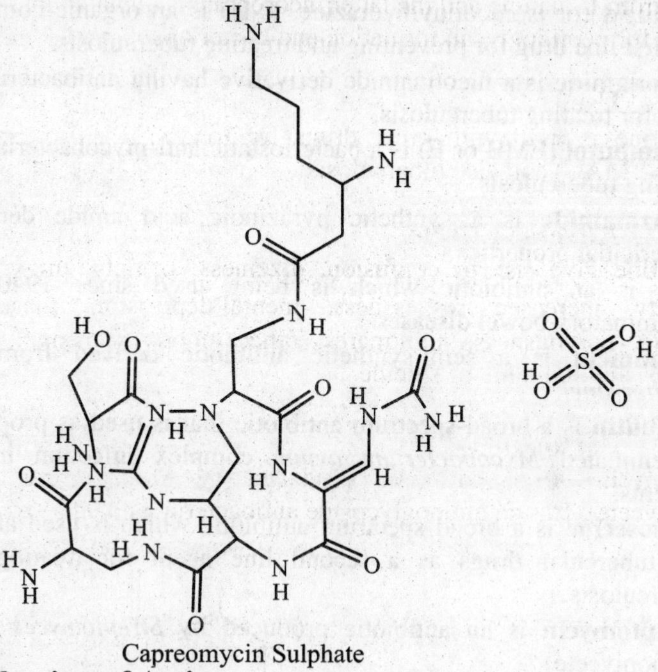

Capreomycin Sulphate

8.3.6.1. Mechanism of Action

The precise mechanism of action of capreomycin is not known, but it is assumed to bind to the 70S ribosomal unit and inhibit protein synthesis. It also binds to bacterial cell components and produce abnormal proteins (normal proteins are essential for bacteria's survival). Therefore, the production of these abnormal proteins is fatal to the bacteria.

8.3.6.2. Use

Capreomycin along with other drugs is used in the treatment of tuberculosis.

8.3.6.3. Adverse Effects

Capreomycin causes black stools, blood in urine, change in the frequency of urination or amount of urine, chest pain, chills, cough, difficult breathing, dizziness, drowsiness, feeling of fullness in the ears, fever, increased thirst, loss of appetite, loss of balance, loss of hearing, nausea or vomiting, painful or difficult urination, ringing or buzzing in ears, sore throat, sores, ulcers, or white spots on lips or in mouth, swelling of feet or lower legs, swollen glands, trouble with hearing, unusual bleeding or bruising, and unusual tiredness or weakness.

8.4. SUMMARY

The details given in the chapter can be summarised as follows:

1) Tuberculosis (TB) is an infective disease, most commonly affecting the lungs, and caused by ***Mycobacterium tuberculosis*** and ***Mycobacterium bovis***.
2) Non-tuberculosis mycobacterial infections are known as ***M. avium* complex (MAC)** as they are caused by *M. avium*, *M. kansaii*, *M. murinum*, and *M. scrofulaceum*.
3) **Isoniazid** (or isonicotinylhydrazine, INH) is an organic compound used as the first line drug for preventing and treating tuberculosis.
4) **Ethionamide** is a nicotinamide derivative having antibacterial activity, and used for treating tuberculosis.
5) **Ethambutol** (EMB or E) is a bacteriostatic anti-mycobacterial drug used for treating tuberculosis.
6) **Pyrazinamide** is a synthetic pyrazinoic acid amide derivative having bactericidal properties.
7) **PAS** is an antibiotic which is being used since 1940s for treating inflammatory bowel diseases.
8) **Rifampicin** is a semi-synthetic antibiotic derived from *Streptomyces mediterranei*.
9) **Rifabutin** is a broad-spectrum antibiotic that is used as prophylaxis against disseminated *Mycobacterium avium* complex infection in HIV-positive patients.
10) **Cycloserine** is a broad spectrum antibiotic which is used along with other anti-tubercular drugs as a second line agent for treating drug-resistant tuberculosis.
11) **Streptomycin** is an antibiotic produced by *Streptomyces griseus* (a soil actinomycete).
12) **Capreomycin** is a cyclic peptide antibiotic produced by *Streptomyces capreolus*.

8.5. EXERCISE

8.5.1. True or False

1) Isoniazid is an organic compound used as the second line drug for preventing and treating tuberculosis.
2) Ethambutol is a nicotinamide derivative having antibacterial activity, and used for treating tuberculosis.
3) Pyrazinamide is a synthetic pyrazinoic acid amide derivative having bactericidal properties.
4) Rifabutin is a semi-synthetic antibiotic derived from *Streptomyces mediterranei*.

8.5.2. Fill in the Blanks

5) Tuberculosis is an infective disease, most commonly affecting the lungs, and caused by ________ and ________.
6) Non-tuberculosis mycobacterial infections are known as ________.
7) ________ is a broad spectrum antibiotic which is used along with other anti-tubercular drugs as a second line agent for treating drug-resistant tuberculosis.
8) Capreomycin is a cyclic peptide antibiotic produced by ________.

Answers

1) False	2) False	3) True
4) False	5) *Mycobacterium tuberculosis* and *Mycobacterium bovis*	
6) *M. avium* complex	7) Cycloserine	8) *Streptomyces capreolus*

8.5.3. Very Short Answer Type Questions

1) Classify anti-tubercular drugs.
2) Give the chemical structure of ethionamide.
3) Give the mechanism of action of ethambutol.
4) Enlist the uses of pyrazinamide.
5) What are the uses of rifampicin?
6) How rifabutin acts?
7) Draw the structure of streptomycin.

8.5.4. Short Answer Type Questions

1) Write a short note on isoniazid.
2) Give the synthesis and SAR of PAS.
3) Discuss about capreomycin sulphate.
4) Give the mechanism of action, uses and adverse effects of cycloserine.

8.5.5. Long Answer Type Questions

1) Discuss the historical background of anti-tubercular drugs.
2) Write an exhaustive note on anti-tubercular antibiotics.

CHAPTER 9

Quinolones and Urinary Tract Anti-Infective Agents

9.1. QUINOLONES

9.1.1. Introduction

Quinolones are synthetic broad-spectrum antibiotics. The term **quinolone** indicates potent synthetic chemotherapeutic antibacterial. In comparison to other antibiotic classes, quinolones have the highest risk of causing colonisation with Methicillin-resistant *Staphylococcus aureus* (MRSA) and *Clostridium difficile*. They are new antibacterial agents that are therapeutically useful in the treatment of urinary tract infections and infections resistant to the available antibacterial agents.

Nalidixic acid is the first therapeutically useful quinolone that is active against gram-negative bacteria, and useful in the short-term therapy of urinary tract infections. **Enoxacilin** is a fluorine-containing compound with increased spectrum of activity against gram-negative and gram-positive bacteria. It is also active against the highly resistant *Pseudomonas aeruginosa*.

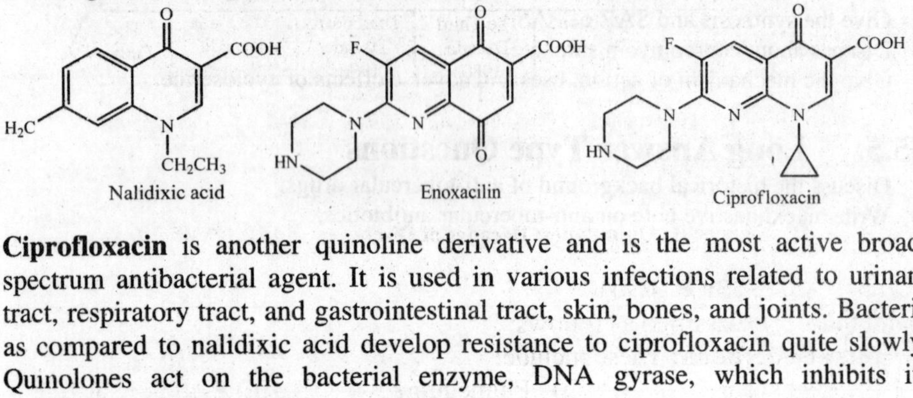

Nalidixic acid Enoxacilin Ciprofloxacin

Ciprofloxacin is another quinoline derivative and is the most active broad-spectrum antibacterial agent. It is used in various infections related to urinary tract, respiratory tract, and gastrointestinal tract, skin, bones, and joints. Bacteria as compared to nalidixic acid develop resistance to ciprofloxacin quite slowly. Quinolones act on the bacterial enzyme, DNA gyrase, which inhibits its replication and transcription.

9.1.2. Historical Background

Based on the 4-quinolone nucleus, quinolones comprise of a relatively large and expanding group of synthetic compounds. **Nalidixic acid** was the first of these compounds to be discovered. It is a naphthyridine agent, an antibacterial by-product of chloroquine synthesis, and rapidly bactericidal. After two years of its discovery, it was described to act by inhibiting the synthesis of bacterial DNA gyrase, thus inhibiting tertiary negative supercoiling of bacterial DNA.

In **1990**, **topoisomerase IV** (a gyrase homologue) was discovered. It had a potent decatenating activity, and is responsible for decatenation of interlinked chromosomes.

The **1960s** mark the **first decade of quinolone development** and use. In **1967**, nalidixic acid was licensed for the treatment of UTIs caused by various gram-negative bacteria, except *Pseudomonas aeruginosa*. Gram-positive organisms are resistant to the early quinolones. Other clinical uses of nalidixic acid (apart from the treatment of urinary infection) were limited due to its low serum concentrations and high Minimum Inhibitory Concentrations (MIC 4-16mg/l). Some derivatives of nalidixic acid, such as **pipemidic acid** (the first piperazinyl quinolone), **oxolinic acid**, and **cinoxacin** were discovered in the **1970s**, however showed minimal improvements over nalidixic acid. These agents proved invaluable in the treatment of uncomplicated UTIs (such as cystitis).

After the introduction of extensive clinical use of nalidixic acid, it was found that a few microorganisms rapidly developed resistance to it. This proved to be a characteristic of the early quinolones. With nalidixic acid, resistance develops readily following serial passages in the laboratory, but primary resistance amongst urinary pathogens is rare. In **1969**, resistance to nalidixic acid in *Escherichia coli* was mapped to chromosomal mutations (nalA, nalB). These resistance loci were identified in **1977** as encoding mutant subunits of DNA gyrase of *E. coli*.

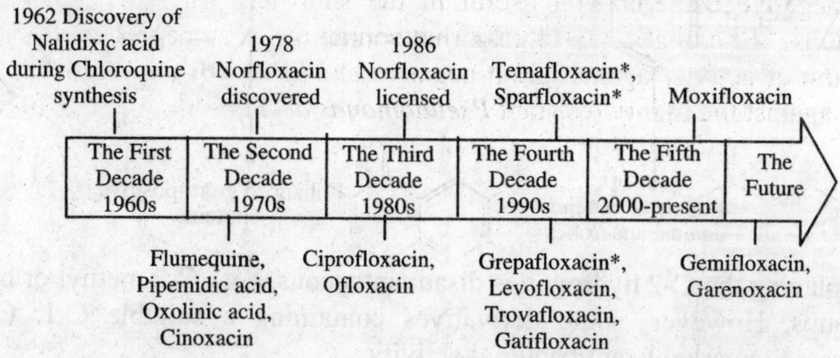

Figure 9.1: Quinolones; Decades of Discovery and Use, * Withdrawn

9.1.3. Classification

Quinolones are classified as follows:

1) **First Generation:** These include:
   i) Cinoxacin ii) Flumequine iii) Nalidixic acid
   iv) Oxolinic acid v) Piromidic acid vi) Pipemidic acid
   vii) Rosoxacin

2) **Second Generation:** This class is sometimes subdivided into Class 1 and Class 2, and include:
   i) Ciprofloxacin ii) Enoxacin iii) Fleroxacin iv) Lomefloxacin
   v) Nadifloxacin vi) Norfloxacin vii) Ofloxaci viii) Pefloxacin
   ix) Rufloxacin

3) **Third Generation:** This class is active against *Streptococci*, and the drugs include:
   i) Balofloxacin ii) Grepafloxacin iii) Levofloxacin iv) Pazufloxacin
   v) Sparfloxacin vi) Temafloxacin vii) Tosufloxacin

4) **Fourth Generation:** This class acts at DNA gyrase and topoisomerase IV. This dual action slows the development of resistance. The drugs include:
i) Clinafloxacin ii) Gatifloxacin iii) Gemifloxacin iv) Moxifloxacin
v) Sitafloxacin vi) Trovafloxacin vii) Prulifloxacin

9.1.4. SAR

The structure-activity relationship aspects of quinolones are mentioned below:

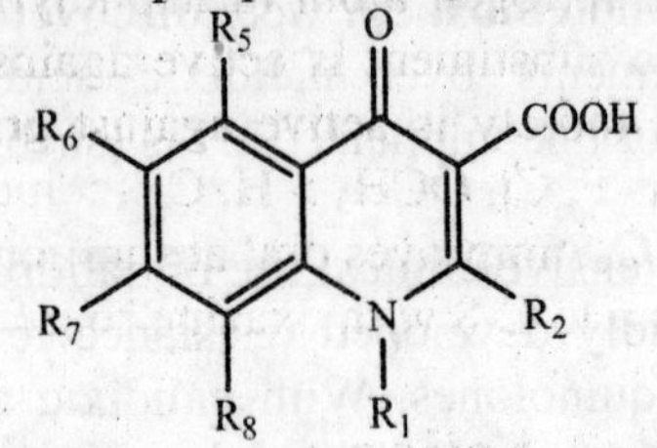

1) A compilation of active N-1 quinolone substituents is shown with overall *in vitro* potency.

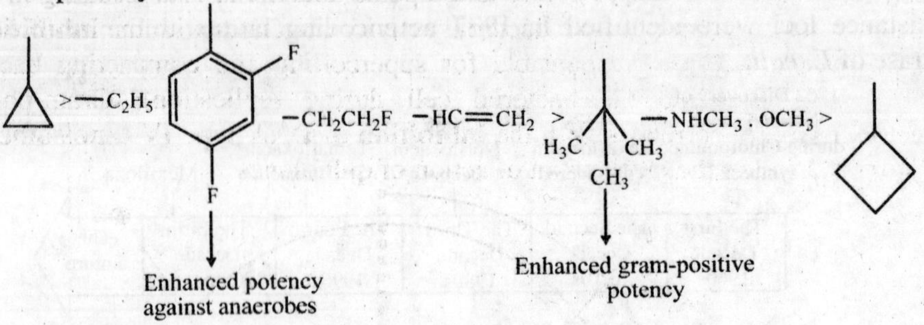

2) Replacing the C-2 hydrogen is disadvantageous, **e.g.,** C-2 methyl or hydroxyl groups. However, some derivatives containing a suitable C-1, C-2 ring possess remarkable antibacterial activity.

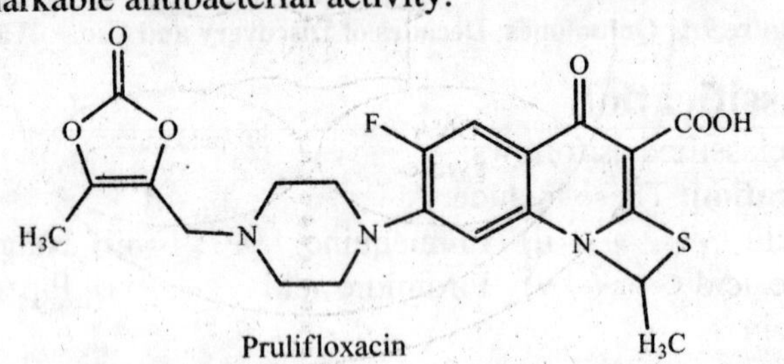

Prulifloxacin

3) The carboxylic acid moiety at C-3 is most commonly encountered. Other acidic groups such as sulphonic acid, phosphonic acid, tetrazole, and derivatisation as an ester results in a loss of antibacterial activity.
4) The oxo group at C-4 of the quinolone nucleus is essential for antibacterial activity. Replacing it with 4-thioxo or sulphonyl group results in loss of activity.
5) Introducing an amino group at C-5 enhances the antibacterial activity. The order of activity at R_5 is NH_2, CH_3 > F, H > OH, OR, SH, SR.
6) Introducing a fluorine atom at C-6 of the quinolone is epic. The order of activity at R_6 is F > Cl, Br, CH_3 > CN.

7) Introducing a piperazine moiety at C-7 was a landmark development. Other aminopyrrolidines also are compatible for activity. The order of activity at R_7 is:

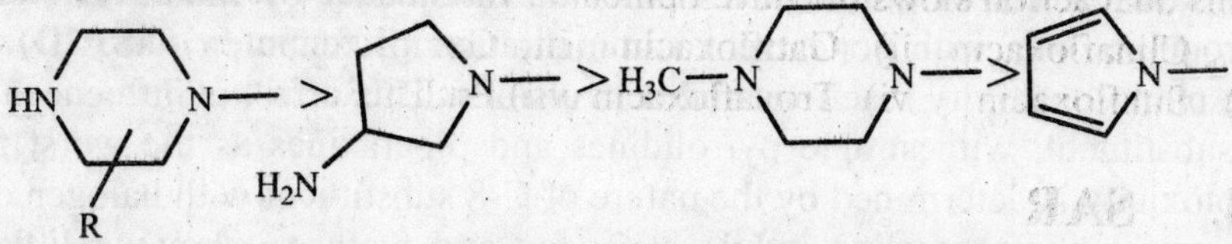

8) A hydrogen atom or a nitrogen atom (a naphthyridone) at C-8 is the most common. A C-8 fluoro substituent is active against gram-negative bacteria, while a C-8 methoxyl moiety is active against gram-positive bacteria. The order of activity at R_8 is F, Cl, OCH_3 > H, CF_3 > methyl, vinyl, propargyl.
9) A halogen (F or Cl) at C-8 improves oral absorption of quinolones.
10) The joining of N1-group to C-8 with oxazine ring forms ofloxacin.

9.1.5. Mechanism of Action

Quinolones **inhibit DNA synthesis** by cleaving bacterial DNA in the DNA-enzyme complexes of DNA gyrase and topoisomerase IV, thus resulting in rapid bacterial death. Gram-negative bacterial activity correlates with the **inhibition of DNA gyrase enzyme** (responsible for supercoiling and compacting bacterial DNA molecules into the bacterial cell during replication). Gram-positive bacterial activity correlates with the **inhibition of DNA type IV topoisomerase. Figure 9.2** shows the mechanism of action of quinolones.

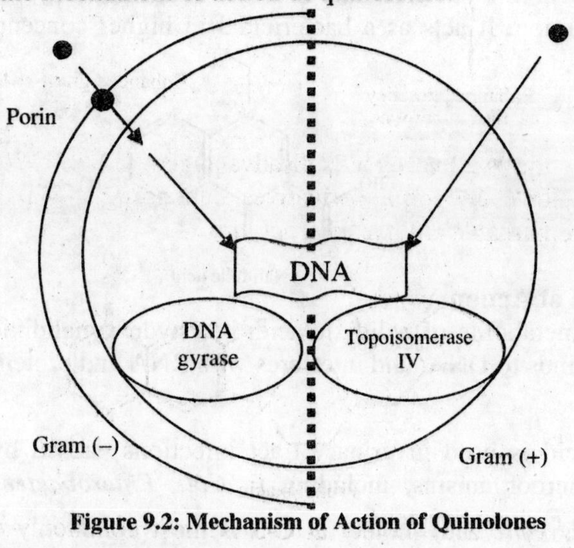

Figure 9.2: Mechanism of Action of Quinolones

9.1.6. Uses

Quinolones have the following uses:

1) Nalidixic acid is used as a urinary antiseptic, as a second line drug in recurrent cases or on the basis of sensitivity reports.
2) It has been used in diarrhoea caused by *Proteus*, *E. coli*, *Shigella*, or *Salmonella*.
3) Floroquinolones are used in urinary tract infection, gonorrhoea, chancroid, bacterial gastroenteritis, typhoid, respiratory infection, tuberculosis, meningitis, conjunctivitis, gynaecological problems, and wound infection.

9.1.7. Adverse Effects

Some side effects of quinolones cannot be modulated by molecular variation. Fluoroquinolones with concurrent administration of fenbufen (NSAID) mostly cause photosensitivity reactions and convulsions. This effect is influenced by the C-7 substituent, with simple pyrrolidines and piperazines as the worst factors. Phototoxicity is determined by the nature of C-8 substituent with halogen causing the greatest photo reaction, while hydrogen and methoxy showing little light-induced toxicity. Arthralgia and joint swelling develop in children receiving fluoroquinolones; thus, their use is not recommended in pre-pubertal children or pregnant women. Genetic toxicity is controlled by the choice of groups at C-1, C-7, and C-8 positions.

9.1.8. Important Products

The following drugs are studied in detail:

1) Nalidixic acid, 2) Norfloxacin, 3) Enoxacin,
4) Ciprofloxacin, 5) Ofloxacin, 6) Lomefloxacin,
7) Sparfloxacin, 8) Gatifloxacin, and 9) Moxifloxacin.

9.1.8.1. Nalidixic Acid

Nalidixic acid is the first synthetic quinolone antibiotic. It is strongly active against gram-negative bacteria, and shows minor activity against gram-positive bacteria. It acts as a bacteriostatic in lower concentrations, i.e., it inhibits growth and reproduction. It acts as a bactericidal in higher concentrations, i.e., it kills bacteria.

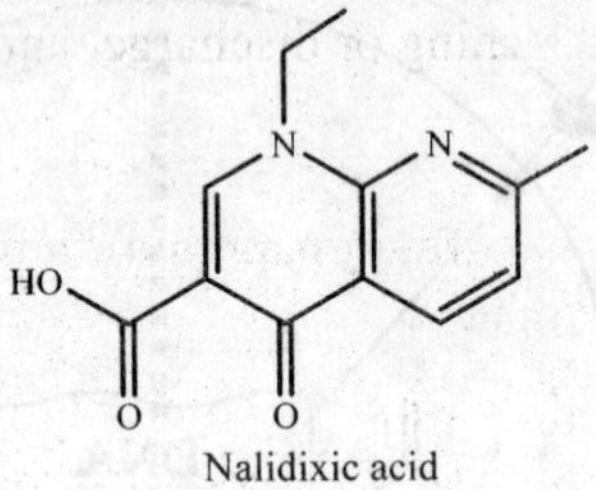

Nalidixic acid

Mechanism of Action

The active metabolite of nalidixic acid, i.e., hydroxynalidixic acid, strongly and reversibly binds to DNA, and interferes with RNA and protein synthesis.

Uses

Nalidixic acid is used in urinary tract infections caused by susceptible gram-negative microorganisms, including E. *Coli*, *Enterobacter* species, *Klebsiella* species, and *Proteus* species.

Adverse Effects

The adverse effects of nalidixic acid include severe allergic reactions (rash, hives, itching, or difficulty breathing), tightness in chest, swelling (of mouth, face, lips, or tongue), blurred vision, burning or tingling sensation, changes in colour vision, convulsions, and decreased ability to sense pain and temperature.

9.1.8.2. Norfloxacin

Norfloxacin is a synthetic fluoroquinolone with broad-spectrum antibacterial activity against a wide range of gram-negative and gram-positive bacteria.

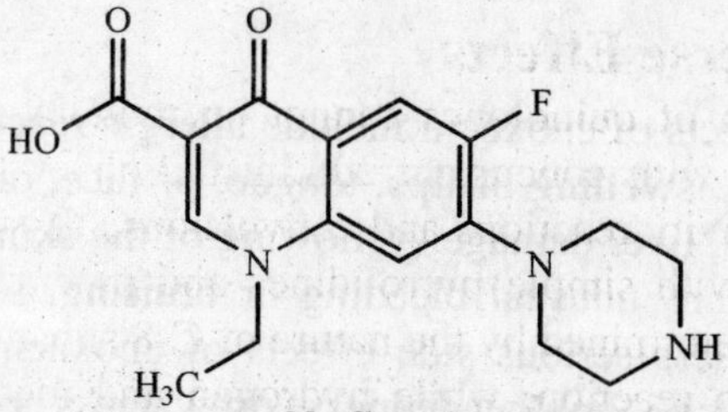

Norfloxacin

Mechanism of Action

Norfloxacin inhibits topoisomerase II (DNA gyrase) and topoisomerase IV enzymes that are required for bacterial DNA replication, transcription, repair, and recombination. It is a broad-spectrum antibiotic with activity against various gram-positive and gram-negative bacteria. Fluorine atom at C-6 of norfloxacin increases its potency against gram-negative microorganisms, and piperazine moiety at C-7 is responsible for its anti-pseudomonal activity.

Uses

Norfloxacin is used as a first-line urinary antibacterial and is useful in genital infection. It is effective in gonorrhoea, typhoid fever, acute bacterial gastroenteritis, and prophylaxis of sepsis in neutropenic patients.

Adverse Effects

Common side effects of norfloxacin include nausea, diarrhoea, dizziness, stomach cramps, heartburn, rectal pain, lightheadedness, muscle and joint aches, back pain, sweating, vaginal itching or discharge, and headache.

9.1.8.3. Enoxacin

Enoxacin is a broad-spectrum 6-fluoronaphthyridinone antibacterial agent that is structurally related to nalidixic acid.

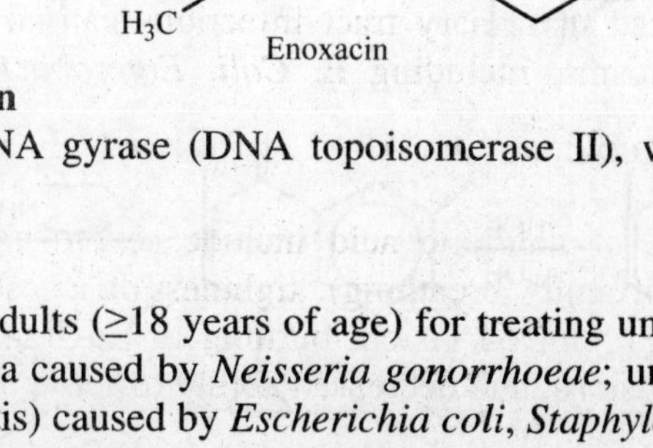

Enoxacin

Mechanism of Action

Enoxacin inhibits DNA gyrase (DNA topoisomerase II), which is an essential bacterial enzyme.

Uses

Enoxacin is used in adults (≥18 years of age) for treating uncomplicated urethral or cervical gonorrhoea caused by *Neisseria gonorrhoeae*; uncomplicated urinary tract infections (cystitis) caused by *Escherichia coli*, *Staphylococcus epidermidis*, or *Staphylococcus saprophyticus*; and complicated urinary tract infections caused by *Escherichia coli*, *Klebsiella pneumoniae*, *Proteus mirabilis*, *Pseudomonas aeruginosa*, *Staphylococcus epidermidis*, or *Enterobacter cloacae*.

Adverse Effects

The adverse effects of enoxacin include allergic reaction (difficulty in breathing, closing of throat, swelling of lips, tongue, or face, or hives), seizures, confusion or hallucinations, liver damage (yellowing of the skin or eyes, nausea, abdominal pain or discomfort, unusual bleeding or bruising, severe fatigue) or muscle or joint pain. The less serious side effects of enoxacin include nausea, vomiting, diarrhoea, headache, lightheadedness, drowsiness, ringing in ears, or increased sensitivity of skin to sunlight.

9.1.8.4. Ciprofloxacin

Ciprofloxacin is a synthetic chemotherapeutic antibiotic of fluoroquinolone class. It is a second generation fluoroquinolone antibacterial. It is a bactericidal and interferes with the enzymes that cause DNA to rewind after being copied, thus blocks DNA and protein synthesis.

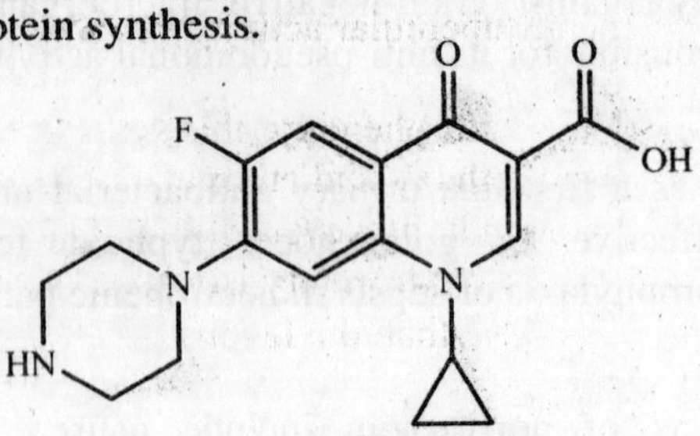

Ciprofloxacin

Synthesis

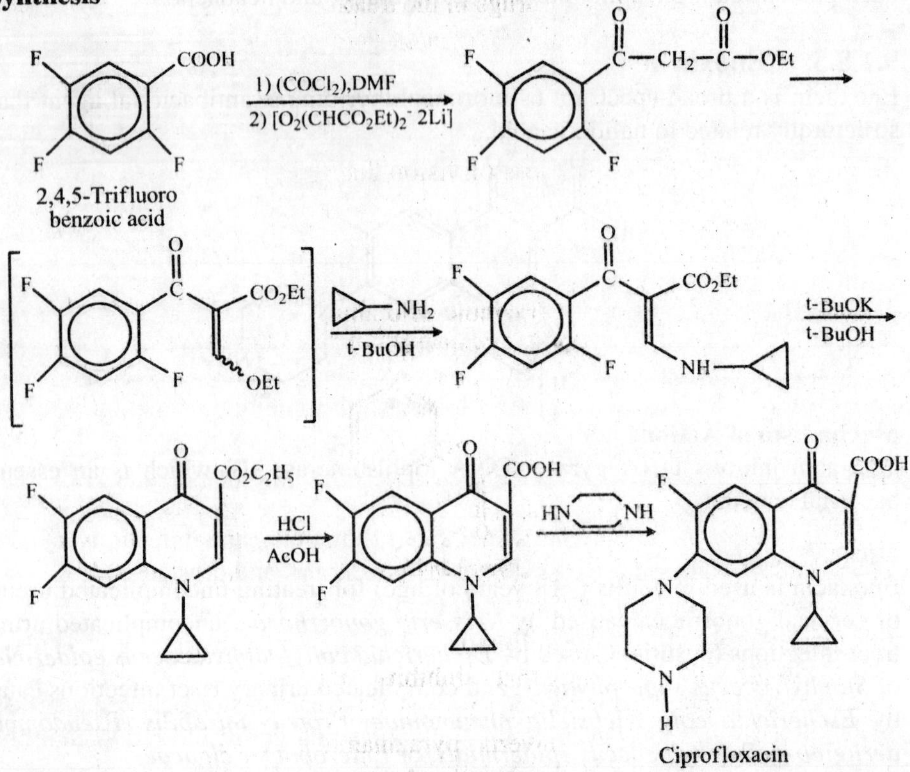

Mechanism of Action

Ciprofloxacin acts on bacterial topoisomerase II (DNA gyrase) and topoisomerase IV. Ciprofloxacin's targeting of the alpha subunits of DNA gyrase prevents it from supercoiling the bacterial DNA that prevents DNA replication.

Uses

1) Ciprofloxacin is used to treat infections of bones and joints, endocarditis, gastroenteritis, malignant otitis externa, respiratory tract infections, cellulitis, and urinary tract infections.
2) It has an important role in treatment guidelines issued by major medical societies for the treatment of serious infections caused by gram-negative bacteria, including *Pseudomonas aeruginosa.*
3) It also play a role in treatment guidelines for acute pyelonephritis, complicated or hospital-acquired urinary tract infections, acute or chronic prostatitis, certain types of endocarditis, certain skin infections, and prosthetic joint infections.

Adverse Effects

The adverse effects of ciprofloxacin include diarrhoea, dizziness, drowsiness, headache, stomach upset, abdominal pain, nausea/vomiting, and blurred vision.

9.1.8.5. Ofloxacin

Ofloxacin is a synthetic chemotherapeutic antibiotic of fluoroquinolone class. It is a second generation fluoroquinolone.

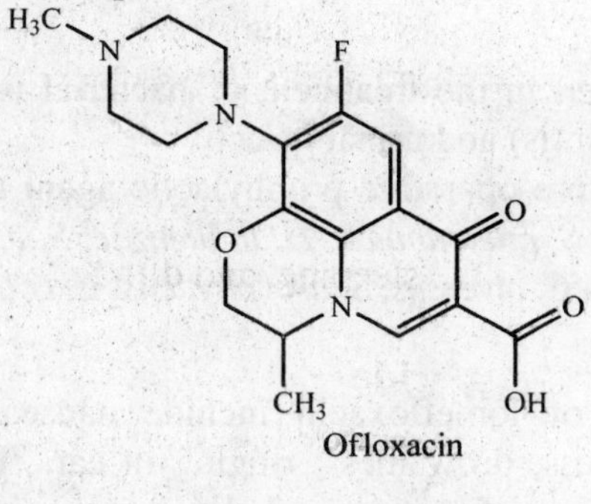

Ofloxacin

Mechanism of Action

Ofloxacin acts on DNA gyrase and topoisomerase IV enzymes, which (like human topoisomerase) prevents excessive supercoiling of DNA during replication or transcription. Therefore, due to this inhibited function, the drug inhibits normal bacterial cell division.

Uses

1) Ofloxacin is used to treat bronchitis, pneumonia, and infections of skin, urinary bladder, urinary tract, reproductive organs, and prostate gland.
2) It is used to treat various bacterial infections.

Adverse Effects

The adverse effects of ofloxacin include abdominal or stomach pain, anxiety, black, tarry stools, blood in urine or stools, bleeding gums, blurred vision, body aches or pain, chest pain, chills, and cloudy urine.

9.1.8.6. Lomefloxacin

Lomefloxacin is a fluoroquinolone antibiotic that is used to treat bacterial infections including bronchitis and urinary tract infections. It has also been used for the prophylaxis of urinary tract infections prior to surgery.

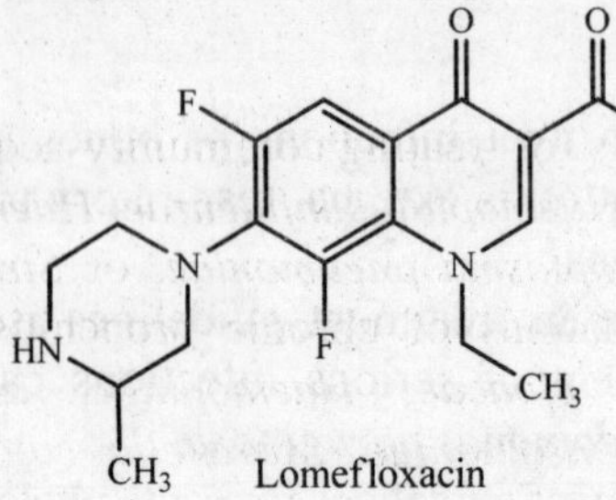

Lomefloxacin

Mechanism of Action

Lomefloxacin is a bactericidal fluoroquinolone that shows activity against various gram-negative and gram-positive organisms. Its bactericidal action results from interference with the activity of DNA gyrase and topoisomerase IV bacterial enzymes, which are required for transcription and replication of bacterial DNA. DNA gyrase is the primary quinolone target for gram-negative bacteria; while topoisomerase IV is the preferred target in gram-positive organisms. Interference with these two topoisomerases results in strand breakage of the bacterial chromosome, supercoiling, and resealing. As a result, DNA replication and transcription is inhibited.

Uses

1) Lomefloxacin is used in the treatment of bacterial infections of respiratory tract (chronic bronchitis) and urinary tract.
2) It is also used as a pre-operative prophylactic agent to prevent urinary tract infections caused by *S. pneumoniae*, *H. influenzae*, *S. aureus*, *P. aeruginosa*, *E. cloacae*, *P. mirabilis*, *C. civersus*, *S. asprphyticus*, *E. coli*, and *K. pneumoniae*.

Adverse Effects

Common side effects of lomefloxacin include nausea, vomiting, diarrhoea, headache, lightheadedness, drowsiness, ringing in ears, increased sensitivity of skin to sunlight, insomnia, indigestion, and abdominal pain.

9.1.8.7. Sparfloxacin

Sparfloxacin is a fluoroquinolone antibiotic that is useful in bacterial infections. It acts by inhibiting a bacterial topoisomerase enzyme, i.e., DNA gyrase, which controls DNA topology and assists in DNA replication, repair, deactivation, and transcription.

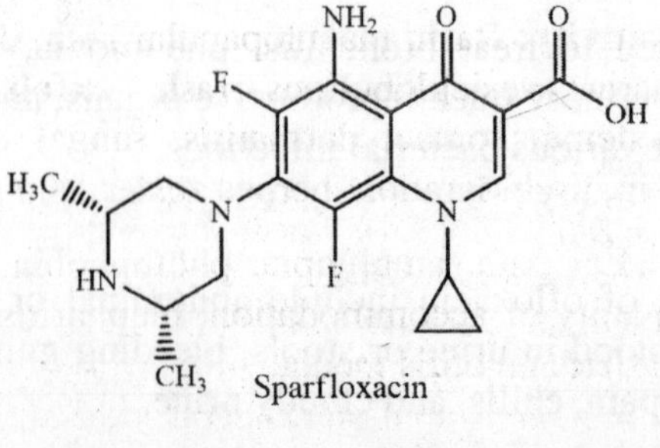

Sparfloxacin

Mechanism of Action

Sparfloxacin is a bactericidal as it inhibits topoisomerase II (DNA gyrase) and topoisomerase IV enzymes, which are required for replication, transcription, repair, and recombination of bacterial DNA.

Uses

Sparfloxacin is used in adults for treating community-acquired pneumonia caused by *Chlamydia pneumoniae*, *Haemophilus influenzae*, *Haemophilus parainfluenzae*, *Moraxella catarrhalis*, *Mycoplasma pneumoniae*, or *Streptococcus pneumoniae*; and acute bacterial exacerbations of chronic bronchitis caused by *Chlamydia pneumoniae*, *Enterobacter cloacae*, *Haemophilus influenzae*, *Haemophilus parainfluenzae*, *Klebsiella pneumoniae*, *Moraxella catarrhalis*, *Staphylococcus aureus*, or *Streptococcus pneumoniae*.

Adverse Effects

1) **Body as Whole:** Fever, chest pain, allergic reactions, cellulitis, back pain, chills, face oedema, malaise, accidental injury, infection, neck pain, and rheumatoid arthritis.

2) **CVS:** Palpitation, abnormal ECG, hypertension, tachycardia, sinus bradycardia, shortened PR interval, angina pectoris, arrhythmia, atrial fibrillation, atrial flutter, complete AV block, first degree AV block, second degree AV block, haemorrhage, migraine, peripheral vascular disorder, \ ventricular extrasystoles, and postural hypotension.

3) **Gastrointestinal:** Constipation, anorexia, gingivitis, oral moniliasis, stomatitis, tongue disorder, tooth disorder, gastroenteritis, increased appetite, mouth ulceration, flatulence, and vomiting.

4) **Hematologic:** Cyanosis, ecchymosis, and lymphadenopathy.

5) **Metabolism:** Gout, peripheral oedema, and increased thirst.

6) **Musculoskeletal:** Arthralgia, arthritis, joint disorder, and myalgia.

7) **CNS:** Paresthesia, nervousness, abnormal dreams, dry mouth, depression, tremor, anxiety, confusion, hallucinations, hyperkinesia, hypokinesia, sleep disorder, vertigo, abnormal gait, agitation, lightheadedness, emotional liability, euphoria, abnormal thinking, amnesia, and twitching.

8) **Respiratory:** Asthma, epistaxis, pneumonia, rhinitis, pharyngitis, bronchitis, haemoptysis, sinusitis, cough increased, dyspnoea, laryngismus, lung disorder, and pleural disorder.

9) **Skin/Hypersensitivity:** Rash, maculopapular rash, dry skin, herpes simplex, sweating, urticaria, vesiculobullous rash, exfoliative dermatitis, acne, alopecia, angioedema, contact dermatitis, fungal dermatitis, furunculosis, pustular rash, skin discolouration, herpes zoster, and petechial rash.

10) **Special Senses:** Ear pain, amblyopia, photophobia, tinnitus, conjunctivitis, diplopia, abnormality of accommodation, blepharitis, ear disorder, eye pain, lacrimation disorder, and otitis media.

11) **Urogenital:** Vaginitis, dysuria, breast pain, dysmenorrhea, haematuria, menorrhagia, nocturia, polyuria, urinary tract infection, kidney pain, leucorrhoea, metrorrhagia, and vulvovaginal disorder.

9.1.8.8. Gatifloxacin

Gatifloxacin is a fourth generation fluoroquinolone antibiotic. It inhibits DNA gyrase and topoisomerase IV bacterial enzymes.

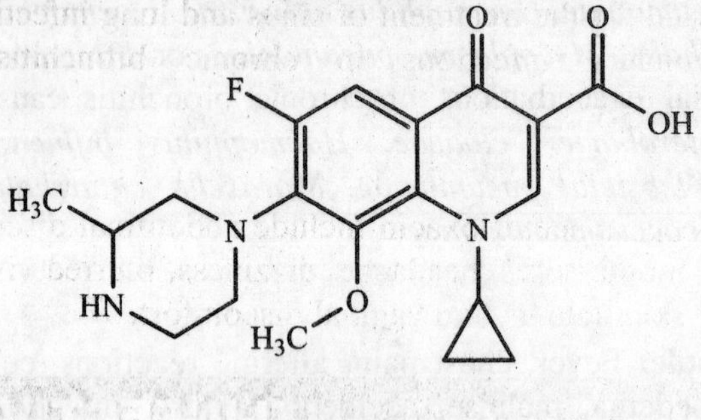

Gatifloxacin

Mechanism of Action

Gatifloxacin acts as a bactericidal by inhibiting topoisomerase II (DNA gyrase) and topoisomerase IV enzymes, which are essential for replication, transcription, repair, and recombination of bacterial DNA.

Uses

Gatifloxacin is used for the treatment of bronchitis, sinusitis, community-acquired pneumonia, and skin infections (abscesses or wounds) caused by *S. pneumoniae*, *H. influenzae*, *S. aureus*, *M. pneumoniae*, *C. pneumoniae*, *L. pneumophila*, and *S. pyogenes*

Adverse Effects

Common side effects of gatifloxacin include blurred vision, watery eyes, headache, eye itching/burning/irritation/pain/dryness/redness, watery eyes, puffy eyelids, headache, or bad or unpleasant taste in mouth after administering the drug, persistent eye redness, or swelling of eye or eyelid.

9.1.8.9. Moxifloxacin

Moxifloxacin is a synthetic fluoroquinolone antibiotic developed by **Bayer AG**. It is marketed in its hydrochloride form for oral treatment.

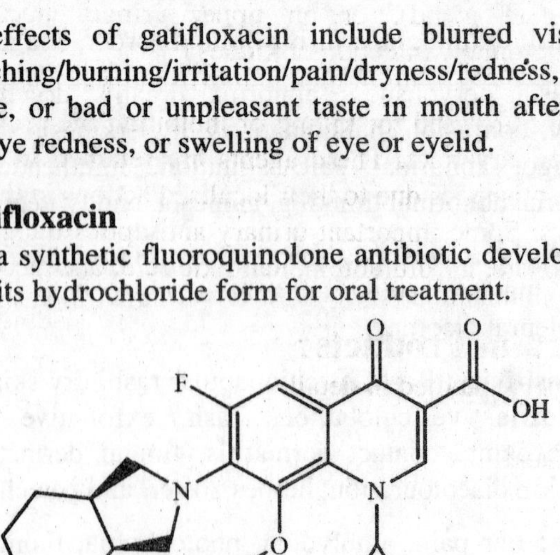

Moxifloxacin

Mechanism of Action

Moxifloxacin acts as a bactericidal by inhibiting topoisomerase II (DNA gyrase) and topoisomerase IV enzymes. The former enzyme is essential for replication, transcription and repair of bacterial DNA; while the latter plays an important role in the partitioning of chromosomal DNA during bacterial cell division.

Uses

Moxifloxacin is used for the treatment of sinus and lung infections (sinusitis and pneumonia), secondary infections in chronic bronchitis, and bacterial conjunctivitis (pinkeye).

Adverse Effects

Common side effects of moxifloxacin include abdominal discomfort, diarrhoea, nausea, vomiting, mouth sores, headache, dizziness, blurred vision, nervousness, anxiety, agitation, skin itching, and vaginal discomfort.

9.2. URINARY TRACT ANTI-INFECTIVE AGENTS

9.2.1. Introduction

Urinary tract infections are among most common bacterial infections of human. These infections range from asymptomatic bacteriuria on one hand to acute pyelonephritis and gram-negative septicaemia (only in men) on the other hand. Females are mostly at risk of developing UTIs because of their short urethra, and certain behavioural factors which include delay in micturition, sexual activity, and the use of diaphragms and spermicides.

A symptomatic bacterial infection of the urinary tract is termed Urinary Tract Infection (UTI). It includes a lower urinary tract infection, e.g., cystitis (symptomatic infection of bladder), urethritis (infection in urethra), prostatitis (infection in prostate gland), or an upper urinary tract infection, e.g., pyelonephritis (symptomatic infection of kidney).

In UTIs, many drugs are used for killing or inhibiting the growth of pathogenic organisms in the urinary tract. These agents are retained in the renal tubules. They are effective antiseptics due to their localised actions in the urinary bladder, ureters, and kidneys. Some important urinary antiseptics include mandelic acid, methenamine mandelate, nitrofurantoin, nalidixic acid, and hexylresorcinol.

9.2.2. Important Products

The following drugs are studied in detail:

1) Furazolidone,
2) Nitrofurantoin, and
3) Methenamine.

9.2.2.1. Furazolidone

Furazolidone is a nitrofuran derivative with antiprotozoal and antibacterial activity. It binds to bacterial DNA and gradually inhibits monoamine oxidase.

Mechanism of Action

Furazolidone and its free radical products bind to bacterial DNA and induce cross-links. Bacterial DNA is susceptible to it, thus causing high levels of mutations (transitions and transversions) in the bacterial chromosome.

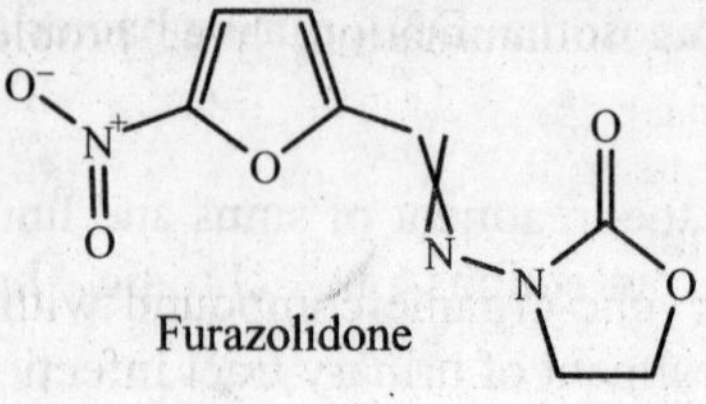

Furazolidone

Uses

Furazolidone is used for specific and symptomatic treatment of bacterial or protozoal diarrhoea and enteritis caused by susceptible organisms.

Adverse Effects

Common side effects of furazolidone include hypotension, hives, fever, joint pain, rash, stomach upset, nausea, vomiting, headache, dizziness, weakness, and malaise.

9.2.2.2. Nitrofurantoin

Nitrofurantoin is a nitrofuran antibiotic used in uncomplicated urinary tract infections. It is more resistant to the development of bacterial resistance because it simultaneously acts on many targets.

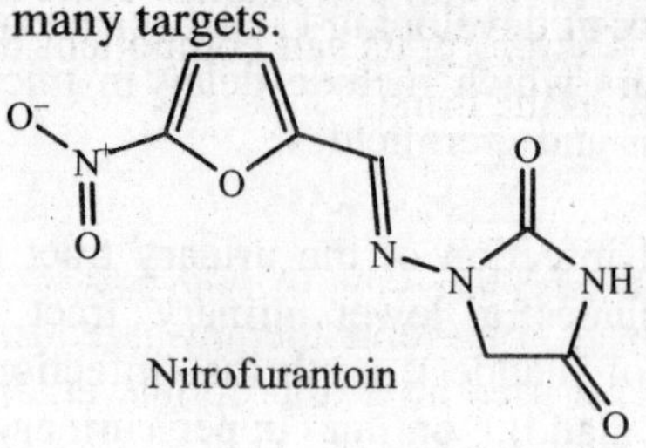

Nitrofurantoin

Synthesis

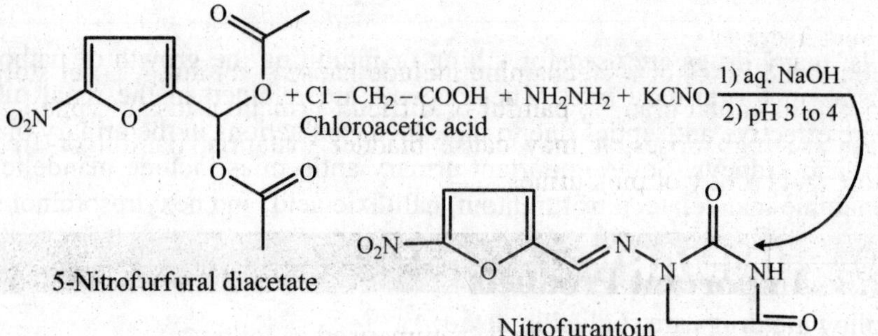

Mechanism of Action

Bacterial nitroreductases convert nitrofurantoin into electrophilic intermediates that inhibit the citric acid cycle and synthesis of bacterial DNA, RNA, and proteins.

Uses

Nitrofurantoin is used in the treatment of acute uncomplicated urinary tract infections.

Adverse Effects

The common side effects of nitrofurantoin include nausea, vomiting, loss of appetite, stomach pain, diarrhoea, numbness in hands and feet, pain in hands and feet, weakness, dizziness, headache, and drowsiness. Serious side effects of nitrofurantoin include lung inflammation, liver problems, nerve damage, and haemolysis.

9.2.2.3. Methenamine

Methenamine is a heterocyclic organic compound with a cage-like structure. Its salt form is used in the treatment of urinary tract infections.

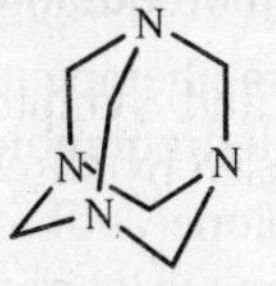

Methenamine

Mechanism of Action

Methenamine does not have antibacterial properties in alkaline environment (pH≥6). However, in an acidic environment (pH<6), it hydrolyses to formaldehyde which is highly bactericidal. Formaldehyde has non-specific antibacterial activity and denatures bacterial proteins and nucleic acids.

Certain bacteria (such as *Proteus* sp.) can alkalise urine and inhibit the beneficial activity of formaldehyde. Therefore, its salt component like hippuric acid is used to maintain the acidic state of the urine.

Uses

Methenamine is used for prophylactic or suppressive treatment of recurring urinary tract infections when long-term therapy is considered. It is not used to treat infection and should be used after appropriate eradication of infection with antimicrobial agents.

Adverse Effects

Common side effects of methenamine include nausea, vomiting, upset stomach, diarrhoea, abdominal cramps, painful or difficult urination, loss of appetite, and skin rash. In high doses, it may cause bladder irritation, painful or frequent urination, and bloody or pink urine.

9.3. SUMMARY

The details given in the chapter can be summarised as follows:

1) **Quinolones** are synthetic broad-spectrum antibiotics.
2) The term **quinolone** indicates potent synthetic chemotherapeutic antibacterial.
3) **Nalidixic acid** is the first therapeutically useful synthetic quinolone antibiotic that is active against gram-negative bacteria, and useful in the short-term therapy of urinary tract infections.

4) **Enoxacilin** is a fluorine-containing compound with increased spectrum of activity against gram-negative and gram-positive bacteria.
5) Quinolones act on the bacterial enzyme, DNA gyrase, which inhibits its replication and transcription.
6) **Norfloxacin** is a synthetic fluoroquinolone with broad-spectrum antibacterial activity against a wide range of gram-negative and gram-positive bacteria.
7) **Enoxacin** is a broad-spectrum 6-fluoronaphthyridinone antibacterial agent that is structurally related to nalidixic acid.
8) **Ciprofloxacin** is a synthetic chemotherapeutic antibiotic of fluoroquinolone class. It is a second generation fluoroquinolone antibacterial.
9) **Ofloxacin** is a synthetic chemotherapeutic antibiotic of fluoroquinolone class. It is a second generation fluoroquinolone.
10) **Lomefloxacin** is a fluoroquinolone antibiotic that is used to treat bacterial infections including bronchitis and urinary tract infections.
11) **Sparfloxacin** is a fluoroquinolone antibiotic that is useful in bacterial infections.
12) **Gatifloxacin** is a fourth generation fluoroquinolone antibiotic.
13) **Moxifloxacin** is a synthetic fluoroquinolone antibiotic developed by **Bayer AG**.
14) A symptomatic bacterial infection of the urinary tract is termed **Urinary Tract Infection** (UTI).
15) **Furazolidone** is a nitrofuran derivative with antiprotozoal and antibacterial activity.
16) **Nitrofurantoin** is a nitrofuran antibiotic used in uncomplicated urinary tract infections.
17) **Methenamine** is a heterocyclic organic compound with a cage-like structure.

9.4. EXERCISE

9.4.1. True or False

1) Ciprofloxacin is the first therapeutically useful synthetic quinolone antibiotic.
2) Lomefloxacin is a broad-spectrum 6-fluoronaphthyridinone antibacterial agent that is structurally related to nalidixic acid.
3) Ciprofloxacin is a first generation fluoroquinolone antibacterial.
4) Sparfloxacin is a fluoroquinolone antibiotic that is useful in bacterial infections.
5) Gatifloxacin is a fourth generation fluoroquinolone antibiotic.
6) Enoxacin is a heterocyclic organic compound with a cage-like structure.

9.4.2. Fill in the Blanks

7) ________ is a fluorine-containing compound with increased spectrum of activity against gram-negative and gram-positive bacteria.
8) Quinolones act on the bacterial enzyme, ________, which inhibits its replication and transcription.

9) ________ is a second generation fluoroquinolone.
10) Moxifloxacin is a synthetic fluoroquinolone antibiotic developed by ________.
11) ________ is a nitrofuran derivative with antiprotozoal and antibacterial activity.
12) ________ is a nitrofuran antibiotic used in uncomplicated urinary tract infections.

Answers

1) False	2) False	3) False	4) True
5) True	6) False	7) Enoxacilin	8) DNA gyrase
9) Ofloxacin	10) Bayer AG	11) Furazolidone	12) Nitrofurantoin

9.4.3. Very Short Answer Type Questions

1) Classify quinolones.
2) Enlist the uses of quinolones.
3) Give the chemical structure of nalidixic acid.
4) Give the mechanism of action of norfloxacin.
5) What are the uses of lomefloxacin?
6) How gatifloxacin and moxifloxacin act?
7) Draw the structure of nitrofurantoin.

9.4.4. Short Answer Type Questions

1) Give the mechanism of action of quinolones.
2) Give the synthesis of ciprofloxacin.
3) Write a short note on enoxacin and ofloxacin.
4) Discuss about the adverse effects of sparfloxacin.
5) Write about any two urinary tract anti-infective agents.

9.4.5. Long Answer Type Question

1) Discuss the historical background of quinolones.
2) Write an exhaustive note on quinolones

CHAPTER 10 Antiviral Agents

10.1. ANTIVIRAL AGENTS

10.1.1. Introduction

Antiviral agents are used for treating viral infections. Similar to antibiotics for bacteria, specific antivirals are effective against specific viruses. Antiviral drugs, instead of destroying their target pathogen, inhibit their development. Since antiviral drugs are harmless to the host, they can be used to treat infections. They should be distinguished from viricides that are not medications but destroy virus particles outside the body.

The available antivirals are mostly designed to help against HIV, herpes viruses (that mainly causes cold sores and genital herpes; however, can cause various other diseases), hepatitis B and C viruses (that cause liver cancer), and influenza A and B viruses. Since the viruses replicate within the host cells, it is difficult to find targets for the drug that would interfere with the virus without harming the host cells. Due to this reason, designing safe and effective antiviral drugs is a difficult task.

10.1.2. Historical Background

History of antiviral drug development has taken many indirect routes ranging from the discovery and development of the first U.S. FDA approved antiviral agent, i.e., 5-Iodo-2′-deoxyuridine (Idoxuridine), by **William H. Prus-off**, to the development of simplified but powerful triple combinations for HIV (such as Atripla and Trizivir). Chemists, biologists, and pharmacologists face many challenges during the development of antiviral agents, including adverse events and development of drug-resistant viruses; thus, they develop improved, more potent, and less toxic medicines with high genetic barrier.

Technologies like Liquid Chromatography (LC)-mass spectrometry, real-time PCR, pharmacokinetic and pharmacodynamics modelling, cryoelectron microscopy, and crystallographic structure determination have advanced the capacity to develop antiviral agents, but the tools available still needs optimisation. To develop early antivirals, researchers grew cultures cell, infected them with the target virus, added chemicals that would inhibit viral activity, and observed whether the virus level in the cultures increased or decreased. Chemicals that showed effect were selected for further detailed study.

This however, was a time-consuming, hit-or-miss procedure, and in the absence of knowledge regarding the working of target virus, not very well at discovering antivirals that were effective and had few side effects. It was not until the 1980s, when the full genetic sequences of viruses began to be unravelled, and the researchers began to learn the working of viruses, and what kinds of molecules can block their mechanism. The general idea for designing modern antiviral drug is to identify viral proteins or protein parts that can be disabled. These targets should unlike any proteins or protein parts in humans reduce the possibility of side effects. The targets should be common across many strains of a virus or among different species of virus in the same family, so a single drug will have broad effectiveness.

10.1.3. Classification

Antiviral drugs are classified into the following classes on the basis of mechanism of action:

1) **Anti-Herpes Virus:** Idoxuridine, Acyclovir, Famciclovir, Ganciclovir, and Foscarnet.
2) **Anti-Retrovirus**
   i) **Nucleoside Reverse Transcriptase Inhibitors (NRTIs):** Zidovudine (AZT), Didanosine, Zalcitabine, and Stavudine.
   ii) **Non-Nucleoside Reverse Transcriptase Inhibitors (NNRTIs):** Efavirenz and Delavirdine.
   iii) **Protease Inhibitors:** Indinavir, Nelfinavir, Saquinavir, Amprenavir, and Lopinavir.
3) **Anti-Influenza Virus:** Amantadine and Rimantadine.
4) **Non-Selective Anti-Viral Drugs:** Ribavirin and Lamivudine.

10.1.4. SAR

The structural-activity relationship of anti-HIV agents involves substitution at the following positions:

1) **3′-Substituted-2′,3′-Dideoxynucleosides:** AZT was the first nucleoside analogue with anti-HIV activity.

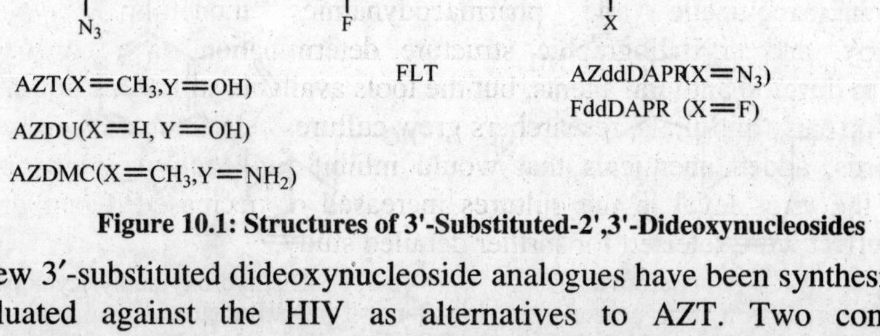

AZT($X{=}CH_3, Y{=}OH$)
AZDU($X{=}H, Y{=}OH$)
AZDMC($X{=}CH_3, Y{=}NH_2$)

FLT

AZddDAPR($X{=}N_3$)
FddDAPR ($X{=}F$)

Figure 10.1: Structures of 3'-Substituted-2',3'-Dideoxynucleosides

A few 3′-substituted dideoxynucleoside analogues have been synthesised and evaluated against the HIV as alternatives to AZT. Two compounds structurally related to AZT are 3′-Azido-2′,3′-Dideoxyuridine (**AZDU**) and 3′-Azido-2′,3′-Dideoxy-5-Methylcytidine (**AZDMC**). The former is less potent than AZT, but is less toxic to bone marrow progenitor cells. This advantage makes it a useful alternative to AZT.

2) **2′-Fluoro-2′,3′-Ara-Dideoxynucleosides:** 2′-Fluro-2′,3′ dideoxyarabinofuranosylcytosine (2′-F-ara-ddC); 2′-fluoro-2′,3′ dideoxyarabinofuranosyladenosine (2′-F-ara-ddA); 2′-fluoro-2′,3′-dideoxy-arabinofuranosylinosine (2′-F-ara-ddI); and 2′-fluro-N^6-methyl-2′,3′-dideoxy-arabinofuranosyladenosine (D2MeFA) are dideoxynucleosides having a fluorine atom at 2′-ara-position. They have been synthesised to stabilise the glycosyl bond against chemical and enzymatic hydrolysis and evaluated for their anti-HIV activity.

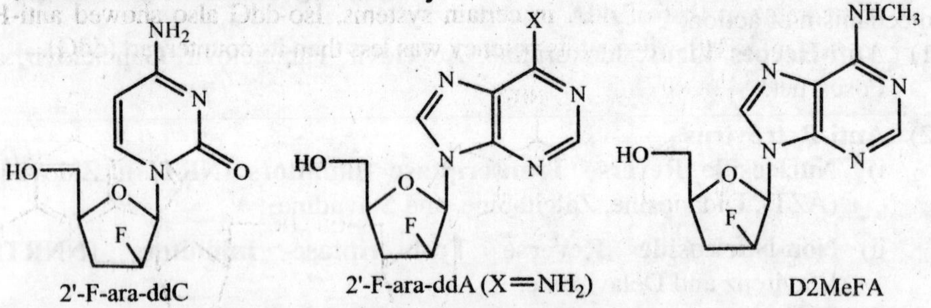

Figure 10.2: Structures of 2'-Fluoro-2',3'-Ara-Dideoxynucleosides

2′-F-ara-ddC presented a potent anti-HIV activity in a human lymphoblastic cell line without cytotoxicity, but showed less potency than ddC. In ATH8 or CEM cells also, 2′-Fara-ddC showed less activity than ddC. This compound in comparison to ddC showed increased stability of glycosyl bond under acidic conditions.

The potency of 2′-F-ara-ddA is 6 times less than that of the parent nucleoside (ddA) in MT-4 cells. However, the potency of 2′-F-ara-ddA and 2′-F-ara-ddI is similar to that of the parent compounds (ddA and ddI) in protecting CD4+ ATH8 cells from the cytopathogenicity of HIV-1, although their toxicity is more than their parent compounds.

3) **Carbocyclic Nucleosides:** Carbocyclic 2′,3′-didehydro-2′,3′-dideoxyguanosine (carbovir), whose furanose ring oxygen atom is replaced with a methylene group, is the most potent and selective *in vitro* inhibitor of HIV-1 discovered from a group of 33 carbocyclic nucleoside analogues.

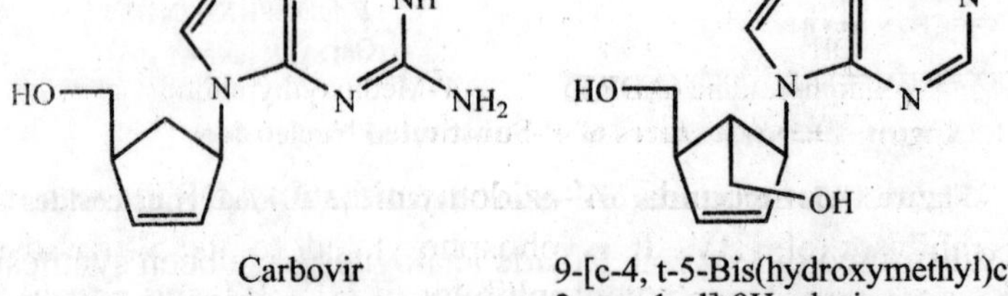

Figure 10.3: Structure of Carbocyclic Nucleosides

Carbovir was first synthesised in racemic form, and (–)-enantiomer with natural nucleoside configuration was synthesised and evaluated in various cell lines. The potency of (–)-carbovir is 2 times more than the racemic carbovir (in MT-4 cells). This indicates that most of the anti-HIV activity resides in the (–)-carbovir. Other recently synthesised analogues of carbovir have a hydroxymethyl group at the methylene carbon which replaced the furanose ring oxygen.

4) **Isodeoxy Nucleosides:** Iso-ddA and Iso-ddG are the isodeoxy nucleosides in which the ring oxygen and 3′-carbon of 2′,3′-dideoxyribose unit are exchanged to enhance chemical and enzymatic stability of the isomeric dideoxynucleosides by eliminating the labile glycosidic bond. In Iso-ddA, the anti-HIV activity was comparable to that of ddA in certain systems. Iso-ddG also showed anti-HIV activity in ATH8 cells, but its potency was less than its counterpart (ddG).

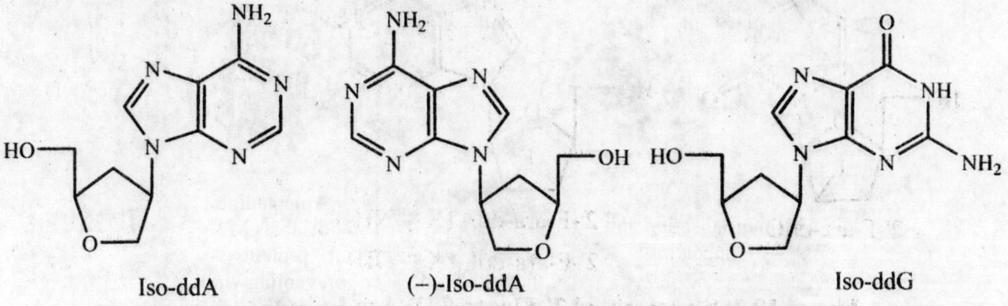

Figure 10.4: Structures of Iso-dideoxy Nucleosides

In nucleoside analogues, the base has been moved from 1′-position to the 2′-position of 2′,3′-dideoxyribose. Among these, the adenine derivative exhibited *in vitro* anti-HIV activity in the low micro-molar range in the MT-4 cells without cytotoxicity.

5) **4′-Substituted Nucleosides:** The 4′-azido-and 4′-methoxynucleoside analogues are potent against HIV *in vitro*. The 4′-methoxy-2′deoxy-β-D-nucleosides were 2-3 times less potent and less toxic than their azido counterparts.

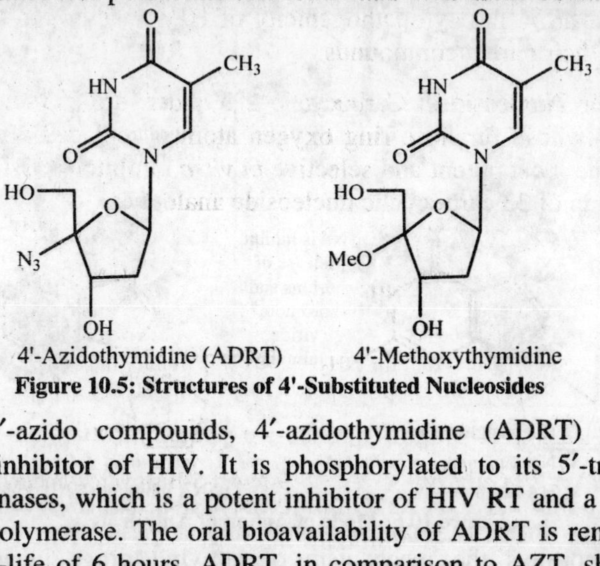

Figure 10.5: Structures of 4'-Substituted Nucleosides

Among 4′-azido compounds, 4′-azidothymidine (ADRT) was the most selective inhibitor of HIV. It is phosphorylated to its 5′-triphosphate by cellular kinases, which is a potent inhibitor of HIV RT and a weak inhibitor of DNA polymerase. The oral bioavailability of ADRT is remarkable and it has a half-life of 6 hours. ADRT, in comparison to AZT, showed reduced toxicity to hematopoietic progenitor cells. However, its metabolism to 4'-amino derivative increases its toxicity.

10.1.5. Mechanism of Action

Anti-viral drugs (**e.g., amantadine and rimantadine**) were the first generation of influenza antiviral agents. They **specifically block the ion channel function of the M2 protein of influenza A virus**, thus interfere with corresponding specific steps in the viral life cycle. Neuraminidase inhibitors are novel drugs that are designed on the basis of the 3-D structure of influenza A and B neuraminidase2. The mechanisms of action of the four available specific anti-influenza viral drugs are summarised in **figure 10.6**.

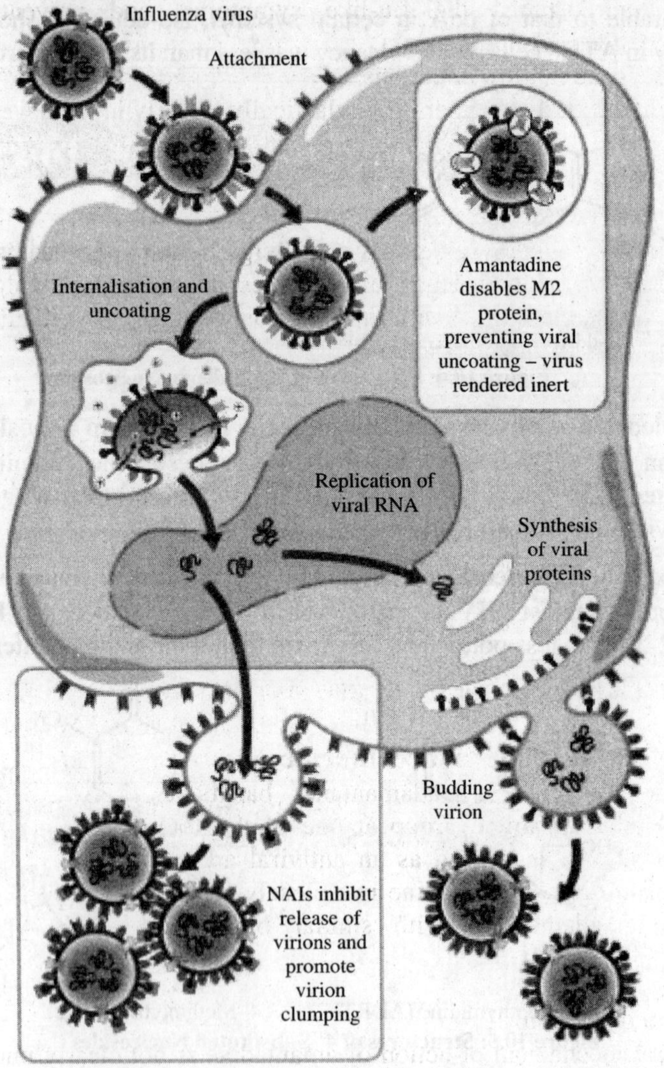

Figure 10.6: Mode of Action of Antivirals

Figure 10.6 portrays the mechanism of antiviral drugs in interrupting the replicative cycle of influenza. M2 inhibitors prevent the M2-mediated acidification of the interior of virus, while it resides in endosomes and subsequent un-coating of the viral genome, thus inhibit viral replication. Neuraminidase Inhibitors (NAIs) prevent cleavage of sialic acid residues, thus the newly formed virus cannot be released from the cell surface to infect adjacent cells.

10.1.6. Uses

Following are the uses of anti-viral drugs:

1) They are used against HIV, herpes viruses, hepatitis B and C viruses, and influenza A and B viruses.
2) They fight against the flu-like symptoms, and prevent serious flu complications, like pneumonia.
3) They are used in viral infections.
4) They should be used either prophylactically or early in the development of an infection.

10.1.7. Adverse Effects

Anti-viral drugs cause hypersensitivity (allergic reactions), bleeding, bone loss, heart disease, high blood sugar and diabetes, lactic acidosis (high lactic acid levels in blood), kidney, liver, or pancreas damage, pancreatitis, peripheral neuropathy, nausea, and diarrhoea.

10.1.8. Important Products

The following drugs are studied in detail:

1) Amantadine hydrochloride,
2) Rimantadine hydrochloride,
3) Idoxuridine trifluoride,
4) Acyclovir,
5) Ganciclovir,
6) Zidovudine,
7) Didanosine,
8) Zalcitabine,
9) Lamivudine,
10) Loviride,
11) Delavirdine,
12) Saquinavir,
13) Indinavir, and
14) Ritonavir.

10.1.8.1. Amantadine Hydrochloride

Amantadine consists of adamantane backbone, substituted with an amino group at one of the four methyne positions. It is used as an antiviral and an anti-Parkinson drug. Rimantadine is a closely related derivative of adamantane with similar biological properties.

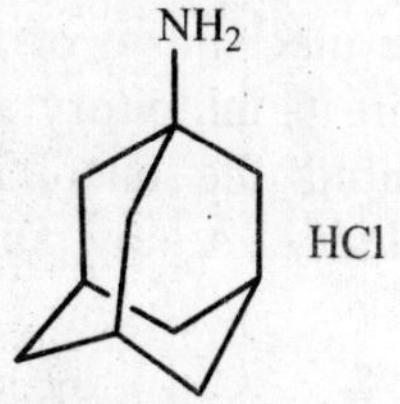

Amantadine Hydrochloride

Mechanism of Action

The antiviral mechanism of action of amantadine is not clearly understood. It is found to interfere with the function of trans-membrane domain of the viral M2 protein, and prevent the release of infectious viral nucleic acid into the host cell. In some cases, amantadine prevents virus assembly during virus replication.

Uses

1) It is used in characteristic fatigue experienced by patients with multiple sclerosis.

2) In low doses it has been used in Attention Deficit Hyperactivity Disorder (ADHD).
3) It has relieved SSRI-induced sexual dysfunction.
4) It is used in Parkinson's disease and similar conditions disease.
5) It also prevents and treats respiratory infections caused by influenza A virus.

Adverse Effects

1) Its CNS side effects include nervousness, anxiety, agitation, insomnia, difficulty in concentrating, exacerbations of pre-existing seizure disorders, and psychiatric symptoms in patients with schizophrenia or Parkinson's disease.
2) Rare cases of severe skin rashes such as Stevens Johnson Syndrome have been reported.
3) Livedo reticularis may occur when amantadine is being used for Parkinson's disease.
4) It can even cause the fatal Neuroleptic Malignant Syndrome (NMS).

10.1.8.2. Rimantadine Hydrochloride

Rimantadine is an orally administered antiviral drug. It is used to treat infections caused by influenza virus A. If it is taken within one to two days of developing symptoms, it can shorten the duration and moderate the severity of influenza.

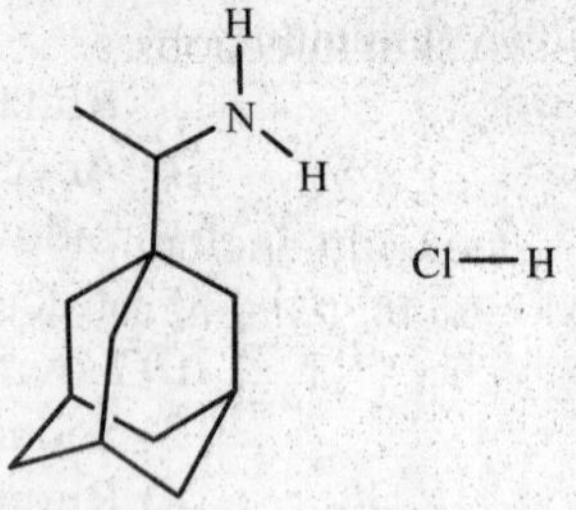

Rimantadine Hydrochloride

Mechanism of Action

The mechanism of action of rimantadine is not fully understood. It is found to exert its inhibitory effect in the early stages of viral replicative cycle. It possibly inhibits the uncoating of the virus. The protein coded by the M2 gene of influenza A may play an important role in rimantadine susceptibility.

Uses

Rimantadine is used for the prophylaxis and treatment of infections caused by various strains of influenza A virus in adults.

Adverse Effects

Common side effects of rimantadine include nausea, upset stomach, nervousness, tiredness, lightheadedness, trouble sleeping, and difficulty in concentrating.

10.1.8.3. Idoxuridine Trifluoride

Idoxuridine is an analog of deoxyuridine. It is used as an antiviral agent that inhibits the synthesis of viral DNA.

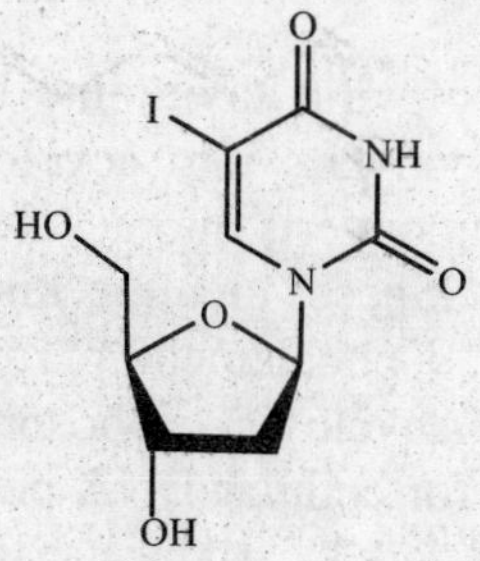

Idoxuridine

Mechanism of Action

Idoxuridine exerts its antiviral activity by inhibiting viral replication by substituting itself for thymidine in viral DNA. This inhibits the proper functioning of thymidylate phosphorylase and viral DNA polymerases. Effect of Idoxuridine results in the inability of the virus to reproduce or to infect/destroy tissue.

Uses

Idoxuridine is used in keratoconjunctivitis and keratitis caused by herpes simplex virus.

Adverse Effects

Serious side effects are not expected with idoxuridine; however, its common side effects include burning, stinging, pain, irritation, itching, redness, blurred vision, eyelid itching, eyelid swelling, or sensitivity to light.

10.1.8.4. Acyclovir

Acyclovir is a nucleotide analog antiviral that is used for treating infections like herpes simplex, herpes zoster, herpes labialis, and acute herpetic keratitis. It is the first line drug to be used in the treatment of infections caused by these viruses.

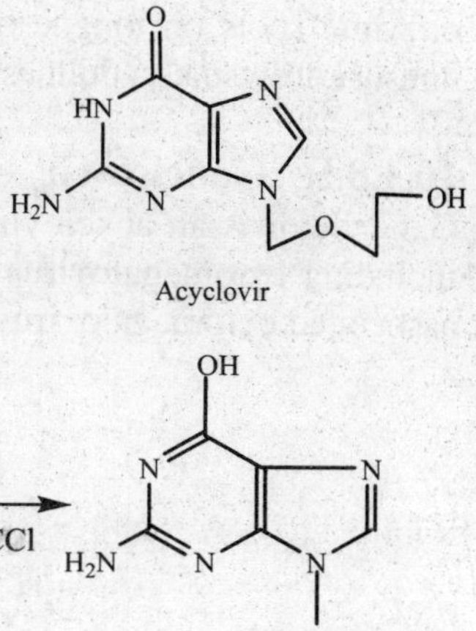

Acyclovir

Synthesis

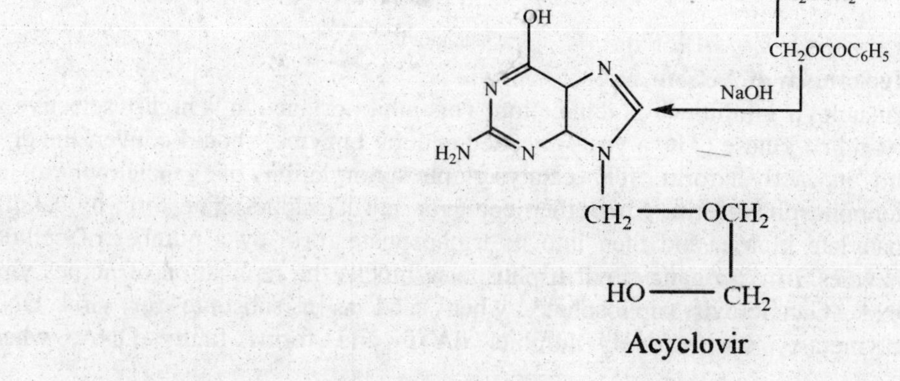

Acyclovir

Mechanism of Action

Acyclovir due to the action of viral thymidine kinase converts into acyclovir monophosphate, which then converts into acyclovir diphosphate by guanylate kinase. This diphosphate form converts into acyclovir triphosphate by nucleoside diphosphate kinase, pyruvate kinase, creatine kinase, phosphoglycerate kinase, succinyl-CoA synthetase, phosphoenolpyruvate carboxykinase, and adenylosuccinate synthetase. Acyclovir triphosphate's affinity for viral DNA polymerase is more than that for cellular DNA polymerase and incorporates into the DNA where the missing 2' and 3' carbons cause DNA chain termination.

Uses

1) Acyclovir topical cream is used in recurrent herpes labialis in 12 years and older immunocompetent patients, initial genital herpes, and limited non-life-threatening mucocutaneous herpes simplex in immunocompromised patients.
2) Acyclovir cream with hydrocortisone is used in recurrent herpes labialis, and shortening lesion healing time in 6 years and older patients.
3) Acyclovir ophthalmic ointment is used in acute herpetic keratitis.
4) Acyclovir oral tablets, capsules, and suspensions are used in herpes zoster, genital herpes, and chickenpox.
5) Acyclovir buccal tablet is used in recurrent herpes labialis.

Adverse Effects

The adverse effects of acyclovir include canker sores, pain in gums, sores, ulcers, or white spots on tongue or inside the mouth, flushing or redness of skin, rash, unusual drowsiness, dullness, tiredness, weakness, or sluggishness, and warm skin.

10.1.8.5. Ganciclovir

Ganciclovir is an acyclovir analog and a potent inhibitor of Herpes virus family including cytomegalovirus. It is used to treat complications arising from AIDS-associated cytomegalovirus infections.

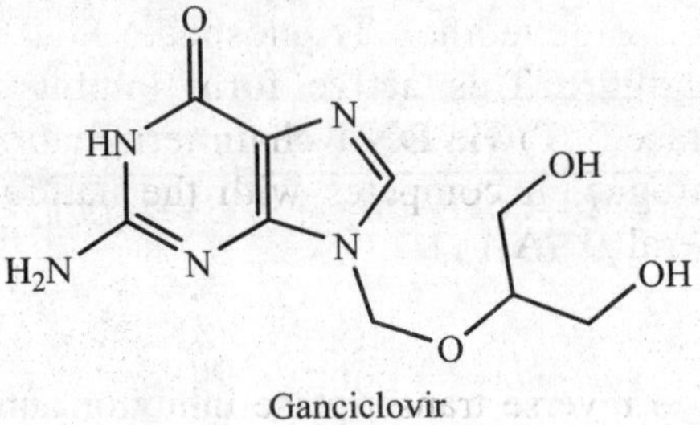

Ganciclovir

Mechanism of Action

Ganciclovir inhibits virus replication. This inhibitory action is highly selective as thymidine kinase (TK, a virus-encoded cellular enzyme) should convert the drug into its active form. TK catalyses phosphorylation of ganciclovir to its monophosphate form, which then converts into its diphosphate form by cellular guanylate kinase, and then into its triphosphate form by a number of cellular enzymes. *In vitro* ganciclovir triphosphate blocks the replication of herpes viral DNA. Ganciclovir triphosphate, when used as a substrate for viral DNA polymerase, competitively inhibits dATP and forms faulty DNA, where ganciclovir triphosphate is incorporated into the DNA strand replacing many of the adenosine bases. This prevents DNA synthesis, as phosphodiester bridges cannot be built, thus the strand destabilises.

Uses

1) It is used for induction and maintenance in the treatment of cytomegalovirus (CMV) retinitis in immunocompromised and AIDS patients.
2) It is also used in severe cytomegalovirus (CMV) disease, including CMV pneumonia, CMV gastrointestinal disease, and disseminated CMV infections in immunocompromised patients.

Adverse Effects

Common side effects of ganciclovir include diarrhoea, upset stomach, nausea, vomiting, decreased appetite, dizziness, drowsiness, unsteadiness, tremors, injection site reactions (pain, redness, or irritation), increased sweating, itching, decreased sperm production, or infertility.

10.1.8.6. Zidovudine

Zidovudine is a dideoxynucleoside compound whose 3'-hydroxy group on the sugar moiety has been replaced with an azido group.

This replacement prevents the formation of phosphodiester linkages required for the completion of nucleic acid chains. Zidovudine is a potent inhibitor of HIV replication that acts as a chain-terminator of viral DNA during reverse transcription.

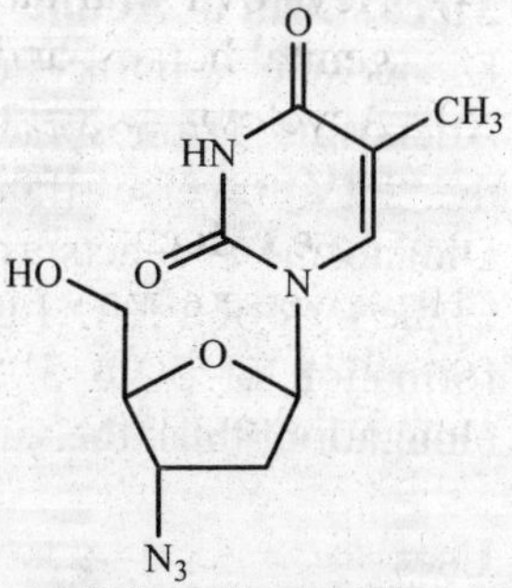

Zidovudine (AZT)

Mechanism of Action

Zidovudine is a structural analog of thymidine, and a prodrug that should be phosphorylated to Zidovudine Triphosphate (ZDV-TP, its active 5′-triphosphate metabolite). This active form inhibits the activity of HIV-1 Reverse Transcriptase (RT) via DNA chain termination after incorporation of the nucleotide analogue. It competes with the natural substrate (dGTP) and incorporates into viral DNA.

Uses

1) It is a nucleoside reverse transcriptase inhibitor antiviral agent used against HIV infection as it slow down the virus growth. It is used with other HIV medications to control HIV infection.
2) It decreases the amount of HIV in body to improve the functioning of immune system.
3) It can also be used in pregnant women to prevent the virus from spreading to the foetus.
4) It is also used in health care workers and other individuals exposed to HIV infection after accidental contact with HIV-contaminated blood, tissues, or **other body fluids.**

Adverse Effects

Zidovudine can cause serious and life-threatening side effects including hypersensitivity reactions, lactic acidosis (buildup of lactic acid in blood), liver problems, myopathy (muscle weakness), and blood disorders, such as severe anaemia or neutropenia (reduced numbers of white blood cells).

10.1.8.7. Didanosine

Didanosine is a dideoxynucleoside compound whose 3'-hydroxy group on the sugar moiety has been replaced with hydrogen. This replacement prevents the formation of phosphodiester linkages required for the completion of nucleic acid chains. Didanosine is a potent inhibitor of HIV replication that acts as a chain-terminator of viral DNA by binding to reverse transcriptase; then it metabolises to its putative active metabolite (dideoxyadenosine triphosphate).

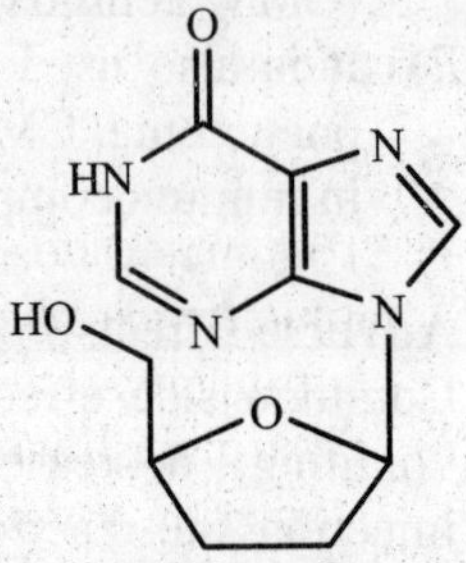

Didanosine

Mechanism of Action

Didanosine is intracellularly metabolised by many cellular enzymes to dideoxy Adenosine Triphosphate (ddATP, its active moiety) that competitively inhibits the HIV reverse transcriptase enzyme by competing with natural dATP. Didanosine also acts as a chain terminator by incorporating itself into viral DNA as the lack of a 3'-OH group in the incorporated nucleoside analogue prevents the formation of 5' to 3' phosphodiester linkage that is required for DNA chain elongation; thus, the viral DNA growth is terminated.

Uses

Didanosine is used along with other antiretroviral agents in the treatment of HIV-1 infection in adults.

Adverse Effects

Didanosine can cause serious, life-threatening side effects including pancreatitis (swelling of pancreas), lactic acidosis, and liver problems.

10.1.8.8. Zalcitabine

Zalcitabine is a dideoxynucleoside compound whose 3'-hydroxy group on the sugar moiety has been replaced with hydrogen. This replacement prevents the formation of 5' to 3' phosphodiester linkages required for the elongation of DNA chains, thus terminating the growth of viral DNA.

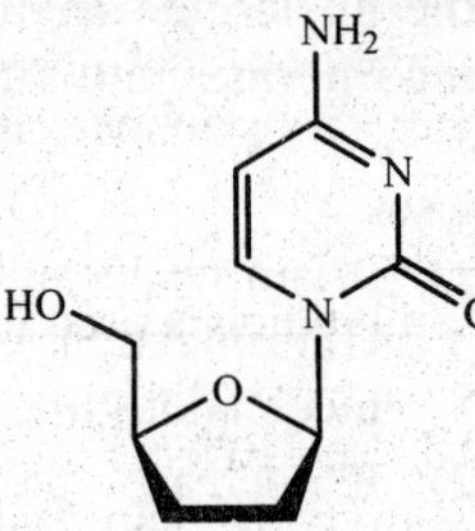

Zalcitabine

Mechanism of Action

Zalcitabine is a nucleoside reverse transcriptase inhibitor that is active against HIV-1 infection. It is intracellularly converted by the sequential action of cellular enzymes to dideoxy Cytidine 5'-Triphosphate (ddCTP, its active metabolite), which interferes with viral RNA-directed DNA polymerase (reverse transcriptase) by competing for utilisation of deoxy Cytidine 5'-Triphosphate (dCTP, the natural substrate), and also incorporating into viral DNA. Due to lack of a 3'-OH group, formation of 5' to 3' phosphodiester linkage (required for DNA chain elongation) is inhibited, thus terminating the growth of viral DNA.

Uses

Zalcitabine is used in combination with other antivirals for the treatment of HIV infections.

Adverse Effects

1) The major dose-limiting adverse effect of zalcitabine is nervous system toxicity. Peripheral neuropathy is characterised by numbness, tingling, and burning dysesthesia in the distal extremities.
2) Gastrointestinal adverse effects include abdominal pain, oral lesions or stomatitis, vomiting or nausea, diarrhoea or constipation, Oesophageal ulceration, and pancreatitis.
3) Dermatologic side effects include rash, pruritus, and urticaria.
4) Blood disorders include thrombocytopenia, leukopenia, eosinophilia, neutropenia, anaemia, and granulocytopenia.
5) Hepatic side effects include elevation in liver function tests and exacerbation of pre-existing hepatic dysfunction.
6) Metabolic side effects include hypertriglyceridemia and hyperlipidemia.
7) Hypersensitivity reactions include anaphylactoid reaction.

10.1.8.9. Lamivudine

Lamivudine is a reverse transcriptase inhibitor and zalcitabine analog. Its sulphur atom replaces the 3' carbon of the pentose ring. It is used to treat Human Immunodeficiency Virus Type 1 (HIV-1) and hepatitis B (HBV).

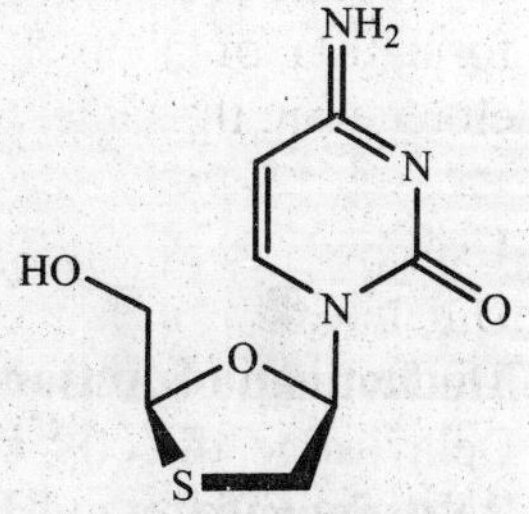

Lamivudine

Mechanism of Action

Lamivudine is a synthetic nucleoside analogue that is intracellularly phosphorylated to Lamivudine Triphosphate (L-TP, its active 5'-triphosphate metabolite) that incorporates itself into viral DNA by HIV reverse transcriptase and HBV polymerase, and causes termination of DNA chain.

Uses

Lamivudine is used in the treatment of HIV infection and chronic hepatitis B.

Adverse Effects

Lamivudine can cause serious, life-threatening side effects including lactic acidosis, severe liver problems, and pancreatitis (in children at risk).

10.1.8.10. Loviride

Loviride is a Non-Nucleoside Reverse Transcriptase Inhibitor (NNRTI) that entered phase III clinical trials in the late 1990s. However, due to poor potency, it failed to gain marketing approval.

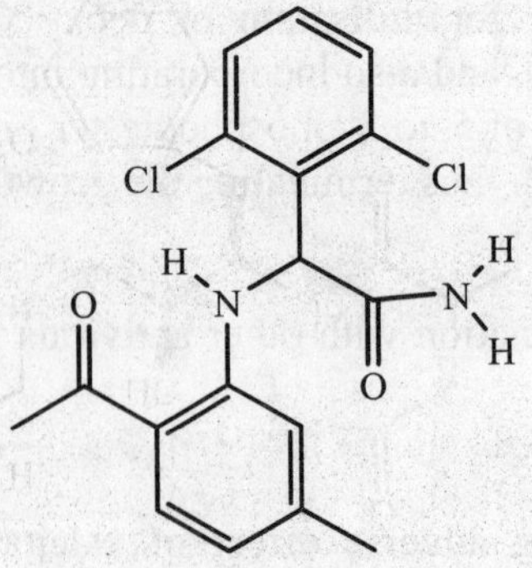

Loviride

10.1.8.11. Delavirdine

Delavirdine is a potent, non-nucleoside reverse transcriptase inhibitor with specific activity against HIV-1.

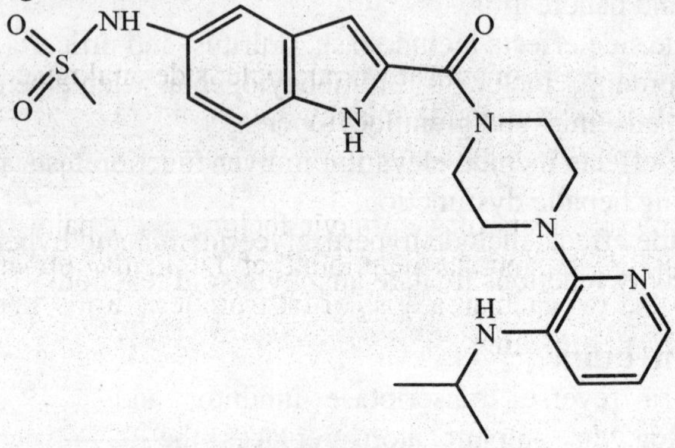

Delavirdine

Mechanism of Action

Delavirdine directly binds to viral Reverse Transcriptase (RT) and blocks the RNA-dependent and DNA-dependent DNA polymerase activities by disrupting the enzyme's catalytic site.

Uses

Delavirdine is used along with appropriate antiretroviral agents in the treatment of HIV-1 infection.

Adverse Effects

Common side effects of delavirdine include nausea, diarrhoea, headache, tiredness, changes in shape and location of body fat (especially in arms, legs, face, neck, breasts, and waist), worsening of a previous medical condition (such as an old infection), itching, rash, or cold symptoms (stuffy nose, sneezing, or sore throat).

10.1.8.12. Saquinavir

Saquinavir is a HIV protease inhibitor that acts as an analog of an HIV protease cleavage site. It is a highly specific inhibitor of HIV-1 and HIV-2 proteases.

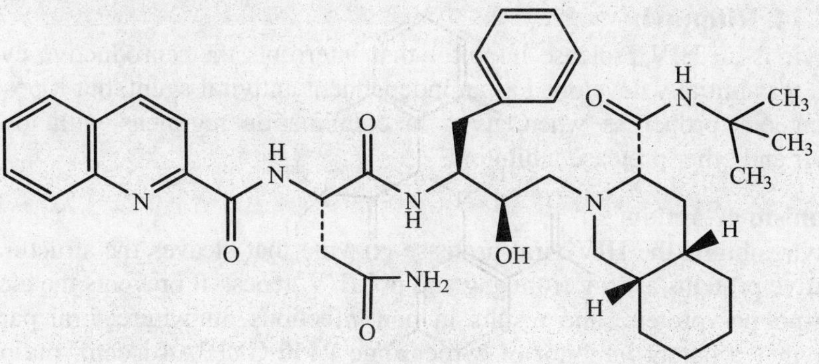

Saquinavir

Mechanism of Action

Saquinavir inhibits the HIV viral protease enzyme that prevents the cleavage of gag-pol polyprotein, and results in non-infectious, immature viral particles.

Uses

Saquinavir is used along with antiretroviral nucleoside analogues in the treatment of HIV-1 with advanced immunodeficiency.

Adverse Effects

The common adverse effects of saquinavir include chest pain, cough, sneezing, fever, sore throat, chills, increased amount of fat in the upper back, neck or around the chest and stomach area, loss of fat from legs, arms, and face, tightness in chest, and troubled breathing.

10.1.8.13. Indinavir

Indinavir is a potent and specific HIV protease inhibitor with a good oral bioavailability.

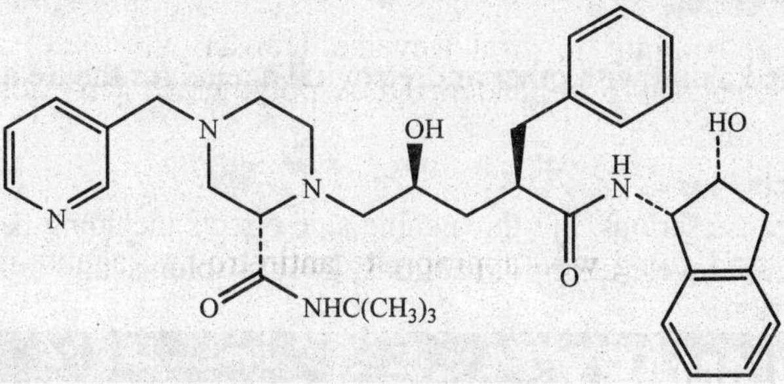

Indinavir

Mechanism of Action

Indinavir inhibits the HIV viral protease enzyme that prevents the cleavage of gag-pol polyprotein, and results in non-infectious, immature viral particles.

Uses

Indinavir is an antiretroviral drug that is used for the treatment of HIV infection.

Adverse Effects

Indinavir causes serious, life-threatening side effects including kidney problems, haemolytic anaemia (rapid breakdown of healthy RBCs), and liver problems.

10.1.8.14. Ritonavir

Ritonavir is an HIV protease inhibitor that interrupts the reproductive cycle of HIV. It was initially developed as an independent antiviral agent, but it possesses advantageous properties when given in combination regimens with low-dose ritonavir and other protease inhibitors.

Mechanism of Action

Ritonavir inhibits the HIV viral protease enzyme that cleaves the structural and replicative proteins arising from gag and pol HIV genes. It prevents the cleavage of gag-pol polyprotein, and results in non-infectious, immature viral particles. Ritonavir is a potent inhibitor of cytochrome P450 CYP3A4 isoenzyme present in the intestinal tract and liver. It is a type II ligand that fits into the CYP3A4 active site and irreversibly binds to the heme iron via thiazole nitrogen, which decreases the redox potential of the protein and prevents its reduction with cytochrome P450 reductase. Ritonavir also limits cellular transport and efflux of other protease inhibitors via P-glycoprotein and MRP efflux channels.

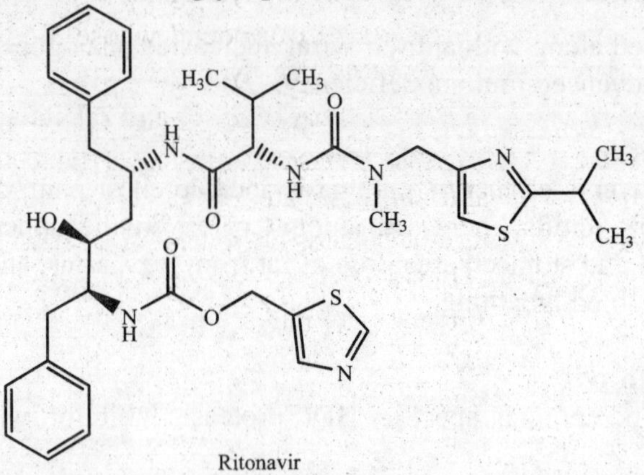

Ritonavir

Uses

Ritonavir is used along with other antiretroviral agents for the treatment of HIV-1 infection.

Adverse Effects

Ritonavir can cause serious, life-threatening side effects including pancreatitis, heart rhythm problems, severe allergic reactions, liver problems, and drug interactions.

10.2. SUMMARY

The details given in the chapter can be summarised as follows:

1) **Antiviral agents** are used for treating viral infections.
2) **AZT** was the first nucleoside analogue with anti-HIV activity.
3) **Carbovir**, whose furanose ring oxygen atom is replaced with a methylene group, is the most potent and selective *in vitro* inhibitor of HIV-1.
4) **Iso-ddA** and **Iso-ddG** are the isodeoxy nucleosides in which the ring oxygen and 3′-carbon of 2′,3′-dideoxyribose unit are exchanged to enhance chemical and enzymatic stability of the isomeric dideoxynucleosides by eliminating the labile glycosidic bond.

5) The **4′-azido**-and **4′-methoxynucleoside** analogues are potent against HIV *in vitro*.
6) **Amantadine** consists of adamantane backbone, substituted with an amino group at one of the four methyne positions.
7) **Rimantadine** is an orally administered antiviral drug.
8) **Idoxuridine** is an analog of deoxyuridine.
9) **Acyclovir** is a nucleotide analog antiviral that is used for treating infections like herpes simplex, herpes zoster, herpes labialis, and acute herpetic keratitis.
10) **Ganciclovir** is an acyclovir analog and a potent inhibitor of Herpes virus family including cytomegalovirus.
11) **Zidovudine** is a dideoxynucleoside compound whose 3'-hydroxy group on the sugar moiety has been replaced with an azido group.
12) **Didanosine** is a dideoxynucleoside compound whose 3'-hydroxy group on the sugar moiety has been replaced with hydrogen.
13) **Zalcitabine** is a dideoxynucleoside compound whose 3'-hydroxyl group on the sugar moiety has been replaced with hydrogen.
14) **Lamivudine** is a reverse transcriptase inhibitor and zalcitabine analog.
15) **Loviride** is a non-nucleoside reverse transcriptase inhibitor (NNRTI) that entered phase III clinical trials in the late 1990s.
16) **Delavirdine** is a potent, non-nucleoside reverse transcriptase inhibitor with specific activity against HIV-1.
17) **Saquinavir** is a HIV protease inhibitor that acts as an analog of an HIV protease cleavage site.
18) **Indinavir** is a potent and specific HIV protease inhibitor with a good oral bioavailability.
19) **Ritonavir** is an HIV protease inhibitor that interrupts the reproductive cycle of HIV.

10.3. EXERCISE

10.3.1. True or False

1) AZT was the first nucleoside analogue with anti-HIV activity.
2) The 4′-azido-and 4′-methoxynucleoside analogues are potent against HIV *in vitro*.
3) Amantadine is an orally administered antiviral drug.
4) Zidovudine is a dideoxynucleoside compound whose 3'-hydroxy group on the sugar moiety has been replaced with an azido group.
5) Zalcitabine is a dideoxynucleoside compound whose 3'-hydroxyl group on the sugar moiety has been replaced with nitrogen.
6) Saquinavir is a HIV protease inhibitor that acts as an analog of an HIV protease cleavage site.

10.3.2. Fill in the Blanks

7) ________ is the most potent and selective *in vitro* inhibitor of HIV-1.
8) ________ is an analog of deoxyuridine.

9) ________ is an acyclovir analog and a potent inhibitor of Herpes virus family including cytomegalovirus.
10) ________ is a reverse transcriptase inhibitor and zalcitabine analog.
11) ________ is an HIV protease inhibitor that interrupts the reproductive cycle of HIV.
12) ________ is a non-nucleoside reverse transcriptase inhibitor (NNRTI) that entered phase III clinical trials in the late 1990s.

Answers

1) True	2) True	3) False
4) True	5) False	6) True
7) Carbovir	8) Idoxuridine	9) Ganciclovir
10) Lamivudine	11) Ritonavir	12) Loviride

10.3.3. Very Short Answer Type Questions

1) Classify antiviral agents.
2) Enlist the uses of antiviral agents.
3) Give the chemical structure of amantadine hydrochloride.
4) Give the mechanism of action of acyclovir.
5) What are the uses of ganciclovir?
6) How zidovudine acts?
7) Draw the structures of lamivudine and loviride.

10.3.4. Short Answer Type Questions

1) Discuss the historical background of antiviral agents.
2) Give the mechanism of action of antiviral agents.
3) Give the synthesis of acyclovir.
4) Write a short note on rimantadine hydrochloride and idoxuridine trifluoride.
5) Discuss about the mechanism of action of zalcitabine and didanosine.

10.3.5. Long Answer Type Questions

1) Discuss the SAR of antiviral agents.
2) Write an exhaustive note on antiviral agents.
3) Write about any three antiviral agents.

CHAPTER 11 Antifungal Agents

11.1. ANTIFUNGAL AGENTS

11.1.1. Introduction

Fungi are neither plants nor animals, and are classified as their own kingdom. Fungi grow either as **yeasts** (single round cells) or as **molds** (many cells forming long, thin threads called hyphae). Some fungi even go through both the forms during their life cycle. Many fungi, including bread molds and mushrooms, can be seen with the naked eye. Fungal infections are often caused by fungi present in the environment. Most fungi are not dangerous, but some of them can be harmful.

Fungal spores are present in the air or in soil, thus fungal infections begin mostly in the lungs or on the skin. These infections progress slowly and are not serious, unless they weaken the immune system. Antifungal agents used to treat fungal infections are either applied topically on the infected site or are taken orally or injected in case the infection is serious.

Table 11.1 enlists some commonly used antifungal drugs:

Table 11.1: Potentially Effective Antifungal Compounds

Diseases	Compounds
Dermatophytoses	Azoles (Butoconazole, Clotrimazole, Econazole, Itraconazole, Miconazole, Oxiconazole, Sulconazole), Griseofulvin, Naftifine, Terbinafine, and Tolnaftate.
Aspergillosis	Amphotericin B, 5-Fluorocytosine, and Itraconazole.
Blastomycosis	Amphotericin B, Itraconazole, and Ketoconazole.
Candidiasis	Amphotericin B, 5-Fluorocytosine, Nystatin, and Azoles (Butoconazole, Clotrimazole, Econazole, Fluconazole, Itraconazole, Ketoconazole, Miconazole, Terconazole, Tioconazole).
Chromomycosis	5-Fluorocytosine, Itraconazole, and Ketoconazole.
Coccidiodomycosis	Amphotericin B, Fluconazole, Itraconazole, and Ketoconazole.
Cryptococcosis	Amphotericin B, 5-Fluorocytosine, and Fluconazole.
Histoplasmosis	Amphotericin B, Itraconazole, and Ketoconazole.
Mucormycosis	Amphotericin B.
Paracoccidioidomycosis	Itraconazole and Ketoconazole.
Pneumocystosis	Trimethoprim/Sulphamethoxazole, Pentamidine isethionate, LY-303, 366, and Deferoxamine.
Pseudallescheriasis	Amphotericin B and Miconazole.
Sporotrichosis	Amphotericin B, Itraconazole, and Potassium iodide.

11.1.2. Historical Background

The 1990s were the most productive period in antifungal development. When the decade began, clinicians had an intravenous fungal agent and an oral fungal agent to choose from when treating systemic fungal infections. However, by the end of the decade, antifungal agents became different in terms of activity, toxicity, and drug interaction potential to allow clinicians to differentiate between agents and tailor therapy to suit specific patient needs.

In **1990**, **fluconazole** was introduced that transformed antifungal development. It is the first broad-spectrum triazole that addressed the inadequacies of imidazoles (i.e., poor solubility and lack of an intravenous formulation). In **1992**, **itraconazole** was introduced that expanded the activity spectrum of triazole class beyond *Candida spp.* up to various filamentous fungi.

These triazoles replaced ketoconazole as the drug of choice for many systemic mycoses. In the **mid-1990s**, **Hydroxypropyl-β-Cyclodextrin** (HP-βCD, the solubilising excipient) enhanced the bioavailability of itraconazole by enabling the development of oral and intravenous formulations. During this time, safer lipid based formulations of the polyenes **Amphotericin B** and **nystatin** were also introduced.

11.1.3. Classification

The antifungal drugs are classified as follows:

1) **Antibiotics**
   i) **Polyenes:** Amphotericin B (AMB), Nystatin, Hamycin, and Natamycin (Pimaricin).
   ii) **Heterocyclic Benzofuran:** Griseofulvin.
2) **Antimetabolite:** Flucytosine (5-FC).
3) **Azoles**
   i) **Imidazoles (Topical):** Clotrimazole, Econazole, and Miconazole. **(Systemic):** Ketoconazole.
   ii) **Triazoles (Systemic):** Fluconazole and Itraconazole.
4) **Allylamine:** Terbinafine.
5) **Other Topical Agents:** Tolnaftate, Undecylenic acid, Benzoic acid, Quiniodochlor, Ciclopirox olamine, and Sodium thiosulfate.

11.1.4. SAR

The structure-activity relationship of different antifungal agents is as follows:

1) **SAR of Azoles:** They are group of synthetic anti-mycotic agents with broad spectrum of anti-fungal activity.

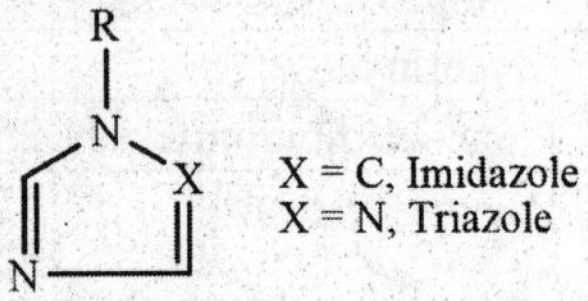

Triazole nucleus

   i) A basic imidazole or 1, 2, 4-triazole is essential for antifungal activity.
   ii) N3 of imidazole and N4 of triazole bind to P450 iron.

iii) The most active ones have two or three aromatic rings, and atleast **one** ring is substituted with halogens or other non-polar groups (2,4-dichlorophenyl or 2,4-difluorophenyl).
iv) The most active azoles have fluorine.
v) Ring substitution at other positions makes the azole inactive.
vi) The big non-polar part resembles the steroid molecule in binding to **the** enzyme.

2) **SAR of Polyene Antifungals**
i) The polyene antibiotic produced by actinomycetes contains a large lactone ring with 4 to 7 unsubstituted conjugated double bonds.
ii) Amphotericin B has 7 and nystatin has 6 conjugated double bonds; **thus,** the former is more active and more toxic.
iii) The conjugated systems are in all-*trans* configuration so that the **ring** contains a planner lipophilic segment and a less rigid **hydrophilic** portion.
iv) Increase in double bond conjugation will increase the activity **and** toxicity.
v) Polyenes have polyhydroxyl groups.
vi) Most polyene antifungal drugs are macrocyclic lactones.
vii) Ring sizes vary from 12 to 37 atoms in size.

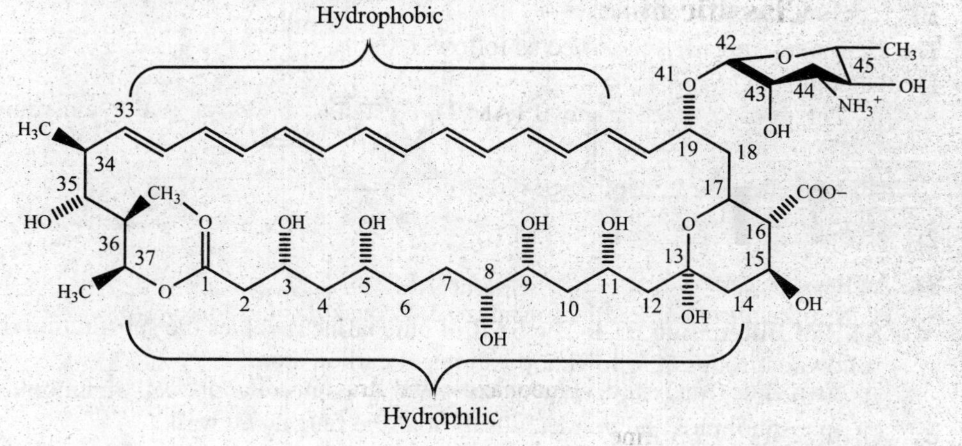

Amphotericin B

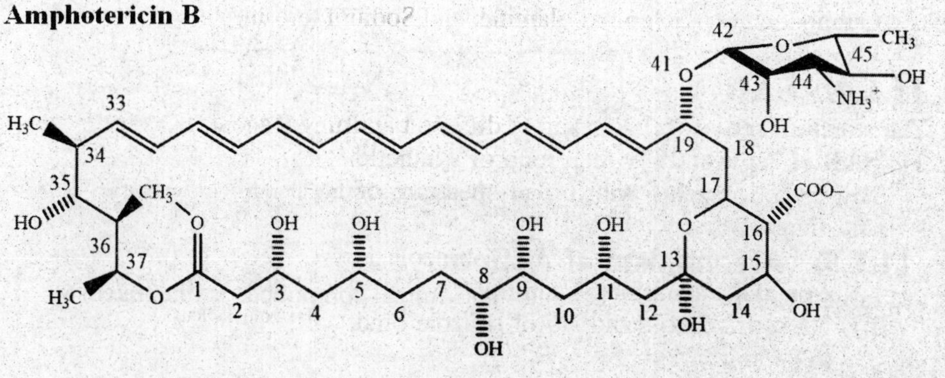

Nystatin

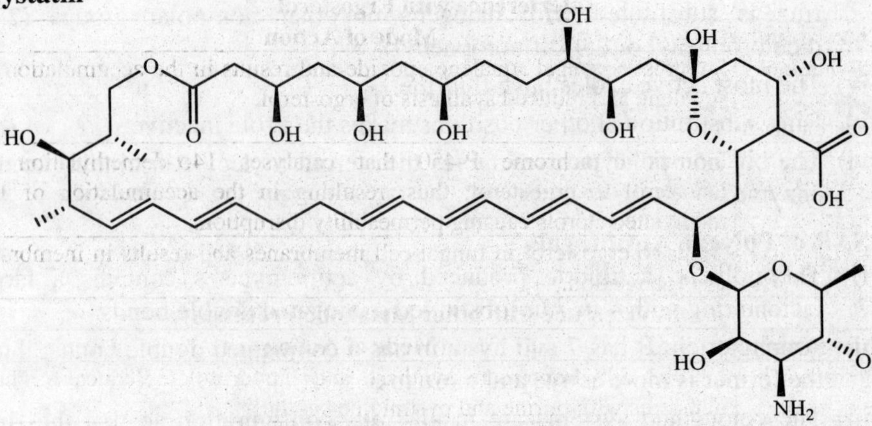

3) **SAR of Griseofulvin:** The SAR of griseofulvin involves the substitution of following groups at following positions of carbon atom:
   i) Out of four possible stereoisomers, only (+)-enantiomer is active.
   ii) On replacing Cl with F, the anti-fungal activity remains unaffected.
   iii) On replacing Cl with Br or H, the anti-fungal activity reduces.
   iv) On substituting a halogen at C-5, the anti-fungal activity reduces.
   v) On replacing CH_3O on ring C with propoxy or butoxy functions, the anti-fungal activity increases.

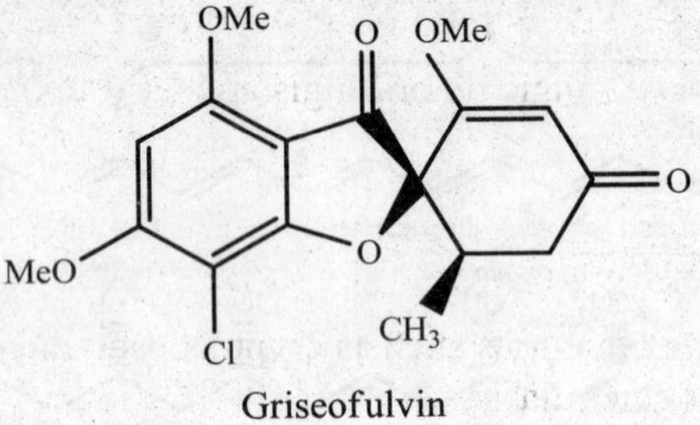

Griseofulvin

4) **SAR of Butenafine HCl:** The SAR of butenafine involves the substitution of following groups at following positions of carbon atom:
   i) Efficacy may be related to an interaction with cell membrane phospholipids and permeabilisation of the fungal cell wall.
   ii) High lipophilicity could account for the long duration of action.

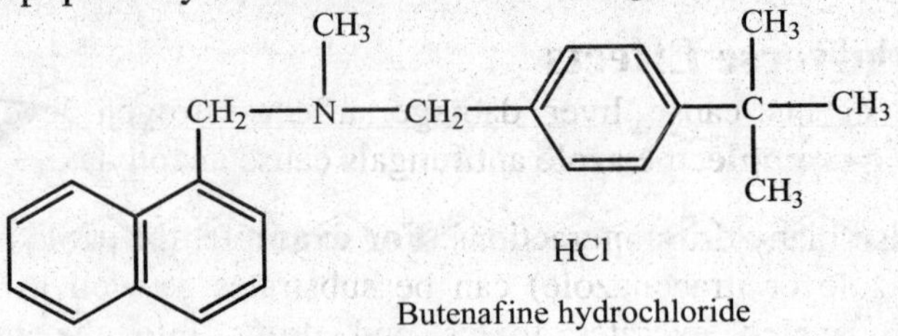

Butenafine hydrochloride

11.1.5. Mechanism of Action

In **table 11.2**, the mode of action of anti-fungal compounds is illustrated:

Table 11.2: Mode of Action of Antifungal Compounds

Interference with Ergosterol	
Compounds	**Mode of Action**
Allylamines and thiocarbamates	Suppresses fungal squalene epoxide and results in the accumulation of squalene and reduced synthesis of ergosterol.
Azoles	Inhibits cytochrome P-450 that catalyses 14α-demethylation of lanosterol to ergosterol; thus, resulting in the accumulation of 14-methylated sterols causing permeability disruption.
Polyene	Binds to ergosterol in fungal cell membranes and results in membrane disorganisation.
Interference with other Metabolic Processes	
Compounds	**Mode of Action**
Antifolates	Inhibits dihydropteroate synthase and dihydrofolate reductase; thus, interferes with purine and pyrimidine synthesis.
Benzofuran cyclohexenes	Binds to fungal proteins involved in tubulin assembly and causes malformation of spindle and cytoplasmic microtubules.
Diamidines	Binds to DNA and interferes with its replication.
Echinocandins	Inhibits β-(1,3)-glucan synthetase and interferes with cell wall formation.
Pyrimidines	Causes deamination of 5-fluorocytosine by fungal cells to 5-fluorouracil incorporated into RNA in place of uracil or is converted to 5-F-2'-deoxyuridylic acid that inhibits thymidine synthetase.

11.1.6. Uses

An antifungal drug is a fungicide or fungistatic used to treat and prevent mycoses such as:

1) Athlete's foot,
2) Ringworm,
3) Candidiasis,
4) Serious systemic infections such as cryptococcal meningitis,
5) Mucocutaneous candidiasis.
6) Coccidioidomycosis,
7) For seborrhoea dermatitis as shampoos,
8) Systemic uses for dermatophytosis (**e.g.,** skin and nail infections, though for the latter terbinafine is preferred), requiring extended treatments (after or with treatment with triazoles).

11.1.7. Adverse Effects

Anti-fungal agents cause liver damage, affect estrogen levels, and allergic reactions; **for example**, the azole antifungals cause anaphylaxis.

There are also many drug interactions. **For example**, the azole antifungals (such as ketoconazole or itraconazole) can be substrates as well as inhibitors of P-glycoprotein, which excretes toxins and drugs into the intestines. Azole antifungals are substrates and inhibitors of cytochrome P-450 family CYP3A4 also, thus cause increased concentration when administering, **e.g.,** calcium channel blockers, immunosuppressants, chemotherapeutic drugs, **benzodiazepines, tricyclic antidepressants, macrolides, and SSRIs.**

11.1.8. Antifungal Antibiotics

The following drugs are studied in detail:

1) Amphotericin B,
2) Nystatin,
3) Natamycin, and
4) Griseofulvin.

11.1.8.1. Amphotericin B

Amphotericin B shows a high order of *in vitro* inhibitory activity against many species of fungi, like *Histoplasma capsulatum*, *Coccidioides immitis*, *Candida* species, *Blastomyces dermatitidis*, *Rhodotorula*, *Cryptococcus neoformans*, *Sporothrix schenckii*, *Mucor mucedo*, and *Aspergillus fumigatus* in 0.03-1.0mcg/ml concentrations.

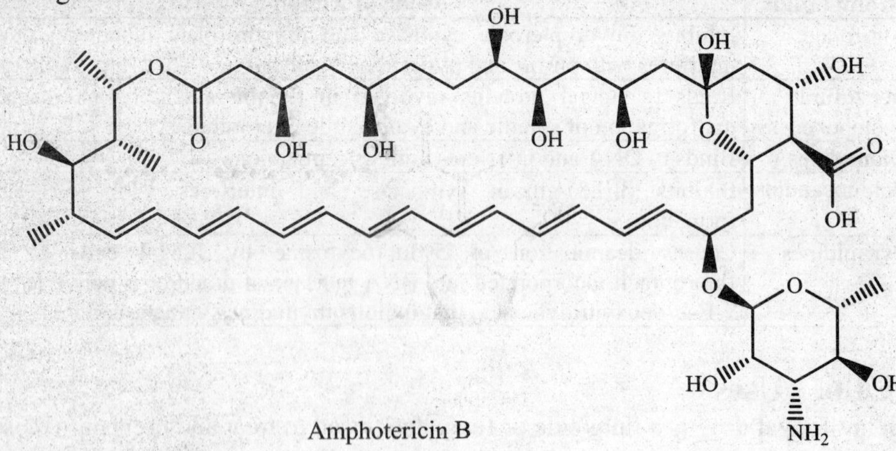

Amphotericin B

Mechanism of Action

Amphotericin B acts either as a fungistatic or fungicidal depending on the concentration obtained in body fluids and the fungus susceptibility. It binds to sterols (ergosterol) in the cell membrane of susceptible fungi, and creates a transmembrane channel. The resultant change in membrane permeability allows leakage of intracellular components. Ergosterol is the principal sterol in the fungal cytoplasmic membrane. It is the target site of action of amphotericin B and azoles. Amphotericin B irreversibly binds to ergosterol and disrupts the membrane integrity, causing cell death.

Uses

1) It is used for treating many serious fungal infections.
2) It is useful in severe mycotic infections such as candidiasis, blastomycosis, aspergillosis, coccidioidomycosis, sporotrichosis and phycomycosis (algae like fungi).
3) It is used for treating mucocutaneous and cutaneous leishmaniasis and candidiasis, primary amoebic meningoencephalitis, and *Cryptococcal* meningitis in combination with flucytosine.
4) It is also used for suppressing oral or intestinal candidiasis.

Adverse Effects

1) **General (Body as a Whole):** Fever (accompanied by shaking chills occurring within 15-20 minutes after initiating the treatment), malaise, and weight loss.

2) **Cardiopulmonary:** Hypotension and tachypnoea.
3) **Gastrointestinal:** Anorexia, nausea, vomiting, diarrhoea, dyspepsia, and cramping epigastric pain.
4) **Hematologic:** Normochromic and normocytic anaemia.
5) **Local:** Pain at the injection site with or without phlebitis or thrombophlebitis.
6) **Musculoskeletal:** Generalised pain, including muscle and joint pains.
7) **Neurologic:** Headache.
8) **Renal:** Decreased renal function and renal function abnormalities including azotemia, hypokalaemia, hyposthenuria, renal tubular acidosis, and nephrocalcinosis.

11.1.8.2. Nystatin

Nystatin is a polyene antifungal which acts against many molds and yeasts (such as *Candida spp*). It is toxic if administered intravenously, but it does not get absorbed across intact skin or mucous membranes. It is thought to be a safer drug in treating oral or gastrointestinal fungal infections.

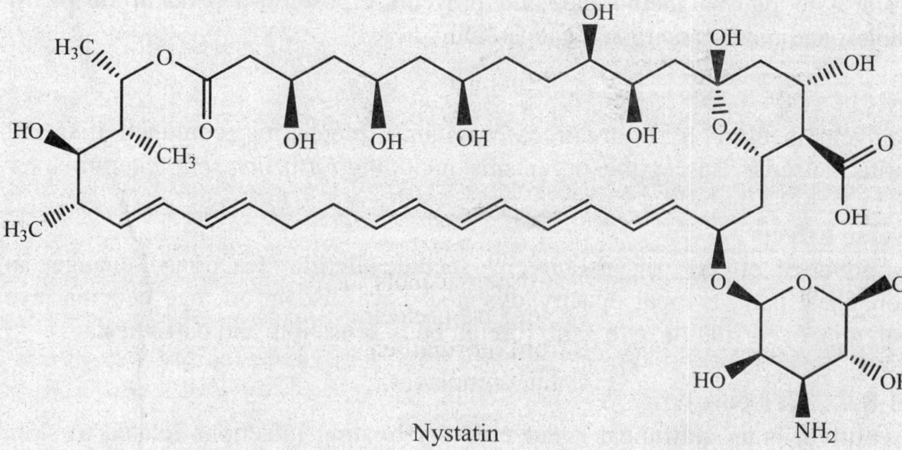

Nystatin

Mechanism of Action

Nystatin exerts its antifungal activity by binding to ergosterol in fungal cell membranes. This binding forms pores in the membrane, through which potassium and other cellular constituents leak and cause cell death.

Uses

1) It is used to treat prophylaxis and candidiasis of skin and mucous membrane.
2) Its tablets are used for treating intestinal and oesophageal candidiasis.
3) Its lozenges are used in candidiasis of mouth.
4) In pessaries or vaginal cream form, it is used to treat candidiasis of vagina.

Adverse Effects

Common side effects of nystatin include diarrhoea, nausea, stomach pain, vomiting, contact dermatitis, Stevens-Johnson syndrome, hypersensitivity reactions, skin irritation or redness, mouth irritation, rash, hives, allergic reaction, slow heart rate, bronchospasm, facial swelling, and muscle pain.

11.1.8.3. Natamycin

Natamycin is an amphoteric macrolide antifungal antibiotic obtained from *Streptomyces natalensis* or *S. chattanoogensis*. It is used for treating a variety of topical fungal infections.

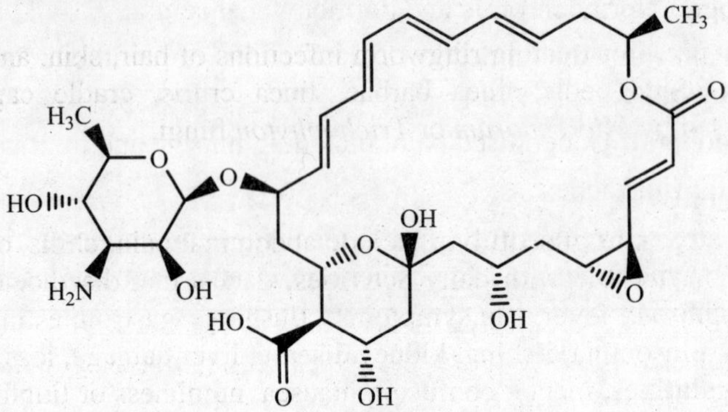

Natamycin

Mechanism of Action

Natamycin binds to sterols and inhibits fungal growth. It specifically binds to ergosterol in plasma membrane, and prevents ergosterol-dependent fusion of vacuoles, and membrane fusion and fission.

Uses

Natamycin is used in the treatment of fungal blepharitis, conjunctivitis, and keratitis caused by susceptible organisms, including *Fusarium solani* keratitis.

Adverse Effects

The adverse effects of natamycin include allergic reactions, change in vision, chest pain, corneal opacity, dyspnoea, eye discomfort, eye oedema, eye hyperemia, eye irritation, eye pain, foreign body sensation, and paresthesia.

11.1.8.4. Griseofulvin

Griseofulvin is an antifungal agent used for treating infections related to skin, nails, scalp, feet, groin, and other body parts. Mostly it is used for treating infections occurring from tinea strains of fungi.

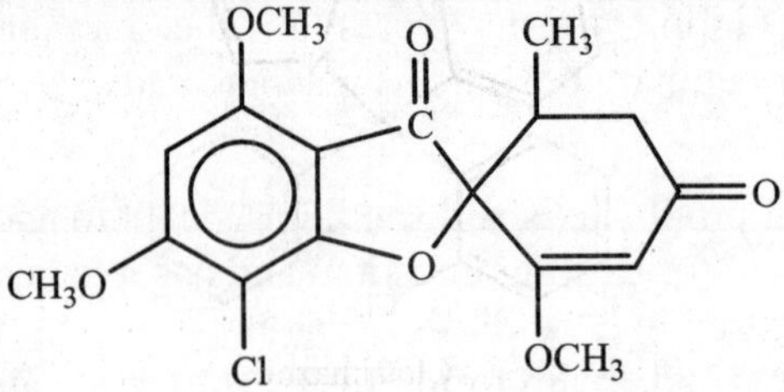

Griseofulvin

Mechanism of Action

Griseofulvin is fungistatic, however its exact mechanism of inhibiting the growth of dermatophytes is not yet understood. It inhibits fungal cell mitosis and nuclear acid synthesis. It binds to and interferes with the function of spindle and cytoplasmic microtubules by binding to α- and β-tubulin. It binds to keratin in human cells, and after reaching the fungal site of action, it binds to fungal microtubes and alters the fungal process of mitosis.

Uses

Griseofulvin is used for treating ringworm infections of hair, skin, and nails, i.e., tinea corporis, tinea pedis, tinea barbae, tinea cruris, cradle cap, or other conditions caused by *Microsporum* or *Trichophyton* fungi.

Adverse Effects

Common side effects of griseofulvin include abdominal pain, chills, clay-colored stools, confusion, trouble with daily activities, dark urine, diarrhoea, dizziness, fatigue, feeling tired, fever, flu symptoms, flushing, gastrointestinal bleeding, headache, hives, insomnia, itching, kidney disease, liver damage, loss of appetite, menstrual irregularities, mental confusion, nausea, numbness or tingling in hands or feet, protein in urine, rash, reduced WBCs, sensitivity to light, severe skin reaction (fever, sore throat, swelling in face or tongue, burning in eyes, skin pain, red or purple skin rash that spreads and causes blistering and peeling), vomiting, white patches or sores inside mouth or lips, yeast infection in mouth, and jaundice.

11.1.9. Synthetic Antifungal Agents

The following drugs are studied in detail:

1) Clotrimazole,
2) Econazole,
3) Butoconazole,
4) Oxiconazole,
5) Tioconazole,
6) Miconazole,
7) Ketoconazole,
8) Terconazole,
9) Itraconazole,
10) Fluconazole,
11) Naftifine hydrochloride, and
12) Tolnaftate.

11.1.9.1. Clotrimazole

Clotrimazole is an antifungal used in the treatment of fungal infections of humans and other animals, such as vaginal yeast infections, oral thrush, and ringworm. It is also used to treat athlete's foot and jock itch.

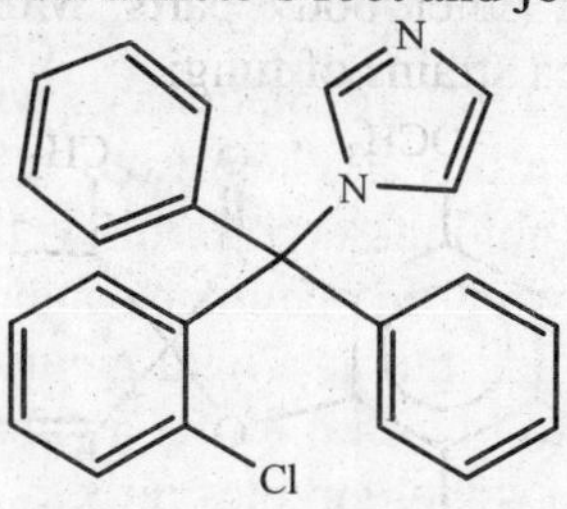

Clotrimazole

Mechanism of Action

Clotrimazole interacts with yeast 14-α demethylase, which is a cytochrome P-450 enzyme that converts lanosterol to ergosterol (an essential component of fungal membrane). Thus, clotrimazole inhibits ergosterol synthesis, and increases cellular permeability. Clotrimazole also inhibits endogenous respiration, interacts with membrane phospholipids, inhibits the transformation of yeasts to mycelial forms, inhibits the uptake of purine, impair triglyceride and/or phospholipid biosynthesis, and inhibits the movement of calcium and potassium ions across the cell membrane by blocking the ion transport pathway, termed **Gardos channel**.

Uses

1) It is available as an OTC drug in various dosage forms, such as a cream and also as a combination medicine.
2) It is also available as a troche (prescription only) and as ear drops for ear infection.
3) It is commonly found in conjunction with betamethasone to add steroid properties.

Adverse Effects

Side effects of clotrimazole include skin rash, hives, blistering, burning, itching, peeling, redness, stinging, swelling, and other sign of skin irritation.

11.1.9.2. Econazole

Econazole is a broad spectrum antimycotic with some action against gram-positive bacteria. It is topically used in dermatomycoses. It can also be used orally and parenterally.

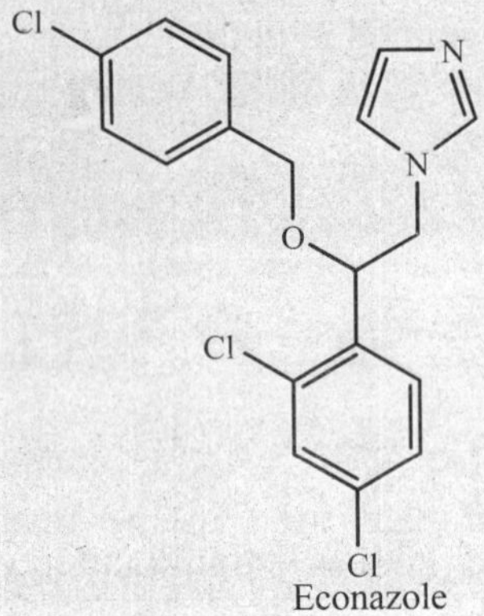

Econazole

Mechanism of Action

Econazole interacts with yeast 14-α demethylase, which is a cytochrome P-450 enzyme that converts lanosterol to ergosterol (an essential component of fungal membrane). Thus, econazole inhibits ergosterol synthesis, and increases cellular permeability, as a result of which the cellular contents leak out. Econazole also inhibits endogenous respiration, interacts with membrane phospholipids, inhibits the transformation of yeasts to mycelial forms, inhibits the uptake of purine, and impairs triglyceride and/or phospholipid biosynthesis.

Uses

1) It is used topically in the treatment of tinea pedis, tinea cruris, and tinea corporis caused by *Trichophyton rubrum*, *Trichophyton mentagrophytes*, *Trichophyton tonsurans*, *Microsporum canis*, *Microsporum audouinii*, *Microsporum gypseum*, and *Epidermophyton floccosum*.
2) It is also used in cutaneous candidiasis and tinea versicolor.

Adverse Effects
Common side effects of econazole cream include burning, stinging, swelling, irritation, redness, pimple-like bumps, tenderness, or flaking of skin.

11.1.9.3. Butoconazole
Butoconazole is an imidazole antifungal used in gynaecology.

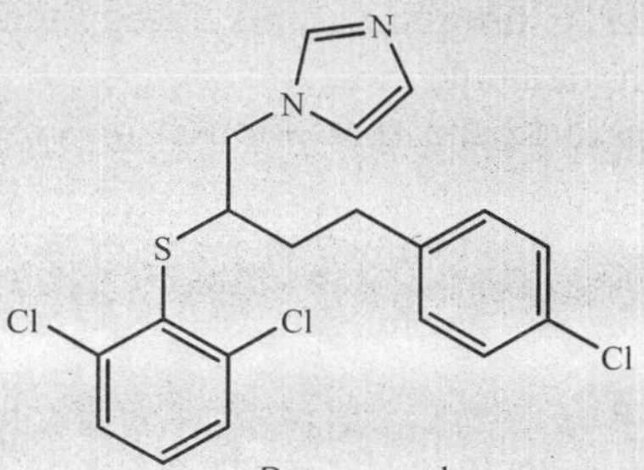

Butoconazole

Mechanism of Action
The exact antifungal mechanism of butoconazole is not clear, however, it is assumed to inhibit steroid synthesis as other imidazole derivatives. Imidazoles inhibit lanosterol conversion into ergosterol by inhibiting cytochrome P-450 14α-demethylase enzyme, thus changing the lipid composition of fungal cell membrane. This structural change alters cell permeability and results in the osmotic disruption or growth inhibition of fungal cell.

Uses
Butoconazole is used for the local treatment of vulvovaginal candidiasis (infections caused by Candida)

Adverse Effects
Butoconazole nitrate vaginal cream USP causes vulvar/vaginal burning, itching, soreness and swelling, pelvic or abdominal pain or cramping.

11.1.9.4. Oxiconazole
Oxiconazole is an antifungal that is found in topical formulations. It is used in the treatment of various skin infections.

Mechanism of Action
Oxiconazole inhibits biosynthesis of ergosterol that is essential for cytoplasmic membrane integrity of fungi. It destabilises the fungal cytochrome P-450 51 enzyme (or Lanosterol 14-α demethylase). This is vital in cell membrane structure of the fungus. Its inhibition leads to cell lysis.

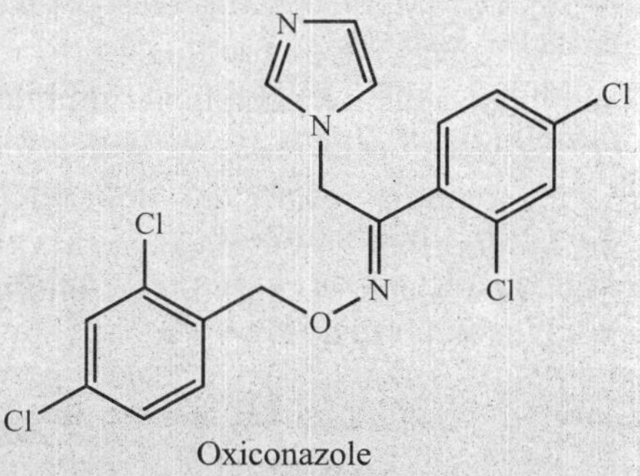

Oxiconazole

Oxiconazole also inhibits DNA synthesis and suppresses intracellular ATP concentrations. Like other imidazole antifungals, oxiconazole increases membrane permeability to zinc, and augments its cytotoxicity.

Uses

Oxiconazole is used in the treatment of various dermal fungal infections such as athlete's foot, jock itch, and ringworm.

Adverse Effects

Oxiconazole nitrate cream causes pruritus, burning, irritation, allergic contact dermatitis, folliculitis, erythema, papules, fissure, maceration, rash, stinging, and nodules. Oxiconazole nitrate lotion causes burning, stinging, pruritus, scaling, tingling, pain, and dyshidrotic eczema.

11.1.9.5. Tioconazole

Tioconazole is an imidazole antifungal used to treat fungal and yeast infections. It interacts with 14-α demethylase, which is a cytochrome P-450 enzyme that converts lanosterol to ergosterol (an essential component of yeast membrane). Thus, tioconazole inhibits ergosterol synthesis and increases cellular permeability.

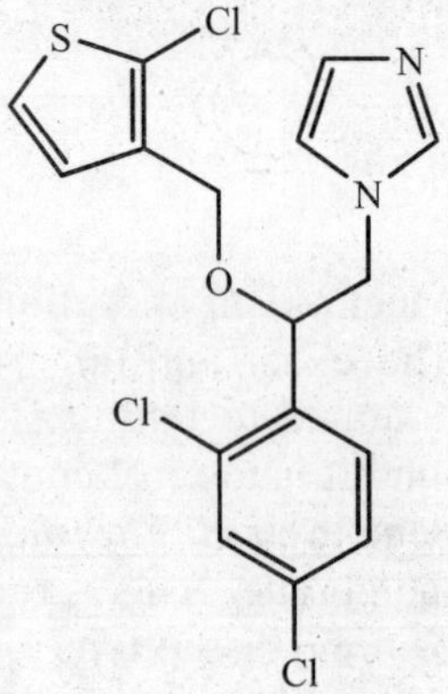

Tioconazole

Mechanism of Action

Tioconazole interacts with 14-α demethylase, which is a cytochrome P-450 enzyme that converts lanosterol to ergosterol (an essential component of fungal membrane). Thus, tioconazole inhibits ergosterol synthesis, and increases cellular permeability. Tioconazole also inhibits endogenous respiration, interacts with membrane phospholipids, inhibits the transformation of yeasts to mycelial forms, inhibits the uptake of purine, impairs triglyceride and/or phospholipid biosynthesis, and inhibits the movement of calcium and potassium ions across the cell membrane by blocking the ion transport pathway, termed **Gardos channel**.

Uses

1) Topical formulations of tioconazole are used for ringworm, jock itch, athlete's foot, and tinea versicolor.
2) It is also used for the local treatment of vulvovaginal candidiasis (moniliasis).

Adverse Effects

Common side effects of tioconazole include headache, vaginal/urethral, burning/itching/pain, or increased urination.

11.1.9.6. Miconazole

Miconazole is an imidazole antifungal agent that is used topically and by intravenous infusion.

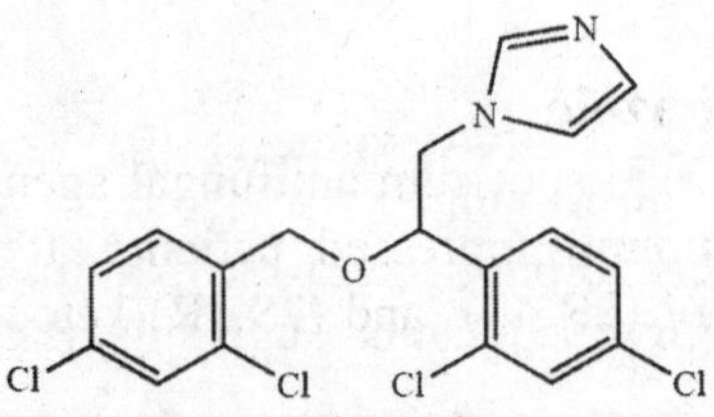

Miconazole

Synthesis

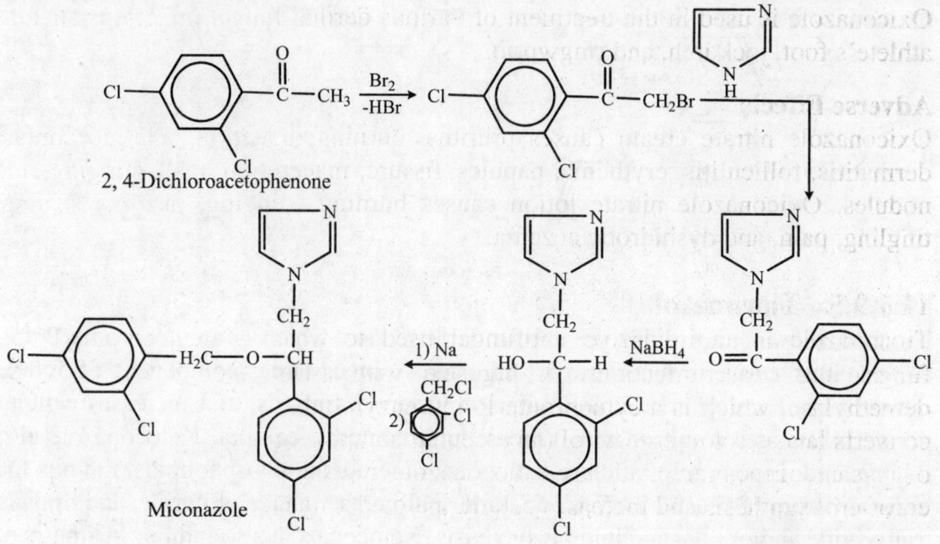

Mechanism of Action

Miconazole interacts with yeast 14-α demethylase, which is a cytochrome P-450 enzyme that converts lanosterol to ergosterol (an essential component of fungal membrane). Thus, clotrimazole inhibits ergosterol synthesis, and increases cellular permeability, as a result of which the cellular contents leak out.

Miconazole also inhibits endogenous respiration, interacts with membrane phospholipids, inhibits the transformation of yeasts to mycelial forms, inhibits the uptake of purine, and impairs triglyceride and/or phospholipid biosynthesis.

Uses

1) Miconazole is topically used in the treatment of tinea pedis (athlete's foot), tinea cruris, and tinea corporis caused by *Trichophyton rubrum*, *Trichophyton mentagrophytes*, and *Epidermophyton floccosum*.
2) It is also used in the treatment of cutaneous candidiasis (moniliasis) and tinea versicolor.

Adverse Effects

Common side effects of miconazole include burning, stinging, swelling, irritation, redness, pimple-like bumps, tenderness, itching, pain, or flaking of treated skin, headache, burning/itching/pain in vagina or urinary opening, an increased need to urinate, and lower abdominal cramps.

11.1.9.7. Ketoconazole

Ketoconazole is a broad spectrum antifungal agent that is used in high doses for long periods in immunosuppressed patients. It is a racemate comprising of equimolar amounts of (2R,4S)- and (2S,4R)-ketoconazole with the chiral centers on acetal ring.

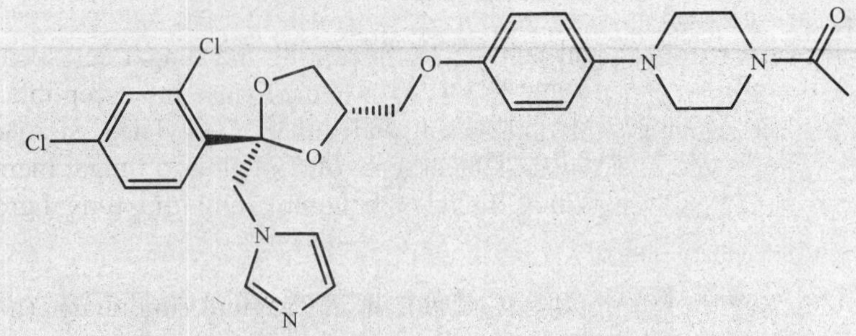

Ketoconazole

Mechanism of Action

Ketoconazole interacts with yeast 14-α demethylase, which is a cytochrome P-450 enzyme that converts lanosterol to ergosterol (an essential component of fungal membrane). Thus, clotrimazole inhibits ergosterol synthesis, and increases cellular permeability, as a result of which the cellular contents leak out. Ketoconazole also inhibits endogenous respiration, interacts with membrane phospholipids, inhibits the transformation of yeasts to mycelial forms, inhibits the uptake of purine, and impairs triglyceride and/or phospholipid biosynthesis. Ketoconazole also inhibits synthesis of thromboxane and sterols (such as aldosterone, cortisol, and testosterone).

Uses

Ketoconazole is used in a wide range of systemic fungal infections, like candidiasis, chronic mucocutaneous candidiasis, oral thrush, candiduria, blastomycosis, coccidioidomycosis, histoplasmosis, chromomycosis, and paracoccidioidomycosis.

Adverse Effects

Common side effects of ketoconazole include nausea, vomiting, stomach pain, itching or skin rash, headache, dizziness, breast swelling, impotence, and loss of interest in sex.

11.1.9.8. Terconazole

Terconazole is an antifungal that is used to treat vaginal yeast infections (or vaginal candidiasis). It is a triazole ketal derivative. It is available as creams and suppositories, both of which have shown high levels of safety, efficacy, and tolerability in clinical trials.

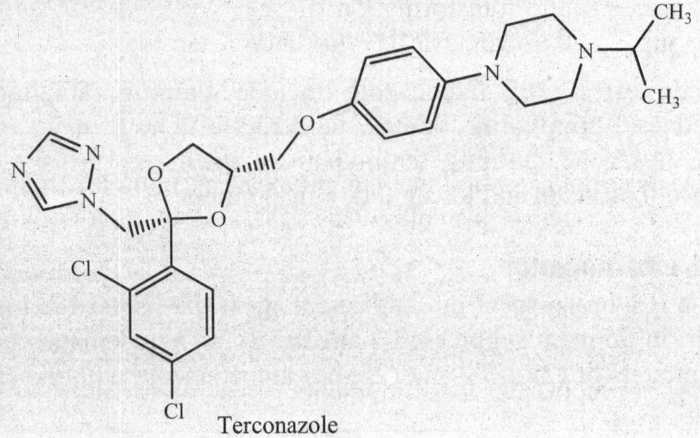

Terconazole

Mechanism of Action

Terconazole exerts its antifungal activity by disrupting the fungal cell membrane permeability. It inhibits cytochrome P-450 14-α-demethylase in susceptible fungi, thus causing accumulation of lanosterol and other methylated sterols, and decreasing ergosterol concentration. This ergosterol depletion in fungal membrane disrupts the structure and function of fungal cell, thereby inhibiting fungal growth.

Uses

Terconazole is used in the treatment of vulvar and vaginal candidiasis (a yeast-like fungal infection).

Adverse Effects

Common side effects of terconazole include headache, increased vaginal/urethral burning/itching/pain, or menstrual cramps. Serious side effects include flu-like symptoms (including fever and chills), foul-smelling discharge from the vagina, and stomach or abdominal pain.

11.1.9.9. Itraconazole

Itraconazole is a triazole antifungal agent that inhibits cytochrome P-450-dependent enzymes, and impairs ergosterol synthesis. It has been used against histoplasmosis, blastomycosis, cryptococcal meningitis, and aspergillosis.

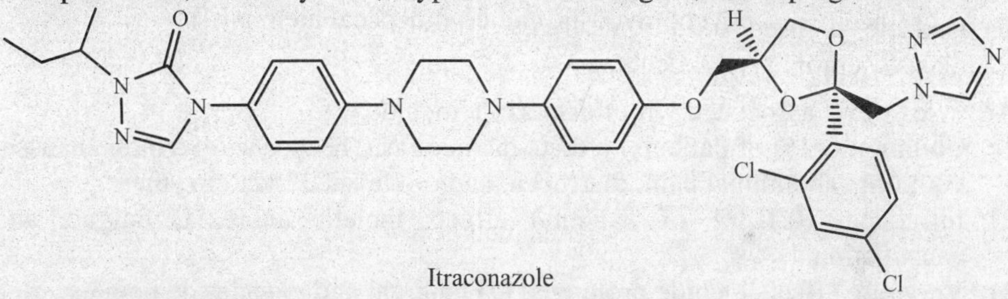

Itraconazole

Mechanism of Action

Itraconazole interacts with yeast 14-α demethylase, which is a cytochrome P-450 enzyme that converts lanosterol to ergosterol (an essential component of fungal membrane). Thus, itraconazole inhibits ergosterol synthesis, and increases cellular permeability, as a result of which the cellular contents leak out. Itraconazole also inhibits endogenous respiration, interacts with membrane phospholipids, inhibits the transformation of yeasts to mycelial forms, inhibits the uptake of purine, and impairs triglyceride and/or phospholipid biosynthesis.

Uses

Itraconazole is used for treating a wide range of fungal infections in immunocompromised and non-immunocompromised patients, like pulmonary and extrapulmonary blastomycosis, histoplasmosis, aspergillosis, and onychomycosis.

Adverse Effects

Common side effects of itraconazole include headache, dizziness, rash, nausea, vomiting, upset stomach, constipation, fever, muscle or joint pain, unusual or unpleasant taste in mouth, hair loss, impotence, erection problems, or irregularity in menstrual periods.

11.1.9.10. Fluconazole

Fluconazole is a triazole antifungal that is used in the treatment and prevention of superficial and systemic fungal infections.

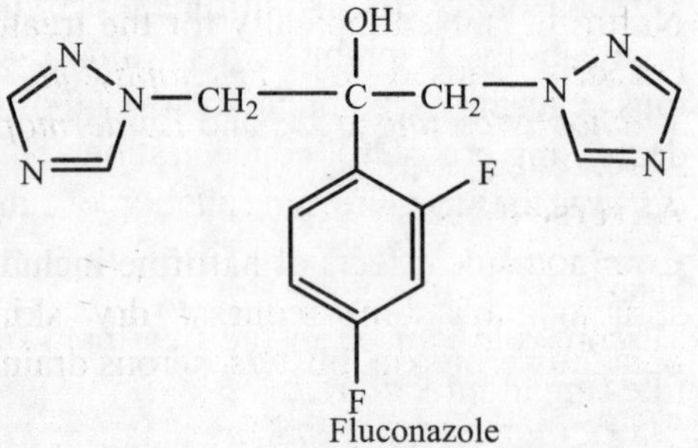

Fluconazole

Mechanism of Action

Fluconazole interacts with yeast 14-α demethylase, which is a cytochrome P-450 enzyme that converts lanosterol to ergosterol (an essential component of fungal membrane). Thus, fluconazole inhibits ergosterol synthesis, and increases cellular permeability, as a result of which the cellular contents leak out. Fluconazole also inhibits endogenous respiration, interacts with membrane phospholipids, inhibits the transformation of yeasts to mycelial forms, inhibits the uptake of purine, and impairs triglyceride and/or phospholipid biosynthesis.

Uses

Fluconazole is used for the treatment and prophylaxis of fungal infections when other antifungals have failed or are not tolerated due to adverse effects, including candidiasis caused by susceptible strains of *Candida,* tinea corporis, tinea cruris or tinea pedis, onychomycosis, and cryptococcal meningitis.

Adverse Effects

Adverse effects associated with fluconazole include:

1) Common (≥1% of patients) effects include rash, headache, dizziness, nausea, vomiting, abdominal pain, diarrhoea, and/or elevated liver enzymes.
2) Infrequent (0.1–1% of patients) effects include anorexia, fatigue, and constipation.
3) Very rare effects include prolonged QT interval and torsades de pointes.

11.1.9.11. Naftifine Hydrochloride

Naftifine is a synthetic, broad spectrum, antifungal and allylamine derivative that is used topically in tinea pedis, tinea cruris, and tinea corporis caused by *Trichophyton rubrum*, *Trichophyton mentagrophytes*, *Trichophyton tonsurans* and *Epidermophyton floccosum.*

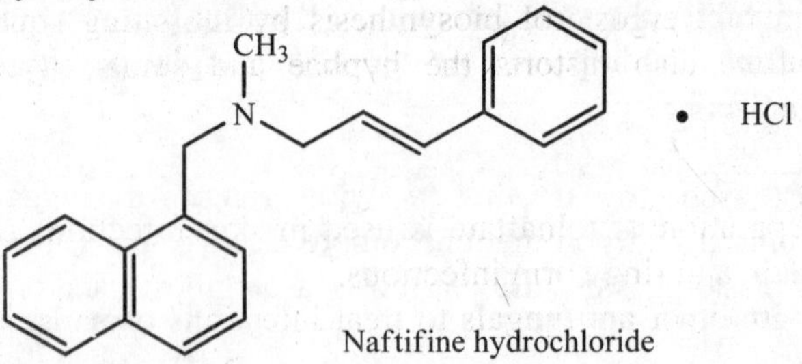

Naftifine hydrochloride

Mechanism of Action

The exact antifungal mechanism of naftifine is not known, but it is assumed to interfere with sterol biosynthesis by inhibiting squalene-2, 3-epoxidase enzyme. This inhibition of enzyme activity decreases the amounts of sterols (especially ergosterol) and a corresponding accumulation of squalene in cells.

Uses

Naftifine is used topically for the treatment of tinea pedis, tinea cruris, and tinea corporis caused by *Trichophyton rubrum*, *Trichophyton mentagrophytes*, *Trichophyton tonsurans* and *Epidermophyton floccosum*.

Adverse Effects

Common side effects of naftifine include reactions at the application site (burning, stinging, irritation, redness, dry skin, itching, inflammation, softening and breakdown of skin, blisters, serous drainage, or crusting), headache, and dizziness.

11.1.9.12. Tolnaftate

Tolnaftate is a synthetic OTC anti-fungal. It is available as creams, powders, sprays, or liquid aerosols. It is used to treat jock itch, athlete's foot, and ringworm.

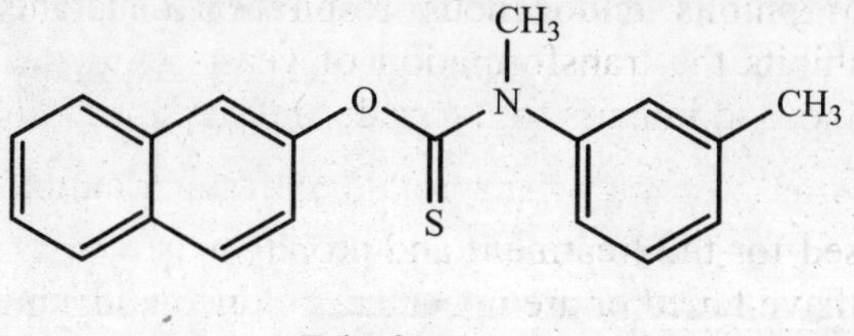

Tolnaftate

Synthesis

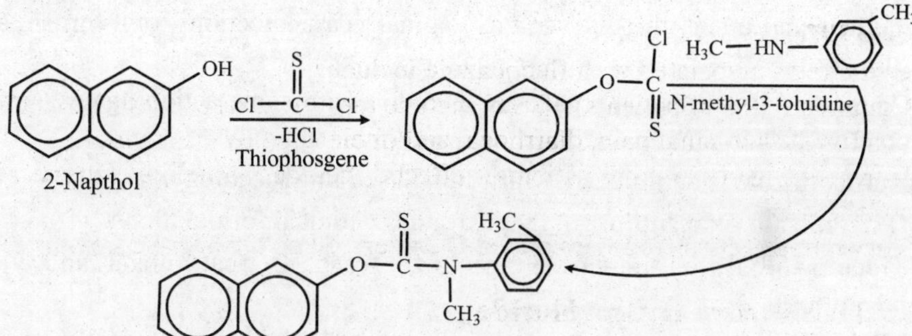

Mechanism of Action

Tolnaftate is a topical fungicide. Its exact mechanism is not clear, but it is presumed to prevent ergosterol biosynthesis by inhibiting squalene epoxidase enzyme. Tolnaftate also distorts the hyphae and stunts mycelial growth in susceptible organisms.

Uses

1) Topical preparation of tolnaftate is used in skin infections such as athlete's foot, jock itch, and ringworm infections.
2) It is used with other antifungals to treat infections of nails, scalp, palm, and soles of feet.
3) Its powder and powder aerosol formulation is used to prevent athlete's foot.

Adverse Effects

Adverse effects of tolnaftate include mild itching, dryness, peeling of treated skin, hives, difficulty in breathing, and swelling of face, lips, tongue or throat.

11.2. SUMMARY

The details given in the chapter can be summarised as follows:

1) In **1992**, **itraconazole** was introduced that expanded the activity spectrum of triazole class beyond *Candida spp.* up to various filamentous fungi.
2) **Azoles** are group of synthetic anti-mycotic agents with broad spectrum of anti-fungal activity.
3) The **polyene antibiotic** produced by actinomycetes contains a large lactone ring with 4 to 7 unsubstituted conjugated double bonds.
4) **Amphotericin B** shows a high order of *in vitro* inhibitory activity against *Histoplasma capsulatum*, *Coccidioides immitis*, *Candida* species, *Blastomyces dermatitidis*, *Rhodotorula*, *Cryptococcus neoformans*, *Sporothrix schenckii*, *Mucor mucedo*, and *Aspergillus fumigatus*.
5) **Nystatin** is a polyene antifungal which acts against many molds and yeasts (such as *Candida spp*).
6) **Natamycin** is an amphoteric macrolide antifungal antibiotic obtained from *Streptomyces natalensis* or *S. chattanoogensis*.
7) **Griseofulvin** is an antifungal agent used for treating infections related to skin, nails, scalp, feet, groin, and other body parts.
8) **Clotrimazole** is an antifungal used in the treatment of fungal infections of humans and other animals, such as vaginal yeast infections, oral thrush, and ringworm.
9) **Econazole** is a broad spectrum antimycotic with some action against gram-positive bacteria.
10) **Butoconazole** is an imidazole antifungal used in gynecology.
11) **Oxiconazole** is an antifungal that is found in topical formulations.
12) **Tioconazole** is an imidazole antifungal used to treat fungal and yeast infections.
13) **Miconazole** is an imidazole antifungal agent that is used topically and by intravenous infusion.
14) **Ketoconazole** is a broad spectrum antifungal agent that is used in high doses for long periods in immunosuppressed patients.
15) **Terconazole** is a triazole ketal derivative antifungal that is used to treat vaginal yeast infections (or vaginal candidiasis).
16) **Itraconazole** is a triazole antifungal agent that inhibits cytochrome P-450-dependent enzymes, and impairs ergosterol synthesis.
17) **Fluconazole** is a triazole antifungal that is used in the treatment and prevention of superficial and systemic fungal infections.
18) **Naftifine** is a synthetic, broad spectrum, antifungal and allylamine derivative that is used topically in tinea pedis, tinea cruris, and tinea corporis caused by *Trichophyton rubrum*, *Trichophyton mentagrophytes*, *Trichophyton tonsurans* and *Epidermophyton floccosum*.
19) **Tolnaftate** is a synthetic OTC anti-fungal. It is available as creams, powders, sprays, or liquid aerosols.

11.3. EXERCISE

11.3.1. True or False

1) Azoles are synthetic anti-mycotic agents with broad spectrum of anti-fungal activity.
2) Natamycin is a polyene antifungal which acts against many molds and yeasts.
3) Oxiconazole is a broad spectrum antimycotic with some action against gram-positive bacteria.
4) Oxiconazole is an antifungal that is found in topical formulations.
5) Miconazole is an imidazole antifungal agent that is used topically and by intraocular administration.
6) Naftifine is a triazole ketal derivative antifungal that is used to treat vaginal yeast infections.
7) Itraconazole is a triazole antifungal agent that inhibits cytochrome P-450-dependent enzymes.

11.3.2. Fill in the Blanks

8) The ________ produced by actinomycetes contains a large lactone ring with 4 to 7 unsubstituted conjugated double bonds.
9) Natamycin is an amphoteric macrolide antifungal antibiotic obtained from ________ or ________.
10) ________ is an antifungal agent used for treating infections related to skin, nails, scalp, feet, groin, and other body parts.
11) ________ is an imidazole antifungal used in gynecology.
12) ________ is a broad spectrum antifungal agent that is used in high doses for long periods in immunosuppressed patients.
13) ________ is a triazole antifungal that is used in the treatment and prevention of superficial and systemic fungal infections.
14) ________ is a synthetic OTC anti-fungal.

Answers

1) True	2) False	3) False
4) True	5) False	6) False
7) True		8) Polyene antibiotic
9) *Streptomyces natalensis* and *Streptomyces chattanoogensis*		10) Griseofulvin
11) Butoconazole		12) Ketoconazole
13) Fluconazole		14) Tolnaftate

11.3.3. Very Short Answer Type Questions

1) Classify antifungal agents.
2) Enlist the uses of antifungal agents.
3) Give the chemical structure of griseofulvin.
4) Give the mechanism of action of amphotericin B.
5) What are the uses of nystatin?
6) How butoconazole acts?
7) Draw the structures of oxiconazole and tioconazole.
8) Give the mechanism of action of fluconazole.

11.3.4. Short Answer Type Questions

1) Discuss the historical background and mechanism of action of antifungal agents.
2) Write a short note on any two antifungal antibiotics.
3) Discuss about the mechanism of action and uses of clotrimazole and econazole.
4) Give the syntheses of miconazole and tolnaftate.
5) Write a short note on ketoconazole and terconazole.
6) Discuss the uses and adverse effects of itraconazole and naftifine.

11.3.5. Long Answer Type Questions

1) Discuss the SAR of antifungal agents.
2) Write an exhaustive note on antifungal agents.
3) Write about any three synthetic antifungal agents.

CHAPTER 12 Anti-Protozoal Agents

12.1. ANTI-PROTOZOAL AGENTS

12.1.1. Introduction

Protozoal infections commonly occur in people living in under-developed tropical and sub-tropical countries, where sanitary conditions, hygienic practices, and control of vectors of transmission are inadequately maintained. However, with increased world travel, protozoal diseases, such as malaria, amoebiasis, leishmaniasis, trypanosomiasis, trichomoniasis, and giardiasis, are no longer confined to specific geographic locales. Because they are eukaryotes, the unicellular protozoal cells have metabolic processes closer to those of the human host than to prokaryotic bacterial pathogens. Thus, the treatment of protozoal diseases is easy than that of the bacterial infections.

Antiprotozoal agents are used in a wide range of diseases caused by protozoa (one-celled organisms, such as amoebas). Some are parasitic and cause infections in the body. African sleeping sickness, giardiasis, amoebiasis, Pneumocystis Carinii Pneumonia (PCP), and malaria are **examples** of diseases caused by protozoa.

Many antiprotozoal drugs cause serious toxic effects in the host, particularly on cells showing high metabolic activity, such as neuronal, renal tubular, intestinal, and bone marrow stem cells. Most antiprotozoal agents have not proved to be safe in pregnant women.

12.1.2. Antiamoebic Agents

Amoeba is a single-celled organism which needs a host to survive and hence, it comes under protozoan category. **Amoebiasis** (or amoebic dysentery) is the most common disease caused by amoeba. This infection is caused in the intestinal tract by *Entamoeba histolytica*. Amoebiasis can be acute or chronic with symptoms ranging from mild diarrhoea to fulminating dysentery. The diagnosis of amoebiasis can be done by isolating *E. histolytica* from fresh faeces.

Anti-amoebic drugs reduce the infections caused by amoeba.

12.1.3. Historical Background

Brazilian and Central American Indians used **ipecacuanha** extracts (*Cephaelis ipecacuanha* or *C. acuminata*) in the treatment of diarrhoea. In Europe, it was bought in use for treating dysenteriae at the middle of 17th century. **Vedder** established its anti-amoebic activity in **1912**. The main alkaloid of ipecacuanha, i.e., emetine, exists in eight racemic forms; out of which (–)-emetine is the natural and the most active. Hundreds of emetine derivatives have been prepared, of which dehydroemetine, having the same absolute configuration as (–)-emetine, is a potent anti-amoebic. **Brosi** synthesised **dehydroemetine** in **1959** and **Schnitzer** and **Russomanno** evaluated it in the same year.

Ehrlich and **Bertheim** synthesised **carbarsone** in **1907**. **Leake** evaluated it in **1931** and observed that it possesses anti-amoebic activity. **Streitwolf** synthesised **glycobiarsol** in **1928**, and **Hauer** evaluated it as an amoebicidal in **1943**. **Claus** prepared **chiniofon** in **1892**, and **Muhlens** and **Menck** first used it for amoebiasis. This led to the introduction of other **haloquinoline derivatives of clioquinol** in **1931**, and **haloquinoline derivatives of iodoquinol** in **1936**. **Burckhalter** and co-workers performed structure-activity relationship studies in these drugs.

The anti-amoebic activity of **chloroquine** (first used as antimalarial agent) was reported by **Conan** in **1948**. **Burckhalter** and associates synthesised **bialamicol** in **1951**. A systematic search for amoebicidal activity among a series of haloacetamides led to the introduction of **diloxanide** in **1956** by **Bristow**. Its derivative, **diloxanide furoate**, was evaluated by **Main** in rats and by **Shaldon** in humans. It was found to be more active than the parent compound (diloxanide) and was also effective in acute intestinal amoebiasis. **Coffey** in **1959** showed that **paromomycin** exerts direct and indirect effects in amoebiasis.

Metronidazole and **niridazole** were obtained in a systematic search of new anti-protozoan agents among nitroimidazoles after the discovery of anti-trichomonal properties of aminitrozole by **Cuckler** in **1955** and of azomycin by **Coser** and **Juliu** in **1959**.

Metronidazole was synthesised in **1957** in Rhone-Poulenc laboratories, and was evaluated as an anti-trichomonal agent and as an anti-amoebic agent by **Coser** and **Juliu** in **1959** and **1961**, respectively. Other nitroimidazole derivatives, like **nimorazole** (1965), **ornidazole** (1966), and **tinidazole** (1969) have been introduced.

12.1.4. Classification

Anti-amoebic drugs are classified as follows:

1) **Luminal Amoebicides:** These agents act against the intestinal forms of amoeba, **e.g.,** Diloxanide furoate.
2) **Systemic Amoebicides:** These agents are used for treating severe amoebic dysentery or hepatic abscesses, **e.g.,** Dihydroemetin and Chloroquine.
3) **Mixed Amoebicides:** These agents act on the intestinal and systemic forms of amoeba, **e.g.,** Metronidazole, Tinidazole, and Ornidazole.

12.1.5. Mechanism of Action

Anti-amoebic drugs act as an artificial electron acceptor after accumulating in the cells as reduced compounds. This diverts electrons from normal pathways of the protozoan. The nitro group of the drugs accepts electrons (source of electrons may be reduced NADPH or sulphide) from electron-transport proteins (such as ferredoxins) and diverts them from normal energy-yielding pathways. This reduction is catalysed by iron-sulphur complexes.

Metronidazole also impairs the ability of DNA to function as a template. The reduced metronidazole damages the helical structure of DNA, causes strand breakage, impairs DNA's function, and ultimately cell death. A disulfiram-like reaction can occur when metronidazole is administered along with an alcoholic beverage.

12.1.6. Uses

Anti-protozoal drugs are used for treating infections caused by anaerobic bacteria, amoeba, and parasites in the urinary tract, vagina, and intestines. Antibiotics are also given to prevent these infections. Some common infections treated by these drugs are amoebic dysentery, bacterial vaginosis, trichomoniasis, giardiasis, hepatic amoebas, and off-label for Crohn's disease.

12.1.7. Adverse Effects

The common adverse effects of anti-protozoal drugs include:

1) Flatulence,
2) Loss of appetite,
3) Nausea,
4) Itching,
5) Hives, etc.

12.1.8. Important Products

The following drugs are studied in detail:

1) Metronidazole,
2) Tinidazole,
3) Ornidazole,
4) Diloxanide,
5) Iodoquinol,
6) Pentamidine isethionate,
7) Atovaquone, and
8) Eflornithine.

12.1.8.1. Metronidazole

Metronidazole is a nitroimidazole used for treating amoebiasis, vaginitis, trichomonas infections, giardiasis, and anaerobic bacterial and treponemal infections. It is also suggested as a radiation sensitiser for hypoxic cells.

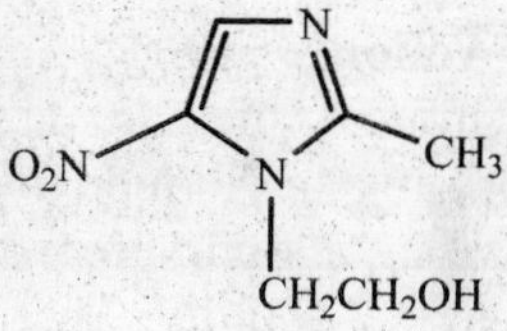

Metronidazole

Synthesis

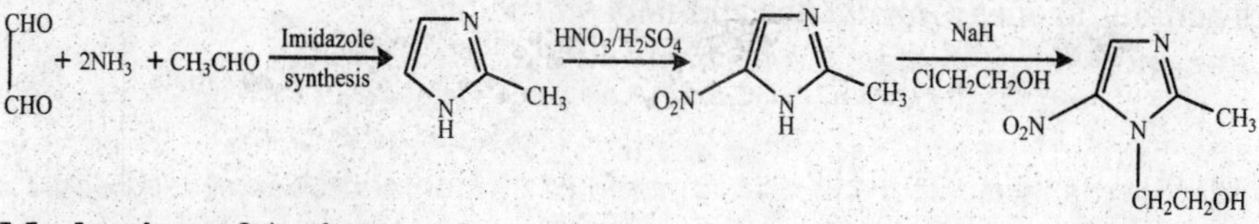

Mechanism of Action

The exact mechanism of action of metronidazole is not yet clear; but, it is possible that an intermediate formed by metronidazole reduction by anaerobic bacteria and protozoa binds to DNA and electron-transport proteins of organisms, and blocks the synthesis of nucleic acids. Metronidazole on administration enters the cells by passive diffusion. Then its nitro group is reduced by ferredoxin or flavodoxin to nitro radicals. The redox potential of the electron transport portions of anaerobic or microaerophilic microorganisms make metronidazole selective to these organisms, which cause nitro group reduction, and thus production of toxic metabolites [N-(2-hydroxyethyl) oxamic acid and acetamide], which may **damage DNA of replicating organisms.**

Uses

Metronidazole is used for treating amoebic dysentery, amoebic hepatitis and liver abscesses (caused by *Entamoeba histolytica*). It is also used in giardiasis characterised by diarrhoea and dysentery (caused by *Giardia lamblia*). Genito-urinary tract infections like vaginitis (caused by *Trichomonas* spp.) are also treated by this drug. Metronidazole is used in septicaemia, brain abscesses, post-operative wound infections (because of its bactericidal action), and necrotising pneumonia. It is also used for treating vincent's disease. It is used for treating balantidiasis (caused by *Balantidiun coli)*.

Adverse Effects

1) Adverse effects associated with systemic metronidazole therapy include nausea, diarrhoea, and/or metallic taste in mouth.
2) Adverse effects associated with intravenous administration of metronidazole include thrombophlebitis, hypersensitivity reactions (rash, itch, flushing, and fever), headache, dizziness, vomiting, glossitis, stomatitis, dark urine, and/or paraesthesia.
3) Adverse effects associated with high doses and/or long-term systemic treatment with metronidazole include development of leukopenia, neutropenia, increased risk of peripheral neuropathy, and/or CNS toxicity.

12.1.8.2. Tinidazole

Tinidazole is a nitroimidazole anti-trichomonal agent that is effective against *Trichomonas vaginalis*, *Entamoeba histolytica*, and *Giardia lamblia* infections.

Mechanism of Action

The nitro group of tinidazole is reduced (in *Trichomonas*) by a ferredoxin-mediated electron transport system to a toxic free nitro radical, which exhibits antiprotozoal activity. These toxic free radicals covalently bind to DNA, cause DNA damage, and lead to cell death. The mechanism by which tinidazole exhibits activity against *Giardia* and *Entamoeba* species is yet to be understood, though it is probably similar.

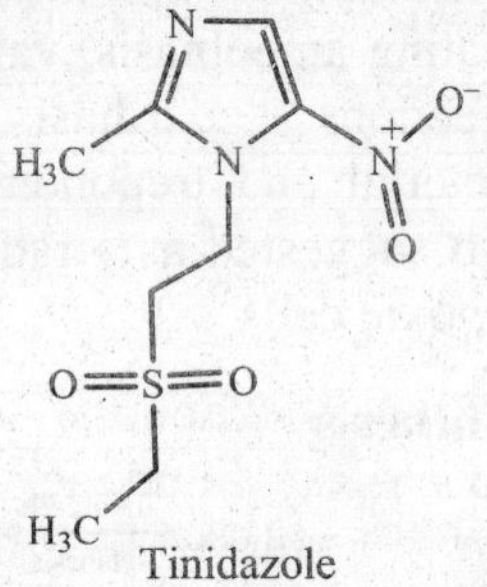

Tinidazole

Uses

1) Tinidazole is used for the treatment of trichomoniasis caused by *T. vaginalis* in females and males.
2) It is also used in giardiasis caused by *G. duodenalis* in adults and pediatrics (>3 years of age).
3) It also helps in intestinal amoebiasis and amoebic liver abscess caused by *E. histolytica* in adults and pediatrics (>3 years of age).

Adverse Effects

1) **CNS:** Convulsions and transient peripheral neuropathy including numbness and paresthesia are the two major adverse effects. Other CNS effects include vertigo, ataxia, giddiness, insomnia, and drowsiness.
2) **Gastrointestinal: Tongue discolouration, stomatitis, and diarrhoea.**

3) **Hypersensitivity:** Urticaria, pruritis, rash, flushing, sweating, dryness of mouth, fever, burning sensation, thirst, salivation, and angioedema.
4) **Renal:** Dark urine.
5) **CVS:** Palpitations.
6) **Hematopoietic:** Transient neutropenia and transient leukopenia.
7) **Other:** Candida overgrowth, increased vaginal discharge, oral candidiasis, hepatic abnormalities including raised transaminase level, arthralgias, myalgias, and arthritis.

12.1.8.3. Ornidazole

Ornidazole is a nitroimidazole having a broad spectrum activity against protozoa and some anaerobic bacteria.

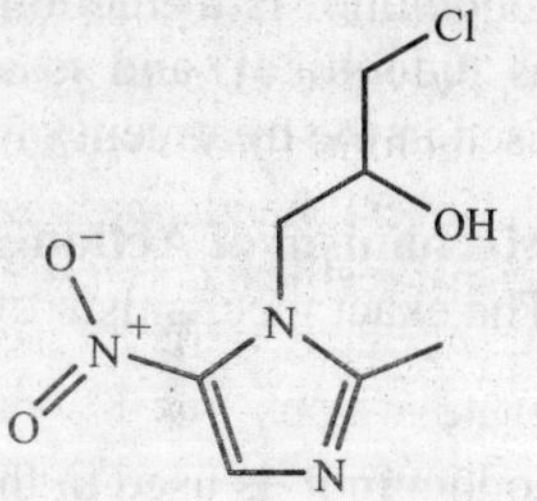

Ornidazole

Mechanism of Action

Ornidazole's selective toxicity to anaerobic microbes involves the following steps:

1) It enters the cell by diffusion,
2) The redox proteins present in anaerobic organisms reduce its nitro group to reactive nitro radical that exerts cytotoxic action by damaging DNA and other critical biomolecules, and
3) This leads to destabilisation and strand breakage in DNA helix.

Uses

Ornidazole is used to treat anaerobic infections, bacterial vaginitis, amoebic liver abscess, amoebic dysentery, hepatic amoebiasis, giardiasis, trichomoniasis, and Crohn's disease.

Adverse Effects

Serious adverse effects of ornidazole include confusion, severe dizziness, severe diarrhoea, numbness, tremors, seizures, jaundice, tingling sensation, bloody stools, rigidity, and lack of coordination.

12.1.8.4. Diloxanide

Diloxanide is an anti-protozoal that is used for treating infections caused by *Entamoeba histolytica* and other protozoa.

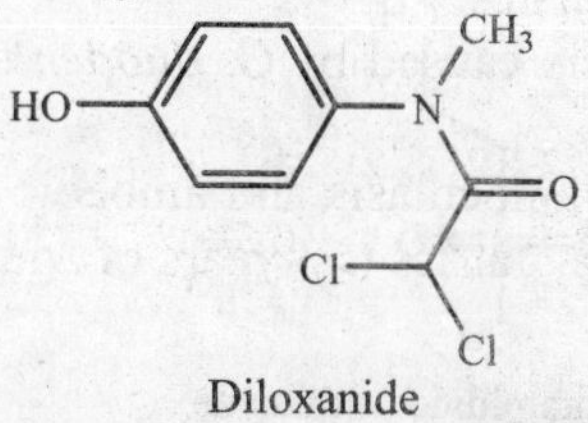

Diloxanide

Mechanism of Action

The mechanism of action of diloxanide is not clear. Since it is structurally related to chloramphenicol, it is presumed to inhibit protein synthesis in microorganisms.

Uses

1) Diloxanide is used as a primary agent for treating asymptomatic intestinal amoebiasis caused by *Entamoeba histolytica*.
2) It is used with or in sequence with other agents like nitroimidazoles (**e.g.,** metronidazole) for treating invasive or extraintestinal forms of amoebiasis.

Adverse Effects

The side/adverse effects of diloxanide include urticarial rash (skin rash), flatulence (full feeling or passing gas), nausea, difficulty in breathing, abdominal cramps, anorexia (loss of appetite), and diarrhoea.

12.1.8.5. Iodoquinol

Iodoquinol is a diiodohydroxyquinoline. It is also known as uidoquinol, and is a quinoline derivative that can be used in the treatment of amoebiasis.

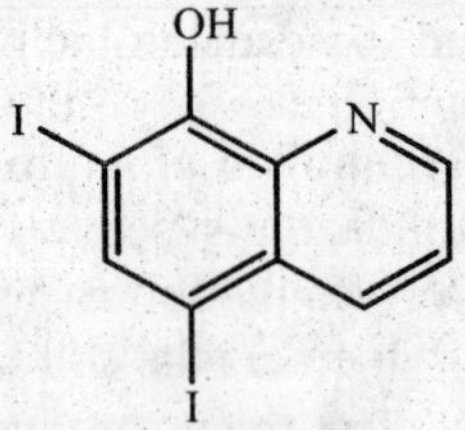

Iodoquinol

Mechanism of Action

The exact mechanism of action of iodoquinol is unknown.

Uses

Iodoquinol is used in the treatment of amoebiasis.

Adverse Effects

Common side effects of iodoquinol include nausea, vomiting, diarrhoea, stomach pain, rectal itching, headache, dizziness and spinning sensation. Serious side effects include hives, difficulty in breathing, swelling on face, lips, tongue or throat, acne-like rash with pus-filled lesions, skin redness or itching, vision problems, pain behind eyes, numbness, tingling, or burning pain in hands or feet, fever, chills, or swelling in neck or throat (enlarged thyroid).

12.1.8.6. Pentamidine Isethionate

Pentamidine is an antiprotozoal that is effective in trypanosomiasis, leishmaniasis, and some fungal infections. It is used in pneumocystis pneumonia in HIV-infected patients.

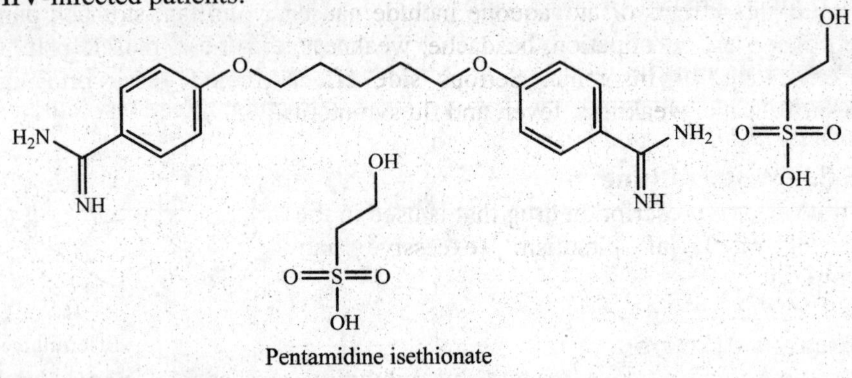

Pentamidine isethionate

Mechanism of Action

The mode of action of pentamidine is not yet clear, but it is presumed to interfere with nuclear metabolism, thus **inhibiting the synthesis of DNA, RNA, phospholipids, and proteins.**

Uses
Pentamidine is used for the treatment of pneumonia caused by *Pneumocystis carinii*.

Adverse Effects
Pentamidine causes diabetes mellitus, CNS damage, and other toxic effects. Common side effects include cough, upset stomach, loss of appetite, nausea, vomiting, diarrhoea, dizziness, headache, burning feeling in throat, unusual taste in mouth, and dry mouth.

12.1.8.7. Atovaquone
Atovaquone is a hydroxynaphthoquinone or an analog of ubiquinone, having antimicrobial and antipneumocystis activity.

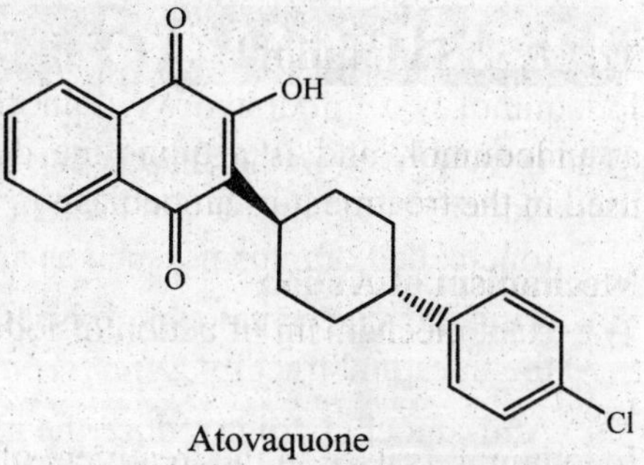

Atovaquone

Mechanism of Action
The mechanism of action of atovaquone against *Pneumocystis carinii* is not fully clear. In *Plasmodium* species, cytochrome bc1 complex (Complex III) is the site of action. Some metabolic enzymes are linked to the mitochondrial electron transport chain via ubiquinone. Atovaquone indirectly inhibits these enzymes by inhibiting the electron transport. The metabolic effects of such blockade include inhibition of nucleic acid and ATP synthesis.

Uses
1) Atovaquone shows good *in vitro* activity against *Toxoplasma gondii*.
2) It is used for the treatment or prevention of *Pneumocystis carinii* pneumonia and acute oral treatment of mild to moderate PCP in patients intolerant to Trimethoprim-Sulfamethoxazole (TMP-SMX).

Adverse Effects
Common side effects of atovaquone include nausea, vomiting, stomach pain or upset, diarrhoea, constipation, headache, weakness, dizziness, muscle pain, skin rash, sweating, or insomnia. Serious side effects include easy bruising or bleeding, unusual weakness, fever, and flu symptoms.

12.1.8.8. Eflornithine
Eflornithine is a prescription drug that is used in the treatment of facial hirsutism (excessive hair growth).

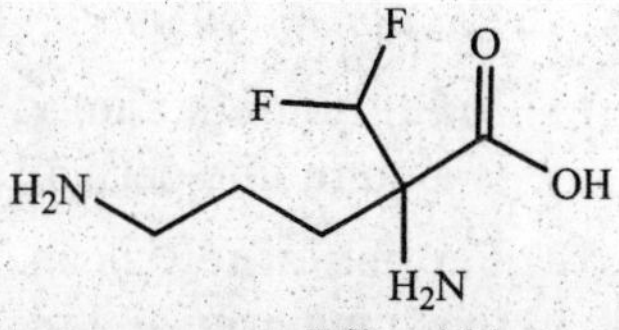

Eflornithine

Mechanism of Action
Eflornithine inhibits hair growth by inhibiting the anagen phase of hair production by irreversibly binding (also called suicide inhibition) to Ornithine Decarboxylase (ODC) and physically preventing the natural substrate ornithine from accessing the active site.

Uses

Eflornithine hydrochloride cream is applied topically in women suffering from facial hirsutism.

Adverse Effects

The most common side effects of eflornithine include acne, swollen patches that sometimes are red and contain a buried hair (pseudofolliculitis barbae), headache, skin itching, stinging, burning, dry or tingling skin, rash, hair loss, and ingrown hairs.

12.2. SUMMARY

The details given in the chapter can be summarised as follows:

1) Antiprotozoal agents are used in a wide range of diseases caused by protozoa (one-celled organisms, such as amoebas).
2) **Amoebiasis** (or amoebic dysentery) is the most common disease caused in the intestinal tract by *Entamoeba histolytica*.
3) Anti-amoebic drugs reduce the infections caused by amoeba.
4) The anti-amoebic activity of **chloroquine** (first used as antimalarial agent) was reported by **Conan** in **1948**.
5) A systematic search for amoebicidal activity among a series of haloacetamides led to the introduction of **diloxanide** in **1956** by **Bristow**.
6) Metronidazole was synthesised in **1957** in Rhone-Poulenc laboratories, and was evaluated as an anti-trichomonal agent and as an anti-amoebic agent by **Coser** and **Juliu** in **1959** and **1961**, respectively.
7) **Metronidazole** is a nitroimidazole used for treating amoebiasis, vaginitis, trichomonas infections, giardiasis, and anaerobic bacterial and treponemal infections.
8) **Tinidazole** is a nitroimidazole anti-trichomonal agent that is effective against *Trichomonas vaginalis*, *Entamoeba histolytica*, and *Giardia lamblia* infections.
9) **Ornidazole** is a nitroimidazole having a broad spectrum activity against protozoa and some anaerobic bacteria.
10) **Diloxanide** is an anti-protozoal that is used for treating infections caused by *Entamoeba histolytica* and other protozoa.
11) **Iodoquinol** is a diiodohydroxyquinoline. It is also known as uidoquinol, and is a quinoline derivative that can be used in the treatment of amoebiasis.
12) **Pentamidine** is an antiprotozoal that is effective in trypanosomiasis, leishmaniasis, and some fungal infections.
13) **Atovaquone** is a hydroxynaphthoquinone or an analog of ubiquinone, having antimicrobial and antipneumocystis activity.
14) **Eflornithine** is a prescription drug that is used in the treatment of facial hirsutism (excessive hair growth).

12.3. EXERCISE

12.3.1. True or False

1) The anti-amoebic activity of metronidazole was reported by Conan in 1948.
2) Diloxanide is an anti-protozoal that is used for treating infections caused by *Entamoeba histolytica* and other protozoa.
3) Ornidazole is an antiprotozoal that is effective in trypanosomiasis, leishmaniasis, and some fungal infections.
4) Atovaquone is a hydroxynaphthoquinone or an analog of ubiquinone, having antimicrobial and antipneumocystis activity.

12.3.2. Fill in the Blanks

5) Amoebiasis is the most common disease caused in the intestinal tract by ________.
6) ________ is a nitroimidazole anti-trichomonal agent that is effective against *Trichomonas vaginalis*, *Entamoeba histolytica*, and *Giardia lamblia* infections.
7) ________ is a prescription drug that is used in the treatment of facial hirsutism.
8) Iodoquinol is a diiodohydroxyquinoline and is also known as ________.

Answers

1) False	2) True	3) False
4) True	5) *Entamoeba histolytica*	6) Tinidazole
7) Eflornithine	8) Uidoquinol	

12.3.3. Very Short Answer Type Questions

1) Classify anti-amoebic agents.
2) Enlist the uses of anti-protozoal agents.
3) Give the chemical structure of metronidazole.
4) Give the mechanism of action of tinidazole.
5) What are the uses of diloxanide?
6) How atovaquone acts?
7) Draw the structures of ornidazole and iodoquinol.
8) Give the mechanism of action of eflornithine.

12.3.4. Short Answer Type Questions

1) Discuss the historical background of anti-protozoal agents.
2) Write a short note on any two anti-protozoal agents.
3) Give the synthesis of metronidazole.
4) Discuss about the mechanism of action and uses of pentamdine isethionate and diloxanide.
5) Discuss the uses and adverse effects of ornidazole and tinidazole.

12.3.5. Long Answer Type Question

1) Write an exhaustive note on anti-protozoal agents.
2) Write about any three synthetic anti-protozoal agents.

CHAPTER 13 Anthelmintics

13.1. ANTHELMINTICS

13.1.1. Introduction

Helminthiasis is an infection caused to human body by helminths. The diseases caused by this worm are known since ancient times, and it still constitutes a major public health hazard worldwide, mainly prevailing in tropical and sub-tropical regions. Mostly, no serious concerns are found to be associated with helminthiasis. Drugs used to kill or eliminate the intestinal parasites from the body are termed **anthelmintics**. Drugs used to remove or expel the intestinal parasites are termed **vermifuges**. Drugs used to kill the intestinal parasites are termed **vermicides**. The name **vermicide** is derived from worms (like hookworm, roundworm, etc.), which are collectively known as **nematehelminthes** or **nematodes**. A number of worms, which are parasitic to humans, carry infections.

Anthelmintics act locally to remove the parasites from gastrointestinal tract. Several types of worms may enter other body tissues; anthelmintic drugs act on these parasitic infections. The worm parasites of humans belong to two phyla, i.e., *Nemathelminthes* (round-worms) and *Platyhelminthes* (flatworms). The round worms are hookworms, whipworms, pinworms, *Strongyloides stercoralis*, *Trichinella spiralis*, and *Wuchereria bancrofti.*

13.1.2. Historical Background

The first anthelmintics were some plant extracts, which are now outdated, but aspidium continues to be in use. Anti-parasitic effects of arsenic and antimony compounds were known since centuries. To improve efficacy and lower the toxicity of these heavy metals, some organic compounds containing these metals have been prepared and are still in use. For example, since 1947, **Friedheim** has synthesised and evaluated some of these compounds, such as **melarsoprol** and **stibocaptate**.

Based on the trypanocidal activity of afridol violet, trypan blue, and trypan red dyestuffs, **Bayer & Co. investigators** synthesised **suramin sodium** in 1916, whose trypanocidal action was evaluated by other German scientists. **Furncau and co-workers** after several years of research (1916-1923) published for the first time the synthesis of suramin sodium.

Cloez synthesised **piperazine** in 1853; **Giroud** discovered its anthelmintic activity in 1942; **Boismare** observed the same effect in 1948; and **Bayard** confirmed the effect in 1949. Structural modification of this molecule in the search for effective filaricides formed **diethylcarbamazine**, which was synthesised by **Kishner** in 1946 and its pharmacological effects were by **Hewitt** in 1947.

In the 1930s it was discovered that some **thioxanthenone derivatives** have schistosomicidal activity, and this resulted in the introduction of **lucanthone** (synthesised by **Mauss** in 1940 and evaluated by **Kikuth** 1946) and its metabolite **hycanthone** (synthesised by **Rosi** in 1965).

Several cyanine dyes possess anthelmintic activity. A systematic investigation of these compounds led to the introduction of **pyrvinium pamoate**, first synthesised by **Van Lare and Brooker** in 1946. **Peters** successfully tested it in helminthiasis in 1949; and other investigators soon confirmed this activity.

Barthel in 1951 first synthesised **metrifonate** as an intermediate in an organic reaction; it was synthesised by **Lorenz** in 1952 as an insecticide; and its anthelmintic action was reported in 1962. **Niclosamide** was synthesised by **Bayer A.G.** in 1955, and **Gonnert and Schraufstatter** introduced it as a taenicide in 1960. **Bephenium hydroxynaphthoate** was introduced by **Copp and co-workers** in 1958.

Thiabendazole is a product of investigation of several hundred substituted benzimidazoles. It was first introduced by **Brown and colleagues** in 1961 in veterinary medicine in 1962. **Vilela** tested it in human helminthiasis. Synthesis and evaluation of a large number of nitrothiazole derivatives led to the development of **niridazole** by **Lambert** in 1964.

Discovery of anthelmintic activity in **isothiouronium salt** encouraged Pfizer laboratories to initiate synthesis and evaluation of its analogues. This led to the introduction of **pyrantel pamoate**, synthesised by **Austin** in 1965; first used in veterinary practice as a broad-spectrum anthelmintic; and introduced in human medicine by **Bumbalo** in 1969. Molecular modification of pyrantel gave rise to **morantel**, synthesised by **Austin** in 1968; **oxantel**, synthesised by **McFarland and Howes** in 1968; and other drugs of the same group.

Tetramisole was developed after **Janssen** conducted biotransformation studies of thiazothienol (a veterinary anthelmintic) in 1966. In the next year, the same researchers synthesised isomers of tetramisole and discovered that the S (–)-isomer, i.e., **levamisole** exhibited anthelmintic activity.

Mebendazole was introduced in 1971 when **Brugmans** conducted a research on benzimidazole derivatives. It was synthesised by **Van Gelder**. Other drugs of this group are **cambendazole** (1970), **albendazole** (1976), and **flubendazole** (1979).

Praziquantel was synthesised by **Seubert** in 1975, after compounds of its group showed anthelmintic activity in 1972.

13.1.3. Classification

Anthelmintic drugs are classified as follows:

1) **Benzimidazoles**

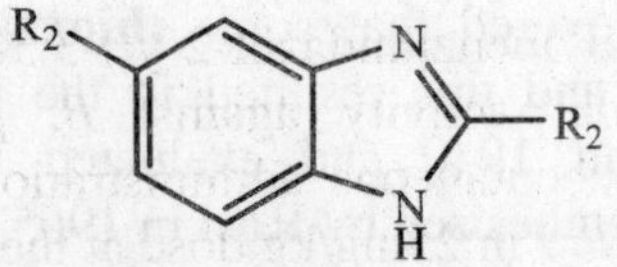

	R_1	R_2
Mebendazole	$-NHCO_2CH_3$	$-COC_6H_5$
Albendazole	$-NHCO_2CH_3$	$-SCH_2CH_2CH_3$
Thiabendazole	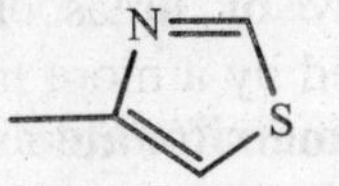	H

2) **Piperazines:** Diethylcarbamazine citrate and Piperazine citrate.
3) **Heterocyclics:** Oxamniquine and Praziquantel.
4) **Natural Products:** Ivermectin and Avermectin.
5) **Vinyl Pyrimidines:** Pyrantel and Oxantel.
6) **Amide:** Niclosamide.
7) **Nitro Derivative:** Niridazole.
8) **Imidazo Thiazole:** Levamisole.

13.1.4. Structure-Activity Relationship

The structure-activity relationships of mebendazole and flubendazole can be studied by choosing the four possible sites (**figure 13.1**):

1) Modification of 2-methyl carbamate group (A),
2) Modification of 5-benzoyl group (B),
3) Modification of keto group (C), and
4) Modification of benzene ring (D) of the benzimidazole.

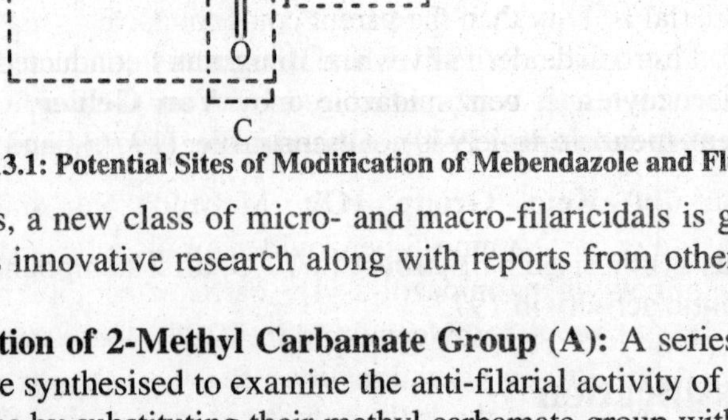

Figure 13.1: Potential Sites of Modification of Mebendazole and Flubendazole

In the process, a new class of micro- and macro-filaricidals is generated and the results of this innovative research along with reports from other laboratories are as follows:

1) **Modification of 2-Methyl Carbamate Group (A):** A series of benzimidolyl ureas were synthesised to examine the anti-filarial activity of benzimidazole-2-carbamates by substituting their methyl carbamate group with other functional groups (alkyl or aryl ureas). Structure-activity relationship studies in this series showed decrease in antifilarial activity against *B. pahangi* and *L. carinii*.

However, 1-(5-benzoylbenzimidazol-2-yl)-3,3-dimethylurea demonstrated 100% macro-filaricidal activity against *B. pahangi* and *L. carinii* in 100mg/kg dose on subcutaneous administration and 87% micro-filaricidal activity against *L. carinii* in 25mg/kg dose at the time of necropsy.

The 1-(5-benzoylbenzimidazol-2-yl)-3-arylureas exhibited marginal macro-filaricidal activity against both *B. pahangi* and *L. carinii* in 100mg/kg dose on subcutaneous administration. This reduced anti-filarial activity may be due to poor water solubility of ureas. In another approach, 2-methyl carbamate moiety was replaced by a more lipophilic group (such as SCO_2R, $SCONR_1R_2$ or $S(CH_2)_nCO_2R$, etc.) to yield more soluble compounds. These compounds showed null anti-filarial activity. These studies prove that carbamate moiety is an essential pharmacophore for anti-filarial activity.

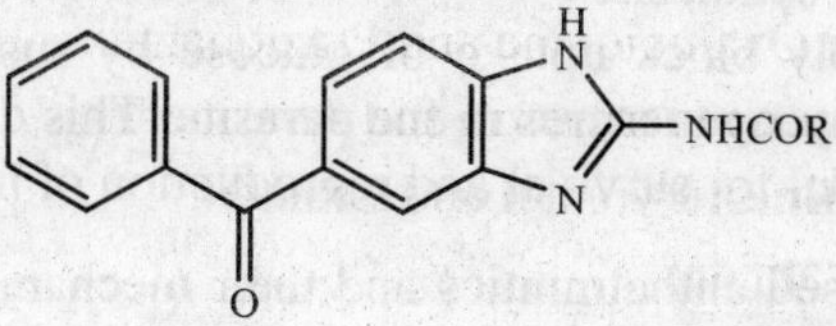

1-(5-benzoylbenzimidazol-2-yl)-3,3-dimethylurea R = NMe_2
1-(5-benzoylbenzimidazol-2-yl)-3-arylureas { R = PhNH; R = 4-FC_6H_4NH

2) **Modification of 5-Benzoyl Group (B):** Substitution of NH group between the benzoyl group and benzimidazole moiety give rise to compounds that are 100% effective against adult *B. pahangi* in 100mg/kg subcutaneous dose. However, if the dose is reduced to 25mg/kg, these compounds are effective at 86% and 60%, respectively. Decrease in anti-filarial activity at lower dose indicates that these target compounds possess poor water solubility and tissue distribution.

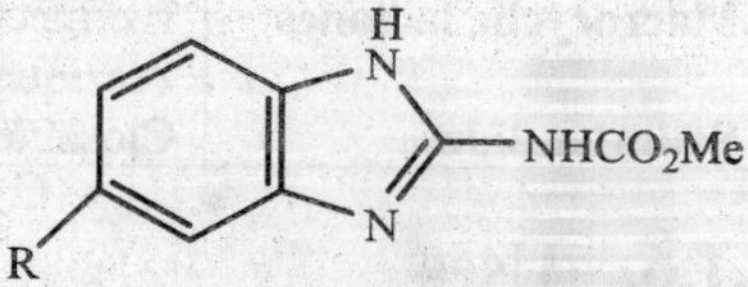

R=2-FC_6H_4CONH
R=4-FC_6H_4CONH
R=4-FC_6H_4NHCO
R=3-$CF_3C_6H_4NHCO$

In another approach, substitution of NH group between the phenyl group and keto function of mebendazole and flubendazole give rise to compounds with lower anti-filarial activity than the parent compounds. This may be due to poor solubility of these amide derivatives and illustrates that increasing the distance between 5-benzoyl and benzimidazole moiety or between phenyl and 5-carbonyl benzimidazole moiety is not essential for macro-filaricidal activity.

3) **Modification of Keto Group (C):** Mebendazole and flubendazole metabolites, i.e., 2-amino-5-benzoylbenzimidazole, methyl [5-α-hydroxyphenylmethylbenzimidazol-2-yl] carbamate, and methyl [5-α-hydroxy-4′ fluorophenylmethylbenzimidazol-2-yl] carbamate are prepared by reducing the ketone functionality. Besides the partially reduced hydroxymethyl derivative, the fully reduced methyl (5-benzylbenzimidazol-2-yl) carbamate was also prepared. It was of considerable interest that the compounds retained the macro-filaricidal activity profile. On the other hand,

metabolite did not show any anti-filarial activity, thus indicating that carbamate moiety is essential for anti-filarial activity. The ketone-reduced derivatives were more soluble in water and ethanol than mebendazole or flubendazole (the parent drugs).

13.1.5. Mechanism of Action

Anthelmintics act in the following ways:

1) They inhibit fumarate reductase enzyme system of the worm, and thus interfere with an important energy source.
2) They inhibit nematode cell division in the metaphase by interfering with microtubule assembly.
3) They have high affinity for tubulin (the precursor protein), which is required for microtubule synthesis.
4) They irreversibly block uptake of glucose by susceptible helminthes, thus depleting the glycogen stores in the parasite. This decreases ATP production, which is essential for survival and reproduction of helminthes.

Some commonly used anthelmintics and their mechanism of action are depicted below:

Classes	Examples	MOA
Benzimidazoles	Albendazole	Tubulin binding and cellular disruption
Tetrahydropyrimidine	Levamisole	Nicotinic-like agonists
Organophosphates	Dichorvos	Acetylcholine esterase inhibitors
Piperazines	Piperazine	GABA agonists
Macrocyclic lactones	Ivermectin	GluCl-potentiators
	Praziquantel	Enhance Ca^{++} permeability
Salicylanilides	Closantel	Proton ionophores

13.1.6. Uses

Anthelminthic drugs have the following uses:

1) They are used in the treatment of intestinal nematode infection and echinococcosis.
2) They are the drugs of choice in the treatment of *Schistosoma japonicum*, (blood fluke), *S. falciolopsiasis* (intestinal flukes), *S. clonorchiasis* (Chinese liver fluke), and *S. opisthorchosis* (liver fluke).
3) They are used in veterinary practice for controlling endoparasite and exoparasite in domestic animals.
4) They are the drugs of choice in the treatment of hookworm, pinworm and roundworm infestations.

13.1.7. Adverse Effects

Common side effects of anthelminthic drugs include dizziness, drowsiness, headache, sweating, dryness of mouth and eyes, and ringing in ears.

Rare side effects of anthelminthic drugs include loss of appetite, diarrhoea, nausea, vomiting, or abdominal cramps.

Serious side effects include fever, chills, confusion, extreme weakness, hallucinations, severe diarrhoea, nausea or vomiting, skin rashes, low back pain, dark urine, blurred vision, seizures, and jaundice.

13.1.8. Important Products

The following drugs are studied in detail:

1) Diethylcarbamazine citrate,
2) Thiabendazole,
3) Mebendazole,
4) Albendazole,
5) Niclosamide,
6) Oxamniquine,
7) Praziquantel, and
8) Ivermectin.

13.1.8.1. Diethylcarbamazine Citrate

DEC is an anthelmintic used as a citrate for treating filariasis, specifically in invasions of *Wucheria bancrofti* or Loa loa.

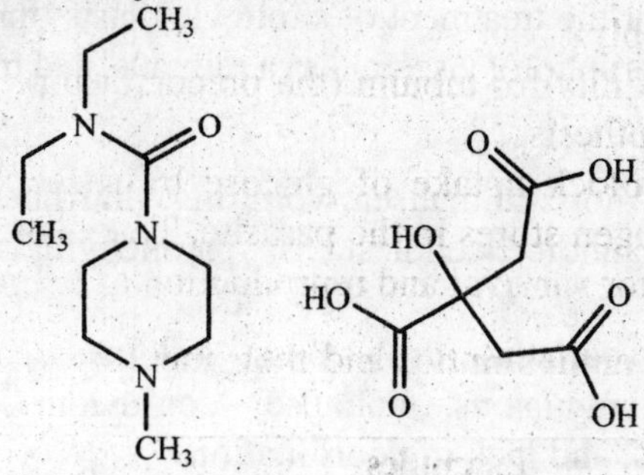

Diethylcarbamazine citrate

Synthesis

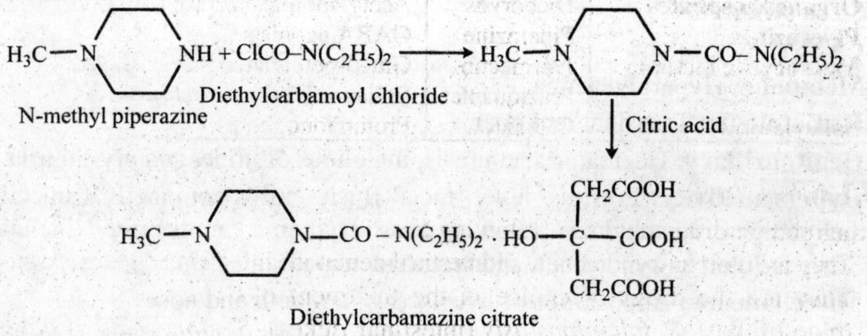

Mechanism of Action

DEC is presumed to sensitise the microfilariae to phagocytosis. A study revealed that its activity against *Brugia malayi* microfilariae depends on inducible nitric-oxide synthase and COX pathway. It confirmed the important role of arachidonic acid metabolic pathway in diethylcarbamazine's mechanism of action *in vivo* and showed that apart from its effects on 5-lipoxygenase pathway, it also targets the cyclooxygenase pathway and COX-1.

Uses

DEC is used for treating round worm infestation (ascariasis) and filarial infections like onchocerciasis (river blindness) and lymphatic filariasis. It is also used in loiasis (infection due to Loa loa) and tropical eosinophilia.

Adverse Effects

Major and minor side effects for DEC include fever, tender, swollen glands in neck, skin rash, visual disturbances, nausea, and dizziness.

13.1.8.2. Thiabendazole

Thiabendazole is a 2-substituted benzimidazole that was first introduced in 1962. It is active against various nematodes and is the drug of choice in the treatment of strongyloidiasis.

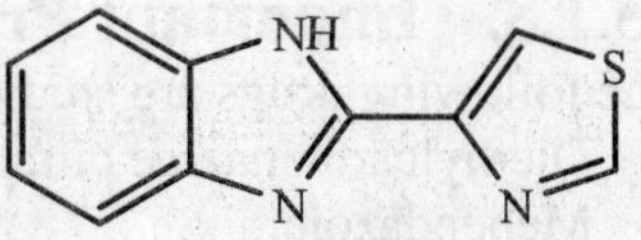

Thiabendazole

Mechanism of Action

The exact mode of action of thiabendazole on the parasite is not yet clear; however, it is presumed to inhibit the helminth-specific enzyme, i.e., fumarate reductase.

Uses

Thiabendazole is used for the treatment of strongyloidiasis (threadworm), cutaneous larva migrans (creeping eruption), visceral larva migrans, and trichinosis.

Adverse Effects

1) **Gastrointestinal:** Anorexia, nausea, vomiting, diarrhoea, epigastric distress, abdominal pain, jaundice, cholestasis, parenchymal liver damage, and hepatic failure.
2) **CNS:** Dizziness, weariness, drowsiness, giddiness, headache, numbness, hyperirritability, convulsions, collapse, confusion, depression, floating sensation, weakness, and lack of coordination.
3) **Special Senses:** Tinnitus, abnormal sensation in eyes, xanthopsia, blurred vision, reduced vision, drying of mucous membranes (mouth, eyes, etc.), and Sicca syndrome.
4) **CVS:** Hypotension.
5) **Metabolic:** Hyperglycaemia.
6) **Hematologic:** Transient leukopenia.
7) **Genitourinary:** Haematuria, enuresis, malodour of urine, and crystalluria.
8) **Hypersensitivity:** Pruritus, fever, facial flush, chills, conjunctival injection, angioedema, anaphylaxis, skin rashes, erythema multiforme (including Stevens-Johnson syndrome), and lymphadenopathy.
9) **Miscellaneous:** Appearance of live ascaris in mouth and nose.

13.1.8.3. Mebendazole

Mebendazole is a benzimidazole which interferes with the metabolism of carbohydrates and inhibits the polymerisation of microtubules.

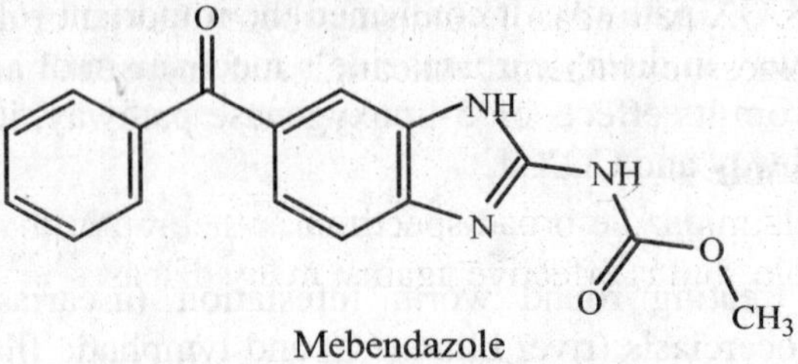

Mebendazole

Synthesis

Nitration of 4-chlorobenzophenone with nitric acid at less than 5°C temperature yields 4-chloro-3-nitrobenzophenone, which when heated at 125°C in a solution of ammonia in methanol gives 4-amino-3-nitrobenzophenone (as its chlorine atom is replaced with an amino group). On reducing the nitro groups of 4-amino-3-nitrobenzophenone with hydrogen using palladium on carbon as a catalyst yields 3,4-diaminobenzophenone, which on reacting with N-methoxycarbonyl-S-methylthiourea (prepared by reacting methyl chloroformate with S-methylthiourea) gives mebendazole.

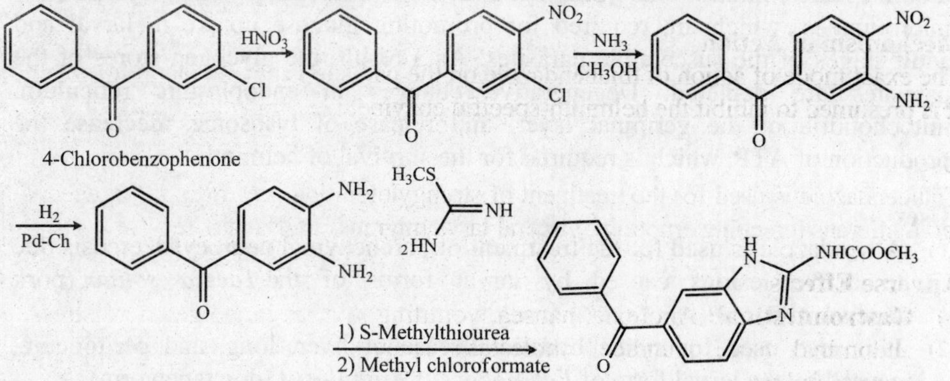

Mechanism of Action

Mebendazole causes degenerative alterations in the tegument and intestinal cells of the worm. It does so by diminishing the parasite's energy production, and causing immobilisation and death. It binds to the colchicine-sensitive site of tubulin, and inhibits its polymerisation or assembly into cytoplasmic microtubules, which are required for promoting glucose uptake in larval and adult stages of the susceptible parasites. As a result, the glycogen stores of the parasites are depleted. Degenerative changes in endoplasmic reticulum, mitochondria of the germinal layer, and release of lysosomes decreases the production of ATP, which is required for the survival of helminth.

Uses

Mebendazole is a broad spectrum anthelmintic, used for treating whipworm infestation (trichuriasis), round worms (ascariasis) infestation, tape worms (taeniasis) infestation, threadworms (stronglyloidiasis) infestation, river blindness (onchocerciasis), hookworms (uncinariasis) infestation, guinea worms (dracantiasis) infestation, and capillaria infection.

Adverse Effects

Common side effects of mebendazole include abdominal pain, diarrhoea, slight headache, fever, dizziness, exanthema, urticarial, and angioedema.

13.1.8.4. Albendazole

Albendazole is a benzimidazole broad-spectrum anthelmintic that is structurally related to mebendazole, and is effective against many diseases.

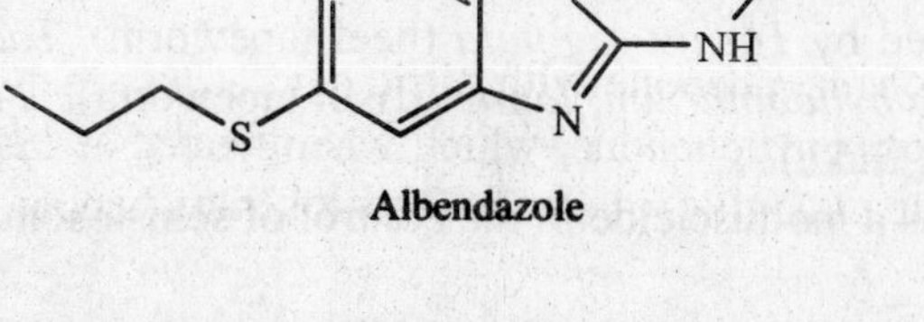

Albendazole

Mechanism of Action

Albendazole causes degenerative alterations in the tegument and intestinal cells of the worm. It does so by diminishing the parasite's energy production, and causing immobilisation and death. It binds to the colchicine-sensitive site of tubulin, and inhibits its polymerisation or assembly into cytoplasmic microtubules, which are required for promoting glucose uptake in larval and adult stages of the susceptible parasites. As a result, the glycogen stores of the parasites are depleted. Degenerative changes in endoplasmic reticulum, mitochondria of the germinal layer, and release of lysosomes decrease the production of ATP, which is required for the survival of helminth.

Uses

1) Albendazole is used for the treatment of parenchymal neurocysticercosis due to active lesions caused by larval forms of the *Taenia solium* (pork tapeworm).
2) It is also used for cystic hydatid disease of liver, lung, and peritoneum, caused by the larval form of *Echinococcus granulosus* (dog tapeworm).

Adverse Effects

1) Albendazole may cause dizziness, headache, fever, nausea, vomiting, or temporary hair loss.
2) It may also cause persistent sore throat, severe headache, seizures, vision problems, jaundice, dark urine, stomach pain, easy bruising, mental/mood changes, very stiff neck, and change in amount of urine.
3) Elevation of liver enzymes during treatment is a common side effect.
4) Allergic reactions can also occur.
5) In rare cases, it may cause bone marrow suppression, agranulocytosis, or aplastic anaemia .

13.1.8.5. Niclosamide

Niclosamide is used for the treatment of most tapeworm infections. Helminths (worms) are multicellular organisms that infect humans and cause a broad range of diseases.

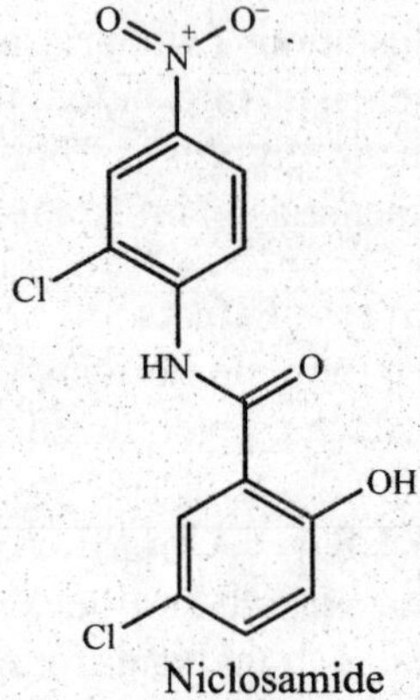

Niclosamide

Mechanism of Action

Niclosamide kills the tapeworms on contact. Adult worms (but not ova) are rapidly killed due to uncoupling of oxidative phosphorylation or stimulation of ATPase activity. The killed worms are either passed in the stool or destroyed in the intestines. Niclosamide may also act as a molluscicide by binding to and damaging DNA.

Uses

1) Niclosamide is used for the treatment of tapeworm and intestinal fluke infections caused by *Taenia saginata* (beef tapeworm), *Taenia solium* (pork tapeworm), *Diphyllobothrium latum* (fish tapeworm), *Fasciolopsis buski* (large intestinal fluke).
2) It is also used as a molluscicide in the control of schistosomiasis.

Adverse Effects

Common side effects of niclosamide include abdominal or stomach cramps or pain, diarrhoea, loss of appetite, nausea, vomiting, dizziness or lightheadedness, drowsiness, itching of rectal area, skin rash, and unpleasant taste.

13.1.8.6. Oxamniquine

Oxamniquine is an anthelmintic with schistosomicidal activity against *Schistosoma mansoni*. It causes the worms to shift from the mesenteric veins to the liver, wherein the male worms are retained, and the female worms return to the mesentery, but no longer release eggs.

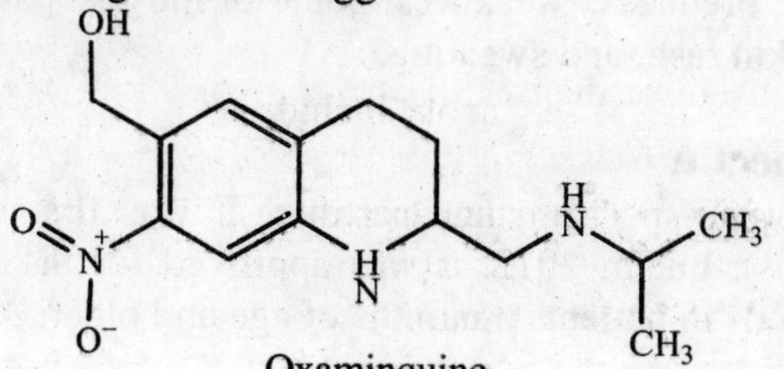

Oxaminquine

Mechanism of Action

Oxamniquine causes an irreversible inhibition of nucleic acid metabolism of the parasites. It is hypothetically believed that the drug is activated when it is converted by schistosome sulfotransferase enzyme into an ester (maybe acetate, phosphate, or sulfate), which spontaneously dissociates. The resulting electrophilic reactant causes alkylation of schistosome DNA.

Uses

Oxamniquine is used for the treatment of schistosomiasis caused by *Schistosoma mansoni*.

Adverse Effects

Common side effects of oxamniquine include allergic reactions (swelling of lips, tongue or face, breathlessness, closing of throat, or hives), headache, dizziness, or drowsiness, abdominal pain, decreased appetite, and vomiting.

13.1.8.7. Praziquantel

Praziquantel is an anthelmintic that is used in most schistosome and many cestode infestations.

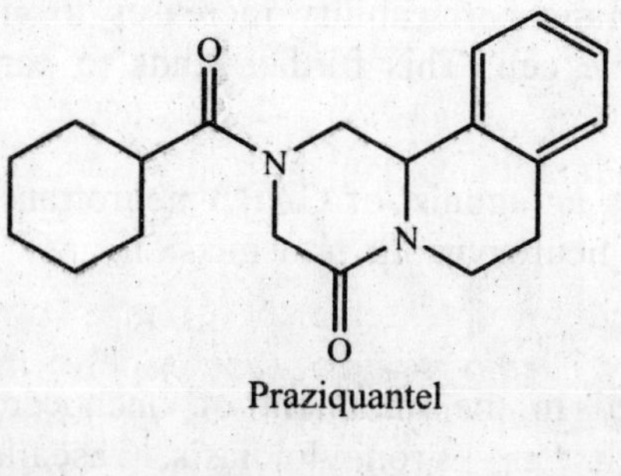

Praziquantel

Mechanism of Action

Praziquantel causes severe spasms and paralysis of the worms' muscles due to rapid Ca^{2+} influx inside the schistosome. Praziquantel also causes morphological alterations, followed by an increased exposure of schistosome antigens at the parasite surface. Then, the worms are either completely destroyed in the intestine or are passed in the stool.

Uses

Praziquantel is used for the treatment of infections due to all species of schistosoma.

Adverse Effects

Common side effects of praziquantel include headache, dizziness, stomach pain or upset, nausea, tiredness, weakness, joint or muscle pain, loss of appetite, vomiting, fever, skin rash, and sweating.

13.1.8.8. Ivermectin

Ivermectin is a broad-spectrum anti-parasite. It was first used against worms (except tapeworms); but in 2012, it was approved for the topical treatment of head lice infestations in patients 6 months of age and older.

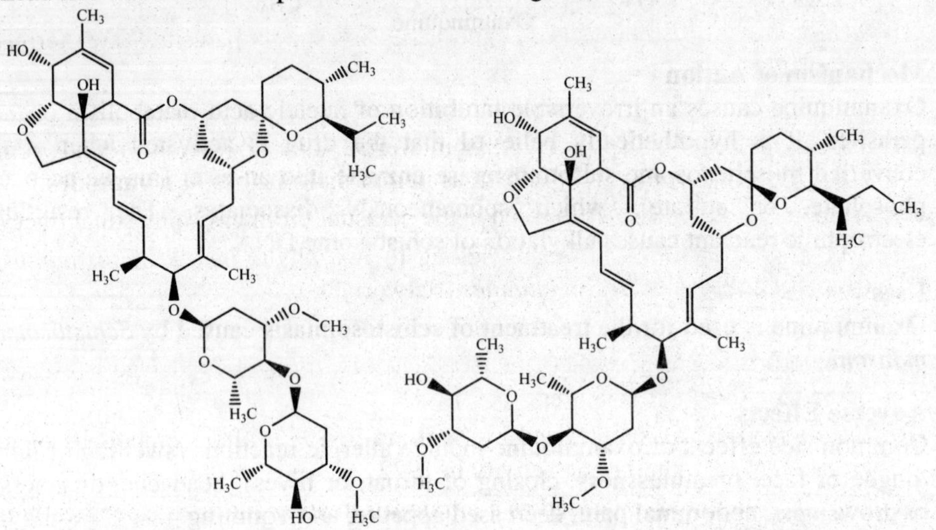

Ivermectin

Mechanism of Action

Ivermectin binds selectively and with high affinity to glutamate-gated chloride ion channels in invertebrate muscle and nerve cells of the microfilaria. As a result, the cell membrane permeability increases to chloride ions and causes hyperpolarisation of the cell. This further leads to paralysis and death of the parasite.

Ivermectin also acts as an agonist of GABA neurotransmitter, thus disrupts the GABA-mediated CNS neurosynaptic transmission.

Uses

1) Ivermectin is used in the treatment of onchocerciasis, and other worm infestations (such as strongyloidiasis, ascariasis, trichuriasis and enterobiasis).

2) It is suitable for the treatment of intestinal (i.e., non-disseminated) strongyloidiasis caused by *Strongyloides stercoralis.*
3) It is also used for the treatment of onchocerciasis (river blindness) caused by *Onchocerca volvulus.*
4) It is used to treat scabies caused by *Sarcoptes scabiei.*

Adverse Effects

Common side effects of ivermectin include headache, dizziness, muscle pain, nausea, diarrhoea, swelling of hands/ankles/feet, swelling or tenderness of our lymph nodes, itching, and skin rash.

13.2. SUMMARY

The details given in the chapter can be summarised as follows:

1) **Helminthiasis** is an infection caused to human body by helminths.
2) Drugs used to kill or eliminate the intestinal parasites from the body are termed **anthelmintics**.
3) Drugs used to remove or expel the intestinal parasites are termed **vermifuges**.
4) Drugs used to kill the intestinal parasites are termed **vermicides**.
5) The name **vermicide** is derived from worms (like hookworm, roundworm, etc.), which are collectively known as **nematehelminthes** or **nematodes**.
6) Anthelmintics act locally to remove the parasites from gastrointestinal tract.
7) The worm parasites of humans belong to two phyla, i.e., *Nemathelminthes* (round-worms) and *Platyhelminthes* (flatworms).
8) **Niclosamide** was synthesised by **Bayer A.G**. in 1955.
9) **Mebendazole** was introduced in 1971 when **Brugmans** conducted a research on benzimidazole derivatives.
10) **Praziquantel** was synthesised by **Seubert** in 1975, after compounds of its group showed anthelmintic activity in 1972.
11) **DEC** is an anthelmintic used as a citrate for treating filariasis, specifically in invasions of *Wucheria bancrofti* or Loa loa.
12) **Thiabendazole** is a 2-substituted benzimidazole that was first introduced in **1962**.
13) **Mebendazole** is a benzimidazole which interferes with the metabolism of carbohydrates and inhibits the polymerisation of microtubules.
14) **Albendazole** is a benzimidazole broad-spectrum anthelmintic that is structurally related to mebendazole, and is effective against many diseases.
15) **Niclosamide** is used for the treatment of most tapeworm infections.
16) **Oxamniquine** is an anthelmintic with schistosomicidal activity against *Schistosoma mansoni.*
17) **Praziquantel** is an anthelmintic that is used in most schistosome and many cestode infestations.
18) **Ivermectin** is a broad-spectrum anti-parasite. It was first used against worms (except tapeworms).

13.3. EXERCISE

13.3.1. True or False

1) Drugs used to remove or expel the intestinal parasites are termed vermicides.
2) Niclosamide was synthesised by Bayer A.G. in 1955.
3) Thiabendazole is a 2-substituted benzimidazole that was first introduced in 1970.
4) Thiabendazole is a benzimidazole broad-spectrum anthelmintic that is structurally related to mebendazole, and is effective against many diseases.
5) Niclosamide is used for the treatment of most tapeworm infections.

13.3.2. Fill in the Blanks

6) Drugs used to kill the intestinal parasites are termed ________.
7) The worm parasites of humans belong to two phyla, i.e., ________ and ________.
8) Praziquantel was synthesised by ________ in 1975.
9) DEC is an anthelmintic used for treating filariasis, specifically in invasions of ________.
10) Oxamniquine is an anthelmintic with schistosomicidal activity against ________.

Answers

1) False	2) True
3) False	4) False
5) True	6) Vermicides
7) *Nemathelminthes* and *Platyhelminthes*	8) Seubert
9) *Wucheria bancrofti*	10) *Schistosoma mansoni*

13.3.3. Very Short Answer Type Questions

1) Classify benzimidazoles.
2) Enlist the uses of anthelmintics.
3) Give the chemical structure of diethylcarbamazine citrate.
4) Give the mechanism of action of mebendazole.
5) What are the uses of albendazole?
6) How niclosamide acts?
7) Draw the structures of oxamniquine and praziquantel.
8) Give the mechanism of action of ivermectin.

13.3.4. Short Answer Type Questions

1) Discuss the historical background of anthelmintics.
2) Write a short note on any two anthelmintics.
3) Give the syntheses of diethylcarbamazine citrate and mebendazole.
4) Discuss about the mechanism of action and uses of albendazole and niclosamide.
5) Discuss the uses and adverse effects of ivermectin and praziquantel.
6) Give the classification and mechanism of action of anthelmintics.

13.3.5. Long Answer Type Question

1) Write an exhaustive note on anthelmintics.
2) Write about any three synthetic anthelmintics.
3) Discuss the SAR of anthelmintics.

CHAPTER 14

Sulphonamides, Sulfones, and Folate Reductase Inhibitorss

14.1. SULPHONAMIDES

14.1.1. Introduction

Several groups of drugs are derived from **sulphonamides** (or **sulpha drugs**). These are synthetic antimicrobial agents containing sulphonamide group. However, some sulphonamides such as anticonvulsant sultiame lack antibacterial activity. Sulphonamides are used for preventing and treating bacterial infections, diabetes mellitus, oedema, hypertension, and gout. Sulfonylureas and thiazide diuretics are newer groups of drugs that are derived from antibacterial sulphonamides.

Sulphonamide was the first antimicrobial agent which acted against pyrogenic bacterial infections. Its molecular structure resembles to the structure of *p*-Aminobenzoic Acid (PABA), required as a substrate of dihydropteroate synthetase enzyme for synthesising Tetrahydrofolic acid (THF) in bacteria. Metabolic processes in bacteria requiring PABA are inhibited by the sulphonamides derived from sulphanilamide.

Allergies commonly occur on administering sulphonamides. Data shows that the adverse drug reactions related to sulpha antibiotics are 3%; so, they are prescribed cautiously. Sulpha drugs are different from other sulphur-containing compounds (such as sulphates and sulphites) which are not chemically related to sulphonamide group and also do not cause the hypersensitivity reactions caused by sulphonamides. Kernicterus (brain damage due to excess bilirubin) is a potential side effect of sulphonamide as it displaces bilirubin from albumin.

14.1.2. Historical Development

Sulphonamides were the first antimicrobial drugs that paved the way for antibiotic revolution in medicine. The first sulfonamide, trade named **Prontosil**, was a prodrug. Experiments with Prontosil began in **1932** in the laboratories of **Bayer AG**. The Bayer team believed that coal-tar dyes that bind to bacteria and parasites might be used to target harmful organisms in the body. After many unsuccessful trial-and-error works on hundreds of dyes, a team led by **Gerhard Domagk** (physician/researcher) found a dye that worked. It was a red dye, synthesised by Bayer chemist, **Josef Klarer** that remarkably prevents some bacterial infections in mice.

The first official communication about the discovery was not published until **1935**, more than two years after **Klarer** and his research partner, **Fritz Mietzsch** patented the drug. Prontosil was the first discovered medicine that could treat various bacterial infections in human body. It had a strong protective action against infections caused by *Streptococci*, including blood infections, childbed fever, and erysipelas. It has a lesser effect on the infections caused by other cocci. Later it was discovered by a French research team, led by **Ernest Fourneau**, at the Pasteur Institute that prontosil metabolised into two pieces inside the body, releasing **sulfanilamide** (a smaller, colourless, active compound) from the inactive dye portion (**figure 14.1**). This discovery established the concept of bioactivation and dashed the German corporation's dreams of enormous profit; the active molecule sulfanilamide was first synthesised in **1906** and was used in dye-making industries.

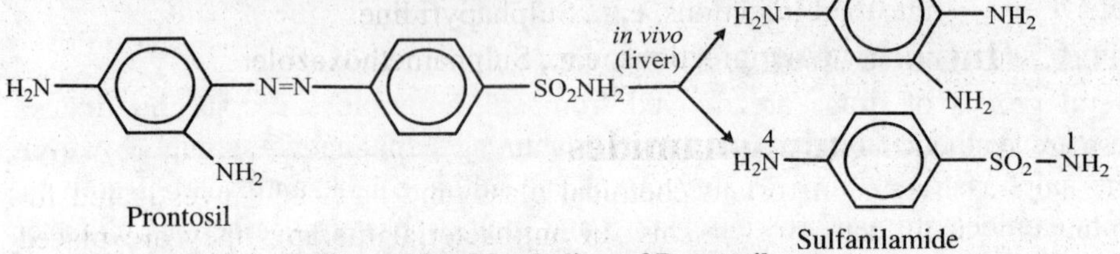

Figure 14.1: Metabolism of Prontosil

For several years in the **late 1930s**, numerous manufacturers produced thousands of tons of myriad forms of sulfa. **Sulfa drugs** being the first and only effective antibiotic available in the years before penicillin, continued to flourish through the early years of World War II. They saved the lives of many patients including Franklin Delano Roosevelt, Jr. (son of President Franklin Delano Roosevelt) (in 1936) and Winston Churchill. Sulfa had a central role in preventing wound infections during the war. American soldiers were issued a first-aid kit containing sulfa pills and powder and were told to sprinkle it on any open wound.

14.1.3. Chemistry

Chemically sulfa drugs are amphoteric. They behave as weak organic acid with pKa ranging from 4.79 to 8.56. They are weakly soluble in water, but their solubility increases at alkaline pH. Their sodium salts are easily soluble in water. Sulfacetamide has a neutral pH and is used in eye infections. The basic structure of sulfanilamide and PABA is given in **figure 14.2**.

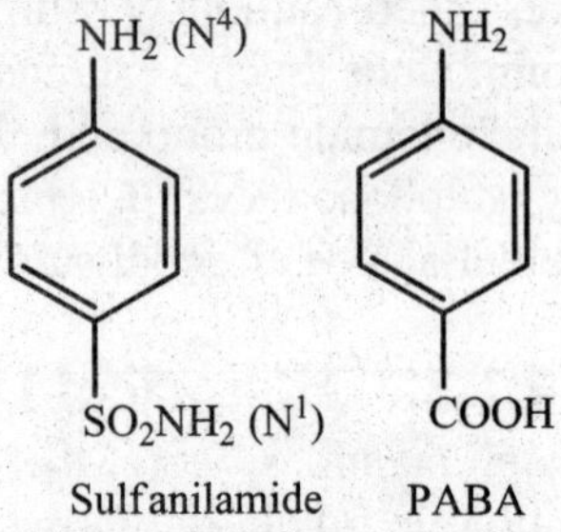

Figure 14.2: Structures of Sulfanilamide and PABA

The nitrogen of amino group at *para* position in sulfanilamide is designated as N^4, and the nitrogen of SO_2NH_2 is designated as N^1. Systemic sulfa drugs are developed by substitution at N^1, and the gut active sulfa drugs are produced by substitution at N^4. Around 5000 compounds are synthesised by substituting at these two positions. Out of these compounds, 30 are clinically significant. Sulfanilamide and its derivatives are popularly known as sulfonamides or sulfa drugs.

14.1.4. Classification

Sulphonamides are classified as follows:

1) **Based on their Duration of Action**
   i) **Short Acting Sulphonamides:** These have 4-8 hours of duration of action, **e.g.,** Sulphadiazine and Sulphamethoxazole.

ii) **Intermediate Acting Sulphonamides:** These have 8-16 hours of duration of action, **e.g.,** Sulphaphenazole and Sulphamethoxazole.

iii) **Long Acting Sulphonamides:** These have 1-7 days of duration of action, **e.g.,** Sulphaphenazole and Sulpha dimethoxine.

2) **Based on their Pharmacological Action**

i) Used in systemic infections, **e.g.,** Sulphadiazine.

ii) Used in eye infections, **e.g.,** Sulphacetamide.

iii) Used in intestinal infections, **e.g.,** Sulphapyridine.

iv) Used in urinary tract infections, **e.g.,** Sulphamethoxazole.

14.1.5. SAR of Sulphonamides

Sulphonamides are an important chemical class, and had been investigated for their activity on infective organisms. In antibacterial therapy, they are placed next to antibiotics, sometimes even preferred over the latter.

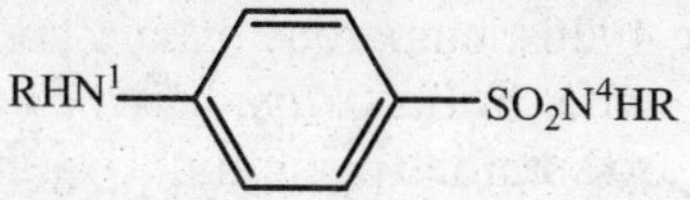

The major features of SAR of sulphonamides include:

1) Sulphanilamide skeleton is the minimum structural requirement for antibacterial activity.
2) Sulphur atom should be directly linked to the benzene ring.
3) In N^1-substituted sulphonamides, nature of the substituent at amide group influences the activity.
4) Substituents that impart electron rich character to SO_2 group increase bacteriostatic activity.
5) Heterocyclic substituents give rise to highly potent derivatives.
6) Sulphonamides containing a single benzene ring at N^1-position are more toxic than the heterocyclic ring analogues.

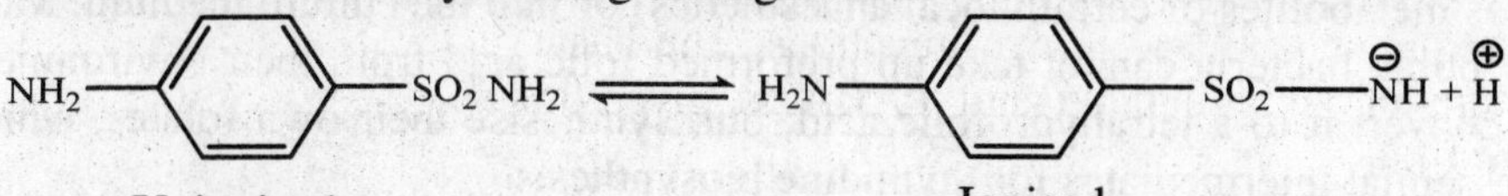

7) The free aromatic amino group should be present *para* to the sulphonamide group. Its substitution at *ortho* or *meta* position will give rise to compounds with no antibacterial activity.
8) Presence of free amino group is essential for activity. Any substitution of amino group either results in prodrug nature or in the loss of activity.
9) The sulphonamides are active in their ionised form. Their maximum activity is observed between 6.6 to 7.4 pKa values.
10) Substitutions in the benzene ring of sulphonamides give rise to inactive compounds.
11) Substitution of free sulfonic acid ($-SO_3H$) for sulphonamide function, destroys the activity; however, replacing with a sulfonic acid group ($-SO_2H$) and acetylation of N_4-position retains the activity.

14.1.6. Mechanism of Action

Sulphonamides are bacteriostatic when administered to humans in achievable doses. They inhibit dihydropteroate synthase enzyme, which is essential for the biosynthesis of folic acid derivatives, and ultimately, thymidine, which is required for DNA. They act by competing at the active site with *p*-aminobenzoic acid (PABA), which is a normal structural component of folic acid derivatives. PABA gets incorporated into the developing tetrahydrofolic acid molecule by enzyme-catalysed condensation with 6-hydroxymethyl-7,8-dihydropterin-pyrophosphate to form 7,8-dihydropteroate and pyrophosphate. Thus, sulphonamides are also classified as antimetabolites (**figure 14.3**).

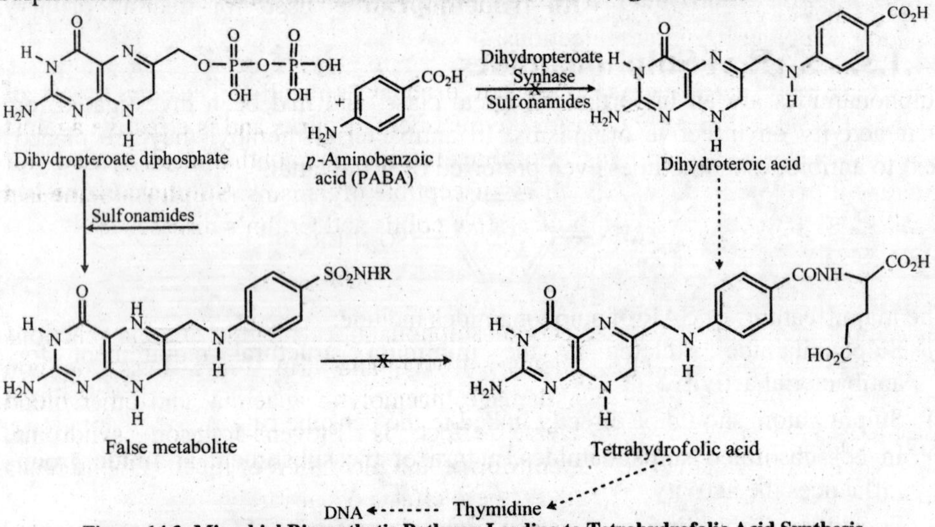

Figure 14.3: Microbial Biosynthetic Pathway Leading to Tetrahydrofolic Acid Synthesis and Major Site of Action of Sulphonamides as well as Site of Action Seen in Some Bacteria Resulting in Incorporation of Sulphonamide as a False Metabolite

The antimicrobial efficacy of sulphonamides can be reversed by adding significant quantities of PABA into the diet (in some multivitamin preparations and as metabolites of certain local anaesthetics) or into the culture medium. Most susceptible bacteria cannot take up preformed folic acid from their environment and convert it to a tetrahydrofolic acid; but, synthesise their own folates, which are essential intermediates for thymidine biosynthesis.

Without thymidine, bacteria fail to multiply. This inhibition is bacteriostatic as well as bactericidal. Humans cannot synthesise folates from component parts, because they lack the required enzymes, including dihydropteroate syntehase, and folic acid is supplied to us in our diet. Consequently, sulphonamides have no similarly lethal effect on human cell growth. The basis for the selective toxicity of sulphonamides thus is clear.

In few bacteria strains, sulphonamides bind to the dihydropteroate diphosphate, and forms an unnatural product which fails to undergo the required glutamic acid condensation. This false metabolite is an enzyme inhibitor, and the net result is inability of the bacteria to multiply as the pre-formed folic acid in their cells is used up and nucleic acid biosynthesis becomes impossible. **Bacteria that are able to take up pre-formed folic acid into their cells are intrinsically resistant to sulphonamides.**

14.1.7. Uses

Sulfisoxazole acetyl along with erythromycin ethylsuccinate is the most popular sulphonamide combination. Sulfisoxazole acetyl is tasteless, and thus is used in pediatric preparations. Its acetyl moiety is removed in the GIT, giving rise to the active sulfisoxazole. Along with the surviving sulfonamides, it has a broad antimicrobial spectrum *in vitro* against gram-negative organisms, but it has a limited clinical use because of bacterial resistance development. Enterobacteriaceae (*Escherichia coli*, *Klebsiella sp.*, and *Proteus sp.*), *Streptococcus pyogenes*, *Streptococcus pneusmoniae*, and *Haemophilus sp* are the susceptible organisms.

Sulphamethoxazole along with trimethoprim is used for treating primary uncomplicated urinary tract infections.

The remaining sulphonamides are not used systemically. The **silver salt of sulphadiazine** is topically used for the treatment of burns and is effective against various bacteria and fungus. **Sulphacetamide** is ophthalmically used for treatment of eye infections caused by susceptible organisms. **Sulphasalazine** is a prodrug used in the treatment of ulcerative colitis and Crohn's disease.

14.1.8. Adverse Effects

The most common adverse effects of sulphonamides include allergic reactions that take the form of rash, photosensitivity, and drug fever. Less common problems are kidney and liver damage, haemolytic anaemia, and other blood problems. Most serious adverse effect is Stevens-Johnson syndrome, characterised by fatal erythema multiforme and ulceration of mucous membranes of eye, mouth and urethra. However, these effects occur rarely.

14.1.9. Important Products

The following drugs are studied in detail:

1) Sulphamethizole, 2) Sulfisoxazole, 3) Sulphamethazine,
4) Sulfacetamide, 5) Sulphapyridine, 6) Sulfamethoxazole,
7) Sulphadiazine, 8) Mafenide acetate, and 9) Sulfasalazine.

14.1.9.1. Sulphamethizole

Sulphamethizole is an antibacterial agent.

Mechanism of Action

Sulphamethizole is a competitive inhibitor of bacterial dihydropteroate synthetase enzyme. It thus prevents the binding of *para*-aminobenzoic acid (PABA) substrate. This inhibited reaction is necessary in these organisms for folic acid synthesis.

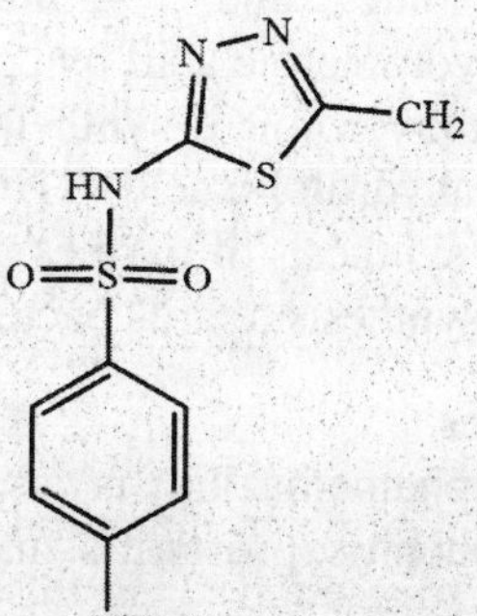

Sulphamethizole

Uses

Sulphamethizole is used in the treatment of gram-negative bacterial infections, gram-positive bacterial infections, and urinary tract infections.

Adverse Effects

Common side effects of sulphamethizole include nausea, vomiting, diarrhoea, vaginitis, dermatitis, allergic reactions, skin rash, red or purple spots under the skin, blood in urine, and swelling of tongue, mouth, or rectum.

14.1.9.2. Sulfisoxazole

Sulfisoxazole is a short-acting sulfonamide antibacterial that shows activity against a wide range of gram-negative and gram-positive organisms.

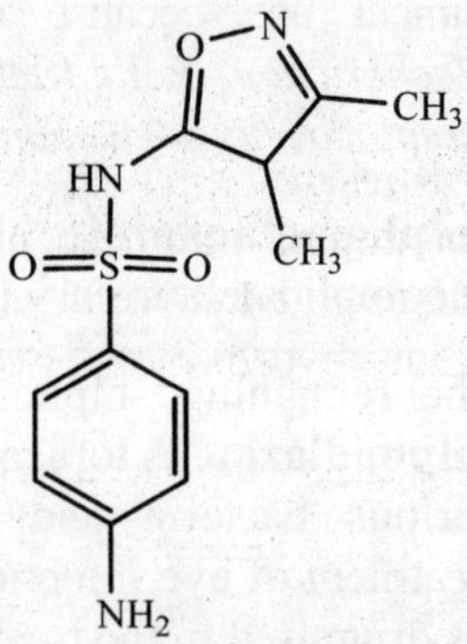

Sulfisoxazole

Mechanism of Action

Sulfisoxazole is a competitive inhibitor of dihydropteroate synthetase enzyme. It inhibits bacterial synthesis of dihydrofolic acid by preventing the condensation of pteridine with *para*-aminobenzoic acid (PABA, a substrate of dihydropteroate synthetase enzyme). This inhibited reaction is necessary in these organisms for folic acid synthesis.

Uses

Sulfisoxazole is used for the treatment of severe, repeated, or long-lasting urinary tract infections, meningococcal meningitis, acute otitis media, trachoma, inclusion conjunctivitis, nocardiosis, chancroid, toxoplasmosis, malaria, and other bacterial infections.

Adverse Effects

Common side effects of sulfisoxazole include stomach pain, bloating, gas, headache, dizziness, ringing in ears, or swollen, black tongue.

14.1.9.3. Sulphamethazine

Sulphamethazine is a sulfanilamide anti-infective agent. Its spectrum of antimicrobial activity is similar to that of other sulfonamides.

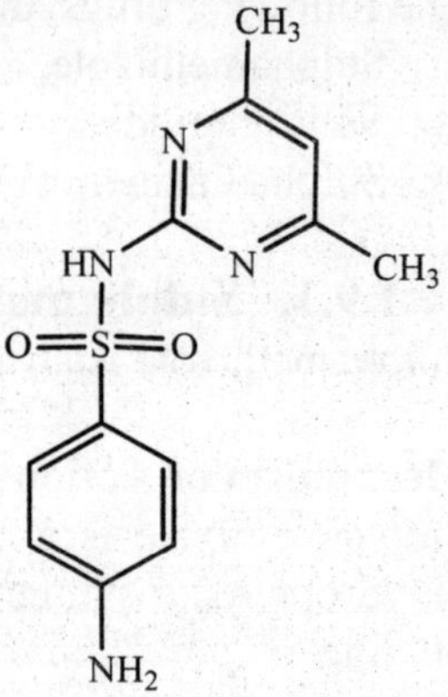

Sulphamethazine

Mechanism of Action

Sulphamethazine inhibits the enzymatic conversion of pteridine and *p*-aminobenzoic acid (PABA) to dihydropteroic acid by competing with PABA for binding to dihydrofolate synthetase, which is an intermediate of tetrahydrofolic acid (THF) synthesis. THF is required for the synthesis of purines and dTMP, and thus inhibition of its synthesis retards bacterial growth.

Uses

Sulphamethazine is used for the treatment of bacterial infections causing bronchitis, prostatitis, and urinary tract infections.

Adverse Effects

Common side effects of sulphamethazine include diarrhoea, dizziness, nausea, head pain, itching, loss of appetite, rash, and sluggishness.

14.1.9.4. Sulfacetamide

Sulfacetamide is a sulphonamide antibacterial agent that is topically used for treating skin infections and orally used for treating urinary tract infections.

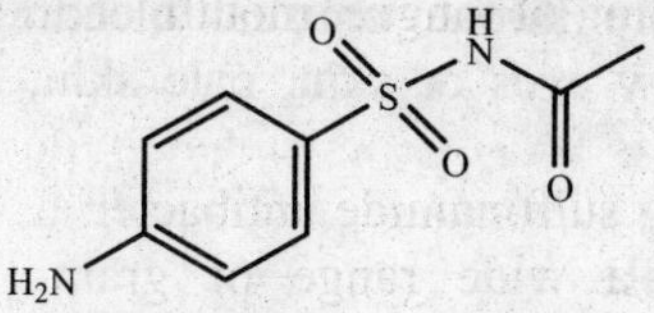
Sulfacetamide

Synthesis

Reaction of 4-aminobenzene sulphonamide with acetic anhydride and subsequent selective, reductive deacylation of the resulting acetamide using a system of zinc-sodium hydroxide yields sulfacetamide.

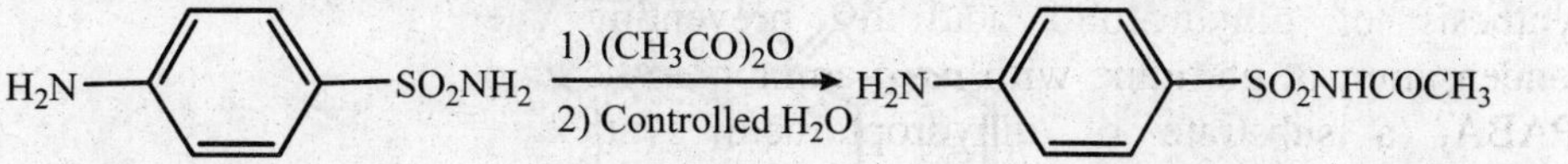

Mechanism of Action

Sulfacetamide is a competitive inhibitor of bacterial *para*-aminobenzoic acid (PABA), which is essential for bacterial growth. This inhibited reaction is necessary in these organisms for folic acid synthesis.

Uses

Sulfacetamide is used for treating bacterial vaginitis, keratitis, acute conjunctivitis, and blepharitis.

Adverse Effects

The adverse effects of sulfacetamide include severe allergic reactions (rash hives; itching; difficulty breathing; tightness in chest; swelling of mouth, face, lips, or tongue), cracked or extremely dry skin, fever, joint pain, severe diarrhoea, sores in mouth, yellowing of skin or eyes, and red, swollen, scaling, or blistered skin

14.1.9.5. Sulphapyridine

Sulphapyridine is an antibacterial, potentially toxic, and previously used to treat certain skin diseases. However, it is no longer prescribed.

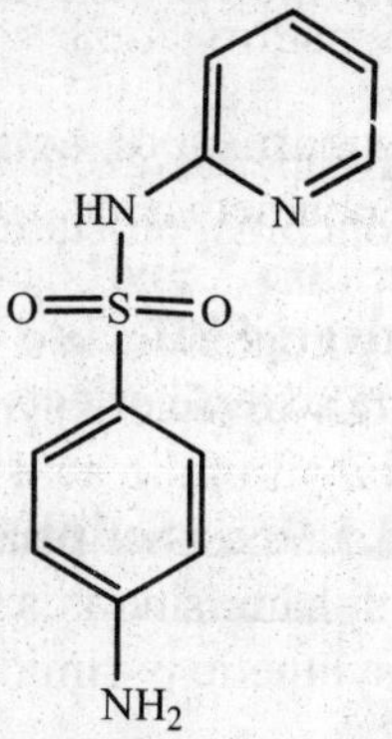
Sulphapyridine

Mechanism of Action

Sulphapyridine is a competitive inhibitor of bacterial dihydropteroate synthetase enzyme. This inhibited reaction is necessary in these organisms for folic acid synthesis by processing the substrate *para*-aminobenzoic acid (PABA). Dihydropteroate synthetase activity is required in the synthesis of folate, which is required for cells to make nucleic acids; and, if DNA molecules cannot be built, the cell cannot divide.

Uses

Sulphapyridine is used for the treatment of dermatitis herpetiformis, benign mucous membrane pemphigoid, and pyoderma gangrenosum

Adverse Effects

More common side effects of sulphapyridine include fever, headache, itching, and skin rash. Less common side effects include aching of joints and muscles, difficulty in swallowing, sore throat, unusual bleeding or bruising, unusual tiredness or weakness, yellow eyes or skin, pale skin, and redness, blistering, peeling or loosening of skin.

14.1.9.6. Sulfamethoxazole

Sulfamethoxazole is a bacteriostatic antibacterial agent that interferes with folic acid synthesis in susceptible bacteria. Its broad spectrum of activity has been limited by the development of resistance.

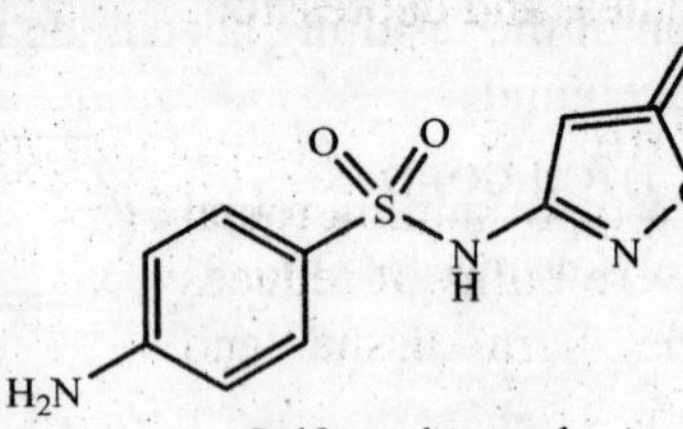

Sulfamethcxazole

Synthesis

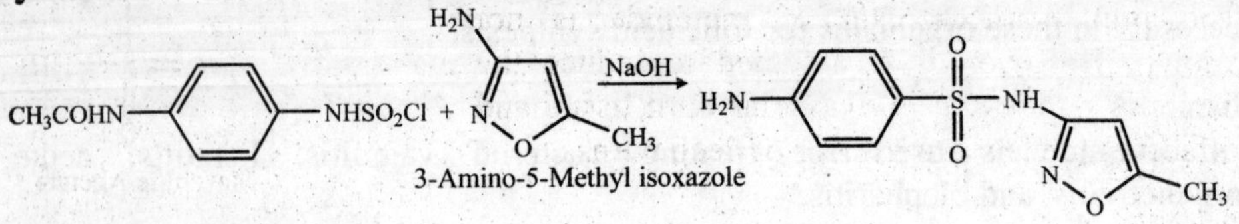

Mechanism of Action

Sulfamethoxazole inhibits the enzymatic conversion of pteridine and *p*-aminobenzoic acid (PABA) to dihydropteroic acid by competing with PABA for binding to dihydrofolate synthetase, which an intermediate of tetrahydrofolic acid (THF) synthesis. THF is essential for the synthesis of purines and dTMP, and inhibition of its synthesis inhibits bacterial growth.

Uses

Sulfamethoxazole is used for the treatment of bacterial infections causing bronchitis, prostatitis, and urinary tract infections.

Adverse Effects

The adverse effects of sulfamethoxazole include fever, itching, rash, and dizziness.

14.1.9.7. Sulphadiazine

Sulphadiazine is a short-acting bacteriostatic and a synthetic pyrimidinyl sulfonamide derivative.

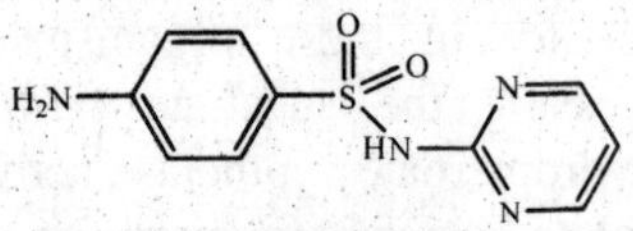

Sulphadiazine

Mechanism of Action

Sulphadiazine is a competitive inhibitor of bacterial enzyme dihydropteroate synthetase, which is required for proper processing of *para*-aminobenzoic acid (PABA), which is essential for folic acid synthesis. This inhibited reaction is necessary in these organisms for folic acid synthesis.

Uses

1) Sulphadiazine can be used for the treatment of upper respiratory tract infections, otitis media, *Meningococcal* meningitis, boils carbuncle, puerperal fever, urinary tract infections, acute dysentery, etc.
2) It is also used for treating infections caused by *Haemolytic streptococcus*, *Meningococci*, *Pneumococcus*, *Neisseria gonorrhoea*, and *E. coli*.

Adverse Effects

The adverse effects of sulphadiazine include anxiety, blurred vision, changes in menstrual periods, chills, cold sweats, coma, confusion, cool, pale skin, decreased sexual ability in males, and depression.

14.1.9.8. Mafenide Acetate

Mafenide is a sulfonamide-type antimicrobial agent that is used to treat severe burns. It reduces bacterial population in the burn tissue and promotes healing of deep burns.

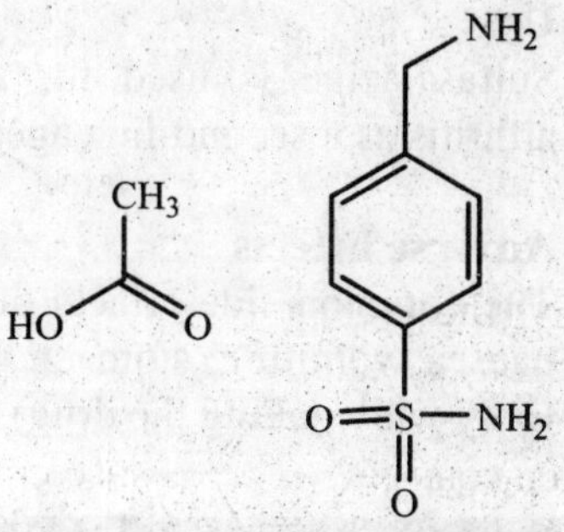

Mafenide Acetate

Mechanism of Action

The precise mechanism of mafenide is not known. However, it is assumed to reduce the bacterial population in avascular burn tissue and promote spontaneous healing of deep burns.

Uses

Mafenide is used as an adjunctive topical antimicrobial agent to control bacterial infection when used under moist dressings over meshed autografts on excised burn wounds.

Adverse Effects

Common side effects of mafenide include rash, redness, blistering, or itching of treated skin; pain or burning of treated skin; or white or pruned appearance of the skin (caused by leaving wound dressings on for long periods of time).

14.1.9.9. Sulfasalazine

Sulfasalazine is a drug that is used in the management of inflammatory bowel diseases. Its activity lies in its metabolic breakdown product, 5-aminosalicylic acid, released in the colon.

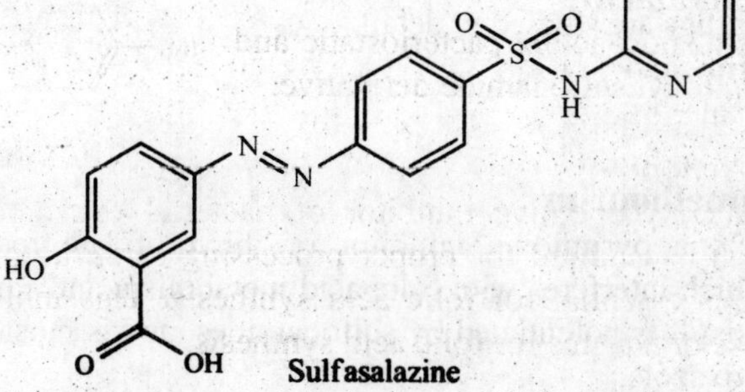

Sulfasalazine

Mechanism of Action

The mode of action of sulfasalazine or its metabolites, 5-aminosalicylic acid (5-ASA) and sulfapyridine (SP), is still unknown, but may be related to anti-inflammatory and/or immunomodulatory properties in animal and *in vitro* models, to its affinity for connective tissue, and/or to the relatively high concentration in serous fluids, liver and intestinal walls, as demonstrated in autoradiographic studies in animals.

In ulcerative colitis, clinical studies with rectal administration of sulfasalazine, SP and 5-ASA have indicated that the major therapeutic action resides in the 5-ASA moiety. Relative contribution of the parent drug and the major metabolites in rheumatoid arthritis is unknown.

Uses

Sulfasalazine is used for the treatment of Crohn's disease and rheumatoid arthritis as a second-line agent.

Adverse Effects

The common side effects of sulfasalazine include decreased appetite, headache, nausea, vomiting, stomach upset and pain, rash, itching, decreased sperm count (only while taking the drug), and dizziness.

14.2. FOLATE REDUCTASE INHIBITORS

14.2.1. Introduction

2,4-Diamino pyrimidine derivatives, like trimethoprim and pyrimethamine, inhibit DHFR enzyme of bacteria and plasmodium, respectively. DHFR converts dihydrofolic acid to tetrahydrofolic acid, which in turn converts into folate cofactors. These drugs inhibit DNA synthesis and cell division.

Sulphonamides and trimethoprim are used in the treatment and prevention of infections. Combination of sulphadiazine and trimethoprim is used in UTIs. Combination of sulphamethoxazole and trimethoprim (cotrimoxazole) is used in bronchitis, middle ear infection, UTI, traveller's diarrhoea, and also in prevention and treatment of Pneumocystis Carinii Pneumonia (PCP).

14.2.2. Important Products

The following drugs are studied in detail:

1) Trimethoprim, and
2) Cotrimoxazole.

14.2.2.1. Trimethoprim

Trimethoprim is a pyrimidine inhibitor of dihydrofolate reductase. It is an antibacterial which interferes with folic acid metabolism and causes a depression of hematopoiesis. It is potentiated by sulfonamides, and is most often used along with sulfamethoxazole.

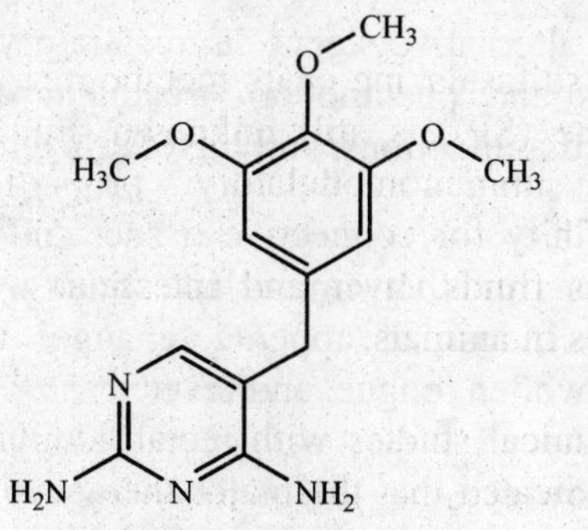

Trimethoprim

Synthesis

3,4,5-Trimethoxybenzaldehyde is condensed with 3-ethoxypropionitrile to give the corresponding benzylidene derivative, which directly reacts with guanidine to yield trimethoprim.

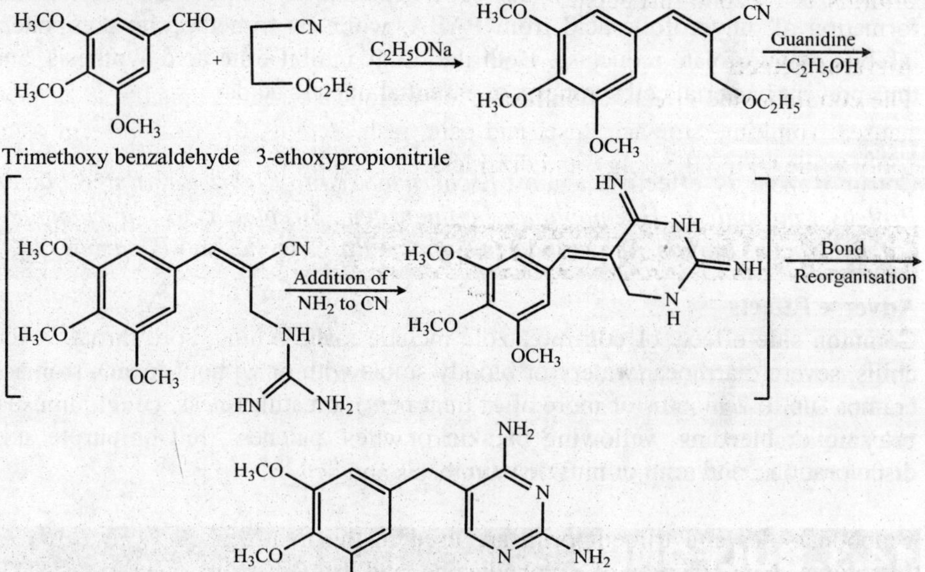

Mechanism of Action

Trimethoprim inhibits dihydrofolate reductase enzyme, and prevents the conversion of dihydrofolic acid (DHF) to tetrahydrofolic acid (THF) in thymidine synthesis pathway. The affinity of its action on bacterial dihydrofolate reductase is thousand times more than that on human dihydrofolate reductase.

Uses

1) Trimethoprim is used for the treatment of UTIs, uncomplicated pyelonephritis (with sulfamethoxazole), and mild acute prostatitis.
2) It is also used as pericoital (with sulfamethoxazole) or continuous prophylaxis in females with recurrent cystitis.
3) It is useful as an alternative in treating asymptomatic bacteriuria during pregnancy (only before the last 6 weeks of pregnancy).

4) Its other uses are alternative agent in respiratory tract infections (otitis, sinusitis, bronchitis and pneumonia), treatment of pneumonia (acute or prophylaxis), Nocardia infections, and traveller's diarrhoea.

Adverse Effects

Common side effects of trimethoprim include itching, rash, diarrhoea, nausea, vomiting, stomach upset, loss of appetite, changes in taste, headache, skin sensitivity to sunlight, swollen tongue, and fever.

14.2.2.2. Cotrimoxazole

Cotrimoxazole is a synthetic antibacterial, and combination of sulfamethoxazole and trimethoprim.

Mechanism of Action

Cotrimoxazole is a bactericidal, and acts by sequential blockade of folic acid enzymes in synthesis pathway. Its sulfamethoxazole component inhibits the formation of dihydrofolic acid from PABA, while its trimethoprim component inhibits dihydrofolate reductase. Both the drugs inhibit folic acid synthesis, and thus prevent bacterial cell synthesis of essential nucleic acids.

Uses

Cotrimoxazole is effective against *Escherichia coli*, *Klebsiella*, *Enterobacter*, *Proteus mirabilis*, *Haemophilus influenzae*, *Streptococcus pneumoniae*, *Staphylococcus aureus*, *Acinetobacter*, *Salmonella*, *Shigella*, and *P. carinii*.

Adverse Effects

Common side effects of cotrimoxazole include rash, itching, sore throat, fever, chills, severe diarrhoea (watery or bloody stools with or without fever), stomach cramps (up to 2 months or more after treatment), breathlessness, cough, unusual bruising or bleeding, yellowing of skin or eyes, paleness, red or purple skin discolorations, and joint or muscle pain.

14.3. SULFONES

14.3.1. Introduction

Studies have suggested that there are about 11 million cases of leprosy in world, of which 60% are in Asia (with 3.5 million in India alone). Diaminodiphenyl sulphone (dapsone) is used for the treatment of infection caused by *Mycobacterium leprae*.

14.3.2. Dapsone

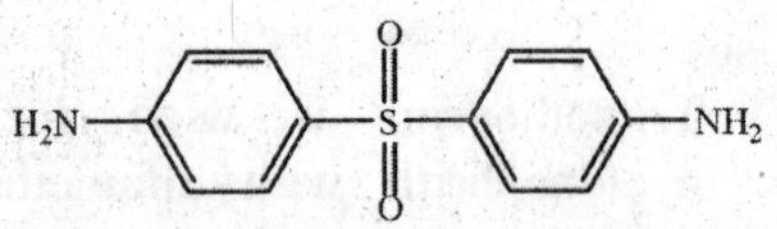

4,4′-Diaminodiphenylsulphone (Dapsone)

Dapsone is a nearly water-insoluble agent that is very weakly basic (pK_a ~ 1.0). Its lack of solubility is somewhat responsible for the occurrence of gastrointestinal irritation. Even if dapsone is poorly soluble, it gets efficiently absorbed from the GIT. Although dapsone is bound to plasma protein (~70%), it is distributed throughout the body.

Synthesis

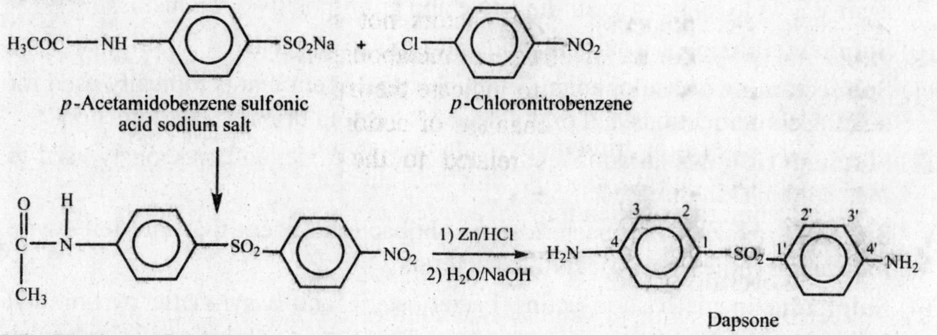

Mechanism of Action

Dapsone acts against bacteria and protozoa by inhibiting the synthesis of dihydrofolic acid through competition with *para*-amino-benzoate for the active site of dihydropteroate synthetase. The anti-inflammatory action of dapsone is unrelated to its antibacterial action and is still not fully understood.

Uses

1) Dapsone is used to control dermatologic symptoms of dermatitis herpetiformis.
2) It is used alone or with other anti-leprosy drugs for leprosy.
3) It is also used to prevent malaria, certain types of arthritis or other inflammatory conditions, or *Pneumocystis Carinii* Pneumonia (PCP).

Adverse Effects

The adverse effects of dapsone include allergic reactions (difficulty in breathing; swelling of lips, tongue, or face; or hives), bluish skin colour, muscle weakness, numbness or tingling, abdominal pain, dark coloured urine or pale coloured stools, and unusual tiredness.

14.4. SUMMARY

The details given in the chapter can be summarised as follows:

1) Several groups of drugs are derived from **sulphonamides** (or **sulpha drugs**). These are synthetic antimicrobial agents containing sulphonamide group.
2) **Sulphonamide** was the first antimicrobial agent which acted against pyrogenic bacterial infections.
3) The first sulfonamide, trade named **Prontosil**, was a prodrug.
4) Chemically sulfa drugs are amphoteric.
5) **Sulfisoxazole acetyl along with erythromycin ethylsuccinate** is the most popular sulphonamide combination.
6) **Sulphamethoxazole along with trimethoprim** is used for treating primary uncomplicated urinary tract infections.
7) The **silver salt of sulphadiazine** is topically used for the treatment of burns and is effective against various bacteria and fungus.
8) **Sulphamethizole** is a competitive inhibitor of bacterial dihydropteroate synthetase enzyme.

9) **Sulfisoxazole** is a short-acting sulfonamide antibacterial that shows activity against a wide range of gram-negative and gram-positive organisms.
10) **Sulphamethazine** is a sulfanilamide anti-infective agent.
11) **Sulfacetamide** is a sulphonamide antibacterial agent that is topically used for treating skin infections and orally used for treating urinary tract infections.
12) **Sulphapyridine** is an antibacterial, potentially toxic, and previously used to treat certain skin diseases.
13) **Sulfamethoxazole** is a bacteriostatic antibacterial agent that interferes with folic acid synthesis in susceptible bacteria.
14) **Sulphadiazine** is a short-acting bacteriostatic and a synthetic pyrimidinyl sulfonamide derivative.
15) **Mafenide** is a sulfonamide-type antimicrobial agent that is used to treat severe burns.
16) **Sulfasalazine** is a drug that is used in the management of inflammatory bowel diseases.
17) **DHFR** converts dihydrofolic acid to tetrahydrofolic acid.
18) **Trimethoprim** is a pyrimidine inhibitor of dihydrofolate reductase.
19) **Cotrimoxazole** is a synthetic antibacterial, and combination of sulfamethoxazole and trimethoprim.
20) **Diaminodiphenyl sulphone** (dapsone) is used for the treatment of infection caused by *Mycobacterium leprae*.
21) **Dapsone** is a nearly water-insoluble agent that is very weakly basic.

14.5. EXERCISE

14.5.1. True or False

1) The first sulfonamide, trade named sulphamethizole, was a prodrug.
2) The silver salt of sulfacetamide is topically used for the treatment of burns.
3) Sulphamethazine is a sulfanilamide anti-infective agent.
4) Sulfisoxazole is a sulfonamide-type antimicrobial agent that is used to treat severe burns.
5) Cotrimoxazole is a pyrimidine inhibitor of dihydrofolate reductase.
6) Dapsone is a nearly water-insoluble agent that is very weakly acidic.

14.5.2. Fill in the Blanks

7) Chemically sulfa drugs are ________.
8) Sulphamethoxazole along with ________ is used for treating primary uncomplicated urinary tract infections.
9) Sulphamethizole is a competitive inhibitor of bacterial ________.
10) Sulphadiazine is a short-acting bacteriostatic and a synthetic ________.
11) DHFR converts dihydrofolic acid to ________.
12) Dapsone is used for the treatment of infection caused by ________.

Answers

1) False
2) False
3) True
4) False
5) False
6) False
7) Amphoteric
8) Trimethoprim
9) Dihydropteroate synthetase enzyme
10) Pyrimidinyl sulfonamide derivative
11) Tetrahydrofolic acid
12) *Mycobacterium leprae*

14.5.3. Very Short Answer Type Questions

1) Classify sulphonamides.
2) Enlist the uses of sulphonamides.
3) Give the chemical structure of sulphamethizole.
4) Give the mechanism of action of sulfisoxazole.
5) What are the uses of sulphamethazine and sulfacetamide?
6) How sulphapyridine acts?
7) Draw the structures of sulfamethoxazole and sulphadiazine.
8) Give the mechanism of action of sulfasalazine.
9) Enlist the uses of trimethoprim and cotrimoxazole.
10) Give the structure of dapsone.

14.5.4. Short Answer Type Questions

1) Discuss the historical background of sulphonamides.
2) Discuss the SAR of sulphonamides.
3) Give the mechanism of action of sulphonamides.
4) Write a short note on any two sulphonamides.
5) Give the syntheses of sulfacetamide and sulfamethoxazole.
6) Discuss about the mechanism of action and uses of sulphapyridine and sulphadiazine.
7) Draw the synthetic pathway of trimethoprim.
8) Give the synthesis, structure, mechanism of action, uses and adverse effects of dapsone.

14.5.5. Long Answer Type Questions

1) Write an exhaustive note on sulphonamides.
2) Write about any three sulphonamides.

CHAPTER 15 Introduction to Drug Design

15.1. DRUG DESIGN

15.1.1. Introduction

In the past few decades, the research and discovery of novel medicinal compounds has stopped. This trend in drug development has increased due to two vital factors; first is the strict empirical and rational approach to drug design and second is the high standards of safety and therapeutic efficacy along with increased cost of research, development and clinical trials.

Drug design or **tailor-made compounds** aim to develop a drug with high chemotherapeutic index and specific action. It is a logical effort to design a drug on a rational basis so that the trial and error approach is minimised. Drug design involves studying the biodynamic of a drug, and the interaction between drug molecules and molecules of the biological objects.

Drug design explains the following:

1) Effects of biological compounds on the basis of molecular interaction in terms of molecular structures or physicochemical properties of the involved molecules.
2) Various processes by which the drugs exert their pharmacological effects.
3) Manner in which the drugs specifically react with the protoplasm to produce a pharmacological response.
4) Manner in which the drugs are modified, detoxicated, metabolised, or eliminated by the organism.
5) Relationship between the biological activities and chemical structure.

Drug design is an integrated whole approach that involves the steps of chemical synthesis, evaluation for activity-spectrum, toxicological studies, drug biotransformation, and study of the formed metabolites, assay procedures, galenical formulation, and bio-pharmaceutics.

Drug design is a random evaluation of synthetic and natural products in bioassay, production of newer drug molecules based on biologically active prototypes of plant or animal origin, synthesis of congeners with biological actions, basic concept of isosterism and bioisosterism, and designing a drug that effectively interacts with a receptor site.

15.1.2. Factors Governing Drug Design

The following factors govern the efficacy towards the evaluation of drug design:

1) Smaller the expenditure of human and material resources involved in the production of a new drug of a particular value, more viable is the program design.

2) Experimental animal and clinical screening operations of the new drugs.
3) Relationships between chemical features and biological properties need to be established retrospectively.
4) QSARs vary based on the nature of evaluation of structure or activity. A relation of structural variables should include steric factors, electronic features of component functional groups, and the whole molecule.
5) The trend to synthesise large number of novel medicinal compounds for exploratory evaluation still succeeds, thus reflecting the creative authenticity and functions of an individualised expression of novelty by a medicinal chemist.
6) Substituting the molecule with functional groups that do not necessarily resemble the metabolites, but undergo bonding interactions with important functional groups of biochemical components of living organisms affords an important basis for exploration.
7) Disease etiologies and various biochemical processes involved prove useful.

15.1.3. Various Approaches Used in Drug Design

The various rational approaches of drug design include the following:

1) **Quantum Mechanical Approach:** Quantum or wave mechanics involve some essential principles derived from fundamental assumptions that effectively describe the natural phenomena. Quantum mechanics satisfactorily explain the properties of protons, neutrons, and electrons. The electronic features of the molecules elicit chemical alterations and form the base of drug molecule phenomena.

2) **Molecular Orbital Approach:** This approach is based on the assumption that electrons in molecules are directly linked to the orbitals engulfing the entire molecule, and this states the molecular orbital theory. The molecular orbital approach shows dependence on electronic charge (as proven by studying three volatile inhalation anaesthetics) and on molecular conformation (as studied with respect to acetylcholine by parameters like bond lengths and torsional angles). Molecular orbital calculations can be done using sophisticated computers, and after result interpretations the molecular structure is established with respect to structure-activity analysis.

3) **Molecular Connectivity Approach:** This approach establishes the presence of structural features like cyclisation, unsaturation, skeletal branching, and presence and position of heteroatom in molecules with a series of numerical indices. **For example,** in the SAR study of amphetamine-type hallucinogenic drugs, an index was found to possess a correlative factor. Molecular connectivity approach has the **limitations** of electronegativity variance between atoms, and non-distinguishable entity of *cis-trans* isomerism.

4) **Linear Free-Energy Approach:** This approach establishes the link between proper selections of physicochemical parameters with a specific biological phenomenon. This correlation, however, does not allow a direct interpretation with regard to molecular structure, but offers a clue towards the selection of candidate molecules for synthesis.

15.1.4. Basic Concepts of Drug Design

Successful drug design is a multi-step, multi-disciplinary and multi-year process. Drug discovery is not a predictable consequence of fundamental basic science; drug design is not just a simple technology of generating drugs for humans based on biological advances; if it were, much better drugs would be available already.

Medicinal chemistry is a science that provides a molecular bridge between the basic science of biology and the clinical science of medicine (analogous to chemistry being the central science between the traditional disciplines of biology and physics).

Drug design may broadly be divided into two phases:
1) Basic concepts about drugs, receptors, and drug-receptor interactions, and
2) Basic concepts about drug-receptor interactions applied to human diseases.

15.1.4.1. First Phase

The first phase of drug design involves the essential building blocks and is divided into the following **three steps**:

Step 1: This step involves studying the properties that convert a molecule into a drug. All drugs may be molecules, but all molecules are not drugs. Drug molecules are small organic molecules (with molecular weight <500gm/mol), **e.g.,** penicillin, acetylsalicylic acid, and morphine.

The geometric, conformational, stereochemical and electronic properties should be controlled if a molecule is going to be emerged as a Drug-Like Molecule (DLM). When a molecule is being designed to be a DLM and a drug, the designer should have the ability to use diverse design tools. Computer-Aided Molecular Design (CAMD) is an important design tool that is available nowadays.

Step 2: This step involves studying the properties that convert a macromolecule into a receptor. All receptors may be macromolecules, but all macromolecules are not receptors. Receptor macromolecules are mostly proteins or glycoproteins. Certain properties should be present if a macromolecule is going to be a druggable target. The receptor macromolecule should be connected with the disease being studied, but not integral to the normal biochemistry of a wide range of processes.

Step 3: This step involves designing a specific DLM to fit into a particular druggable target. Many molecules are taken into consideration during this task, but only one or two emerge out as promising starting points around which the design process is preceded further. This prototype compound is the **lead compound**.

15.1.4.2. Second Phase

After putting in place the basics of drug design, the drug designer focuses on connecting a drug-receptor interaction to a human disease; and this is the objective of this phase. The second phase of drug design requires an understanding of biochemistry and molecular pathology of the disease being treated.

This phase of drug development connects the drug-receptor interactions to human diseases, and is divided into the following **three approaches**:

1) Know how the body's endogenous control systems are manipulated,
2) Know how the body's endogenous macromolecules are manipulated, and
3) Know how a harmful exogenous substance is inactivated.

A researcher is able to design drugs only if he/she has a full understanding of the three steps of first phase and the three approaches of second phase.

15.2. QSAR (QUANTITATIVE STRUCTURE-ACTIVITY RELATIONSHIP)

15.2.1. Introduction

Corwin Hansch in the **early 1960s**, extended the concept of Linear Free Energy Relationships (LFER) to describe the efficacy of a biologically active molecule. This approach quantitatively related the structure of a compound to its activity and the resulting equations were named **Quantitative Structure-Activity Relationships (QSAR)** or **Quantitative Structure-Property Relationships (QSPR)**. QSAR studies are in part retrospective and predictive, since a training set of compounds of known pharmacological activity should be first established.

This method increases the probability of finding active compounds among the eventually synthesised ones, thus keeping synthetic and screening efforts within reasonable limits in relation to the success rate.

15.2.2. Physicochemical Parameters Used in QSAR

QSAR studies are conducted in groups of related compounds. However, QSAR studies on structurally diverse sets of compounds are more common. In both the cases, a wide range of parameters should be considered.

15.2.2.1. Partition Coefficient (P)

In order to reach its site of action a drug has to pass through a few biological membranes. Therefore, organic medium/aqueous system partition coefficients (P) are the parameters considered for measuring the ease of movement of the drug through these membranes. Accuracy of the drug activity correlation with partition coefficients depends on the solvent system used as a membrane model. **For example,** consistent results for drugs absorbed in the GIT can be obtained using n-octanol; consistent correlations for drugs crossing the blood-brain barrier can be obtained using less polar solvents (like olive oil); and more consistent values for buccal absorption (soft tissues in the mouth) can be obtained using more polar solvents (like chloroform).

Nature of the relationship between partition coefficient (P) and drug activity depends on the range of P values obtained for the compounds used. If the range is small, the results are expressed as a straight line equation:

$$\log (1/C) = k_1 \log P + k_2$$

Where, k_1 and k_2 = Constants.

This equation shows a linear relationship between the drug activity and its partition coefficient. If the range P value is large, the graph of log 1/C *versus* log P yields a parabolic form (**figure 15.1**) with a maximum value (log P^0).

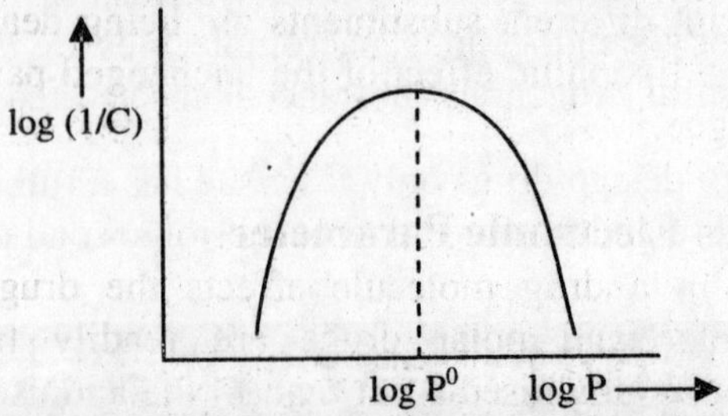

Figure 15.1: Parabolic Plot for log (1/C) against logP

This maximum value indicates that an optimum balance exists between aqueous and lipid solubility for maximum biological activity. Below P^0, the drug will not enter the membrane; whereas above P^0, the drug will leave the membrane. Log P^0 represents optimum partition coefficient for biological activity. This indicates that analogues with partition coefficients near this optimum value are the most active and can be further investigated. **Hansch *et al.*** showed that these parabolic relationships can be represented accurately as:

$$\log (1/C) = -k_1(\log P)^2 + k_2 \log P + k_3 \quad \text{..... (1)}$$

Where, k_1, k_2 and k_3 = Constants determined by regression analysis.

15.2.2.2. Lipophilic Substituent Constants (π)

Lipophilic substituent constants (or **hydrophobic substituent constants**) represent the contribution a group makes to the partition coefficient and were defined by **Hansch *et al.*** by the equation:

$$\pi = \log P_{RH} - \log P_{RX} \quad \text{..... (2)}$$

Where, P_{RH} and P_{RX} = Partition coefficients of standard compound and its mono-substituted derivative, respectively.

However, in the presence of several substituents, the π value for the compound is the sum of π values of each separate substituent. The π value for a specific substituent varies with the structural environment of the substituent. As a result, average values or the values relevant to the type of structure being investigated can be used for determining the activity relationships. It also depends on the solvent system used to determine the partition coefficients. The π values also depend on the solvent system used to determine the partition coefficients used in their calculation.

Most π values are determined using the n-octanol/water system. A positive π value indicates that a substituent's lipophilicity is higher than that of hydrogen and so it will increase the compound concentration in the n-octanol layer and in the lipid material of biological systems. On the contrary, a negative π value indicates that a substituent's lipophilicity is lower than that of hydrogen and so it will increase the compound concentration in aqueous media of biological systems.

Biological activity π relationships having high regression constants and low standard deviations demonstrate that the substituents are important in determining the drug's lipophilic character. Lipophilic constants are used when a series of analogues with different substituents are being dealt. This is based on the assumption that the lipophilic effect of the unchanged part of the structure is similar for each analogue.

15.2.2.3. Hammet's Electronic Parameter

Electron distribution in a drug molecule affects the drug's distribution and activity. The non-polar and polar drugs are readily transported through membranes when in their unionised form than in their ionised forms. When the drug reaches its target site, the electron distribution in its structure controls the type of bond it will form with the target; the bond formed influences the drug's biological activity. **Hammett** made the first attempt to quantify the electronic effects of groups on the physicochemical properties of compounds.

Hammet substitution constant (σ_X) is a measure of a substituent's (i.e., the functional moiety) ability to either withdraw or donate electrons. It may be determined by measuring the dissociation of a series of benzoic acid substituted derivatives in relation to the dissociation of pure benzoic acid itself.

However, since benzoic acid is a weak-acid, it gets partially ionised in an aqueous medium as follows:

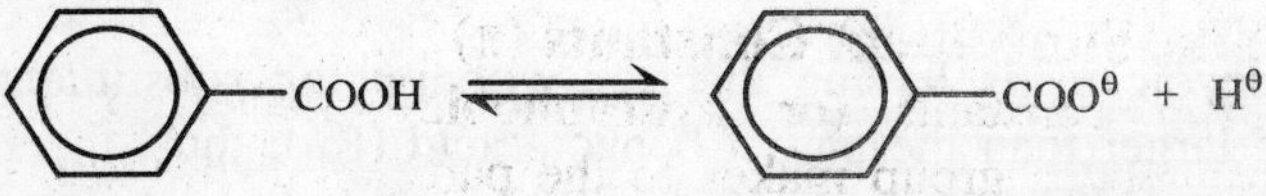

Explanation

An equilibrium is attained between the ionised and non-ionised forms. Thus, the relative proportion of these two distinct species is termed the **dissociation** or **equilibrium constant**, which is designated by $\mathbf{K_H}$ (the subscript H indicates that no substituents are attached to the aromatic nucleus, i.e., the phenyl ring).

$$\therefore\ K_H = \frac{[PhCOO^{\theta}]}{[PhCOOH]} \qquad \text{..... (3)}$$

When a substituent is strategically positioned on the aromatic (phenyl) ring, the equilibrium undergoes an imbalance. At this junction two situations may arise due to the fact that an electron-withdrawing moiety and an electron-releasing (donating) moiety could be present in the aromatic ring, thereby giving rise to different electronic status to the 'Aryl Nucleus'.

Electron-Withdrawing Moiety

A large number of electron-withdrawing groups, **e.g.,** $-NO_2$, –CN, –COOH, –COOR, $-CONH_2$, –CONHR, $-CONR_2$, –CHO, –COR, $-SO_2R$, and –NO, permit the aromatic ring (with π-electron cloud on its top and bottom) to have a stronger electron-withdrawing and stabilising influence on the carboxylate anion. Hence, the overall equilibrium influences and shifts towards the ionised form, making the substituted weak benzoic acid a much stronger acid. This so obtained substituted strong benzoic acid shows a larger K_X value (the subscript X indicates the substituent on the aromatic nucleus) (**figure 15.2**).

Electron-Donating Moiety

A large number of electron-donating groups, **e.g.,** –R, –Ar, –F, –Cl, –I, –Br, –SH, –SR, $–O^-$, $–S^-$, $–NR_2$, –NHR, $–NH_2$, –NHCOR, –OR, –OH, and –OCOR, influence and make the aromatic ring too less stable to stabilise the carboxylate ion. Thus, the equilibrium shifts towards the left, and ultimately forms a much weaker acid with a smaller K_X value (**figure 15.2**).

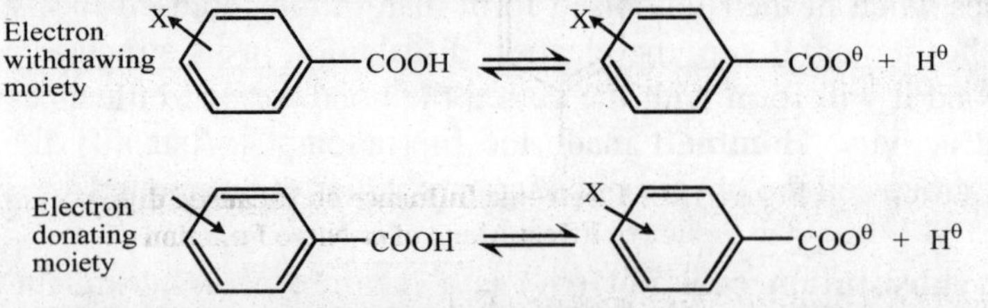

Figure 15.2: Influence of Substituent Moiety X on the Status of Equilibrium in Reaction

Now, the Hammett substitution constant with reference to a specific substituent (X) is defined as follows:

$$\sigma_X = \log \frac{K_X}{K_H} = \log K_X - \log K_H$$

Therefore, the benzoic acids having electron-withdrawing substituents should exhibit K_X values larger than the parent benzoic acid (K_H); thus, the **Hammett substitution constant (σ_X) for electron-withdrawing substituents should always have a positive value**. The benzoic acid having electron-donating substituents should exhibit K_X values smaller than the parent benzoic acid; therefore, the **Hammett substitution constant for an electron-donating substituent should always be a negative value**.

The Hammett substitution constant takes cognizance of two vital and critical suppcrtive effects, i.e., resonance effect and inductive effect. As a result, the value of σ_X with respect to a specific substituent depends on whether the attached substituent is located at *meta-* or at *para-*position. Such particular substituent is usually indicated with the symbol σ followed by the subscript m or p.

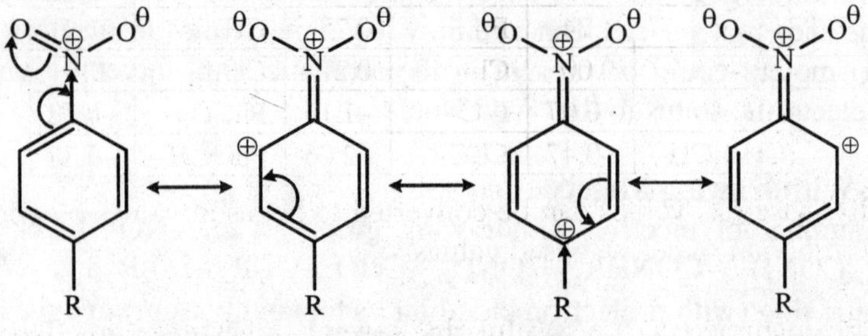

Figure 15.3: Electronic Influence on R caused due to Resonance and Inductive Effects of *p*-Nitro Function

For example, the nitro ($-NO_2$) substituent on benzene nucleus has two distinct σ values, namely $\sigma_m = 0.71$ and $\sigma_p = 0.78$. It is observed that the electron-withdrawing strength at *para*-position is due to the combined effect of inductive and resonance effects, thus justifying the greater value of σ_p (**figure 15.3**).

Similarly, the electron-withdrawing strength at *meta*-position is due to the inductive effect of the substituent ($-NO_2$ group) (**figure 15.4**).

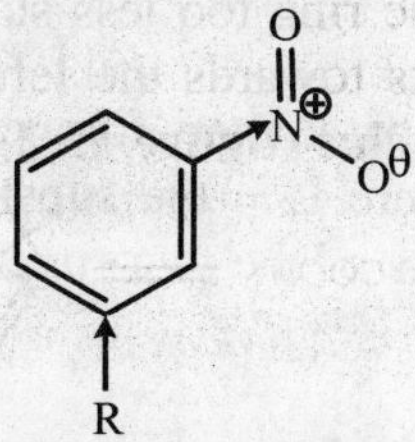

Figure 15.4: Electronic Influence on R caused due to Inductive Effect Alone of *m*-Nitro Function

15.2.2.4. Taft Steric Parameter (E_s)

Taft steric parameter (E_s) was the first parameter used to demonstrate the relationship between the shape and size (bulk) of a drug, the dimensions of its target site, and its activity. It was followed by Charton's steric parameter (ν), Verloop's steric parameters, Molar Refractivity (MR), etc.

Taft used the relative rate constants of the acid-catalysed hydrolysis of α-substituted methyl ethanoates to define the steric parameter because it had been shown that these hydrolysis rates were dependent on steric factors. Taft used methyl ethanoate as the standard and defined E_s as:

$$E_s = \log \frac{k_{(XCH_2COOCH_3)}}{k_{(CH_3COOCH_3)}} = \log k_{(XCH_2COOCH_3)} - \log k_{(CH_3COOCH_3)} \quad \text{..... (4)}$$

Where,

k = Rate constant of the appropriate hydrolysis

Value of $E_s = 0$ when, $X = CH_3$.

The E_s values (**table 15.1**) obtained for a group using the hydrolysis data are assumed to be applicable to other structures containing that group.

Table 15.1: Examples of the Taft Steric Parameter (E_s)

Groups	E_s	Groups	E_s	Groups	E_s
H–	1.24	F–	0.78	CH_3O–	0.69
CH_3–	0.00	Cl–	0.27	CH_3S–	0.19
C_2H_5–	–0.07	F_3C–	–1.16	$PhCH_2$–	–0.38
$(CH_3)_2CH$–	–0.47	Cl_3C–	–2.06	PhOCH–	–0.33

The methyl based E_s values can be converted to H based values by adding –1.24 to the corresponding methyl based values.

Taft steric parameters are useful in several investigations. They have a **disadvantage** of getting determined experimentally. This limits the number of values recorded in the literature.

15.2.2.5. Verloop's Steric Parameter

The unique revelation and wisdom of a latest computer researched programme, **Sterimol** has helped in measuring the steric factor accurately. It relies on various standard physical parameters, such as Van der Waals radii, bond lengths, bond angles, and the proposed substituent under examination to assist in calculating the desired steric substituent values (otherwise known as Verloop steric parameters). However, the Verloop steric parameters can be accurately measured for any substituent.

For example, the Verloop steric parameters for a carboxylic acid moiety are duly measured as in **figure 15.5**, where L = the substituent length, and B_1 to B_4 = longitudinal and horizontal radius of the two functional groups, i.e., carboxyl (–COOH) and hydroxyl (–OH).

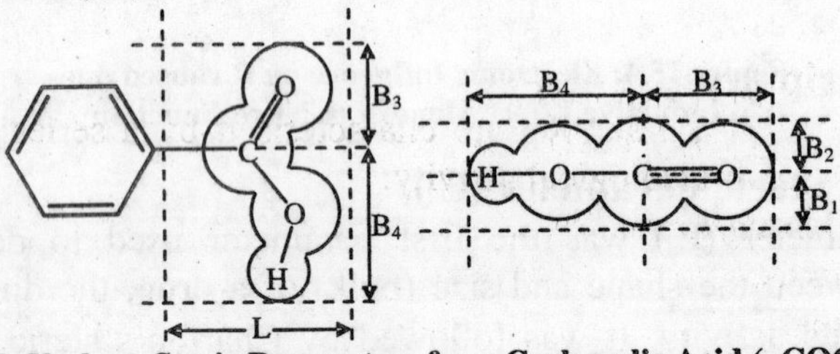

Figure 15.5: Verloop Steric Parameters for a Carboxylic Acid (–COOH) Moiety

Most QSAR studies commence by considering the Hammett substitution constant, and if there is more than one substituent, the σ values are represented as a summation value (Σσ). Due to the huge quantum of synthetic newer target drug molecules, it has become possible either to modify or fine tune-up the QSAR equation. A substituent's resonance effect (R) and inductive effect (F) can be quantified using the available tables of constants. In some cases, one may observe that:

1) A substituent's effect on biological activity is due to F rather than R, and *vice versa.*
2) A substituent exerts a prominent and appreciable activity when strategically located at a specific position on the aromatic nucleus; and it can also be appropriately expressed as an equation.

15.2.2.6. Molar Refractivity (MR)

Molar refractivity is a measure of the volume of a compound and how easily it is polarised. It is defined as:

$$MR = \frac{(n^2 - 1)M}{(n^2 + 2)\rho} \quad \text{..... (5)}$$

Where, n = Refractive index.
M = Relative mass.
ρ = Density of the compound.

The term M/ρ is the molar volume, while the term **refractive index** is the polarisability of the compound. Although MR is calculated for a whole molecule, it is an additive parameter. So the MR values for a molecule can be calculated by adding the MR values for its component parts.

15.2.3. 2D-QSAR – Pattern Recognition Analysis

2D-QSAR is an advanced method for correlating activity and structure. In 2D-QSAR method, the **first step** involves selecting the training set, which is a subset of molecules showing diversity in terms of structure and bioactivity. The available compounds cover the entire bioactivity spectrum that ranges from active (fully and partially, covering a 10^3-fold range in receptor binding affinities) to inactive.

Determining what makes a molecule bioactive or bio-inactive, if all the tested compounds have similar bioactivities, is difficult. The more molecules the better, but initially the process should be started using ten compounds. It is not necessary to use all the available molecules, as one more subset is retained as a test set that will be used for evaluating any prediction algorithm developed by studying the training set.

15.2.3.1. Descriptors

All the molecules in a training set are characterised by a series of descriptors, regardless of their pharmacological activity:

1) **Geometric Descriptors**
   i) Bond lengths,
   ii) Bond angles,
   iii) Torsional angles, and
   iv) Interatomic distances.

2) **Electronic Descriptors**
   i) Charge densities on individual atoms,
   ii) Energy of the highest occupied molecular orbital,
   iii) Energy of the lowest unoccupied molecular orbital, and
   iv) Molecular dipole.

3) **Topological Descriptors**
   i) Graph theory indices:
      a) Randic indices, and
      b) Kier-Hall indices.
   ii) *Ad hoc* indices:
      a) Number of rings in the molecule, and
      b) Number of aromatic rings in the molecule.

4) **Physicochemical Descriptors**
   i) Octanol-water partition coefficients:
      a) Log P, and
      b) $(\text{Log P})^2$.
   ii) Hydrogen bonding number:
      a) Number of hydrogen bonding donor sites, and
      b) Number of hydrogen bonding acceptor sites.

These descriptors can be calculated using various **approaches of molecular and quantum mechanics**:

1) **Geometric descriptors** reflect molecular geometry and are conceptually straightforward.

2) **Electronic descriptors** reflect properties that arise from variations in electron distribution throughout the drug molecule framework.
3) **Topological descriptors** describe molecular branching and complexity through notion of molecular connectivity.
4) **Graph theory indices** differentiate between an n-butyl substituent and a tert-butyl substituent.
5) **Physicochemical indices** reflect the drug's ability to partition itself into the lipid surroundings of the receptor micro-environment.

15.2.3.2. Hansch Analysis

Hansch analysis is the most popular mathematical approach to QSAR. It majorly contributes in recognising the importance of log P (P = octanol-water partition coefficient), which is the most important parameter for determining the solubility of a drug molecule. The value of log P describes the drug's ability to partition itself into the lipid surroundings of the receptor micro-environment.

Hansch analysis mathematically relates the drug activity to measurable chemical properties. It relies on **Hansch's proposal** that **drug action** could be divided into **two stages**:

1) Transport of drug to its site of action, and
2) Binding of drug to the target site.

The drug's chemical and physical properties and its target site influence these stages. **Hansch** postulated that the biological activity of a drug can be related to these parameters by simple mathematical relationships:

$$\log 1/C = k_1 \text{ (Partition Parameter)} + k_2 \text{ (Electronic Parameter)} + k_3 \text{ (Steric Parameter)} + k_4 \quad \text{..... (6)}$$

Where,

C = Minimum concentration to produce a specific biological response.

k_1, k_2, k_3 and k_4 = Numerical constants obtained by feeding the values of the parameters, selected by the investigating team, into a suitable computer statistical package.

These parameter values are obtained either from the literature (**e.g.,** π, σ, and E_s) or are experimentally determined (**e.g.,** C, P, etc.). In investigations involving change in more than one substituent, the value of a specific parameter can be expressed in the Hansch equation as either independent individual parameters or the sum of the values of that parameter for the individual substituents.

For example, in a hypothetical case of a benzene ring with two substituents (X and Y), the Hammett constants are expressed as either $k_1\Sigma(\sigma_X + \sigma_Y)$ or $k_1\sigma_X + k_2\sigma_Y$ in the Hansch equation. The equations obtained from the selected data are termed **Hansch equations**. Their nature varies (**table 15.2**), but in an investigation using P, σ, and E_s parameters, Hansch equations become as follows:

$$\log 1/C = k_1P - k_2P^2 + k_3\sigma + k_4E_s + k_5 \quad \text{..... (7)}$$

Hansch equations can be derived using the parameters other than those shown in **equation (7).**

Table 15.2: Examples of Simple Hansch Equation

Compound	Activity	Hansch Equation
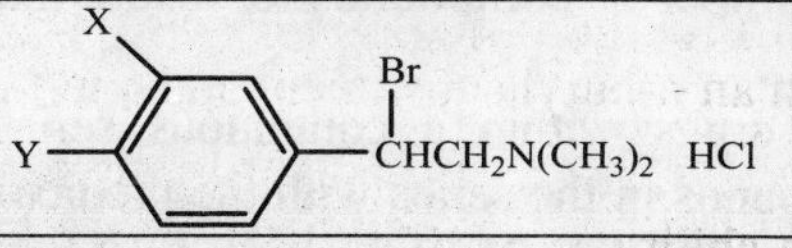	Antiadrenergic	$\log 1/C = 1.22\pi - 1.59\sigma + 7.89$ ($n = 22; s = 0.238; r = 0.918$)
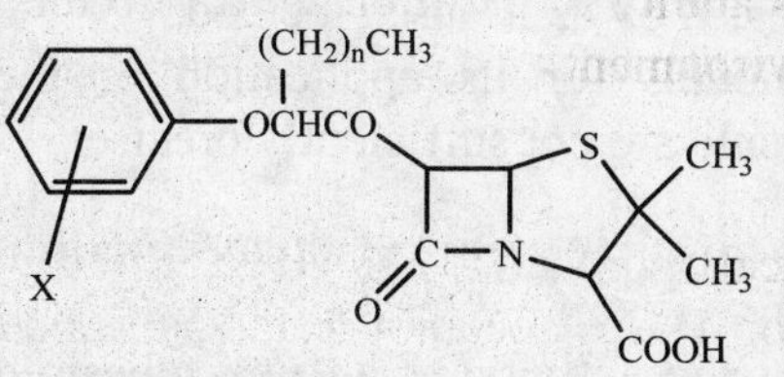	Antibiotic (*in vivo*)	$\log 1/C = -0.445\pi + 5.673$ ($n = 20; r = 0.909$)
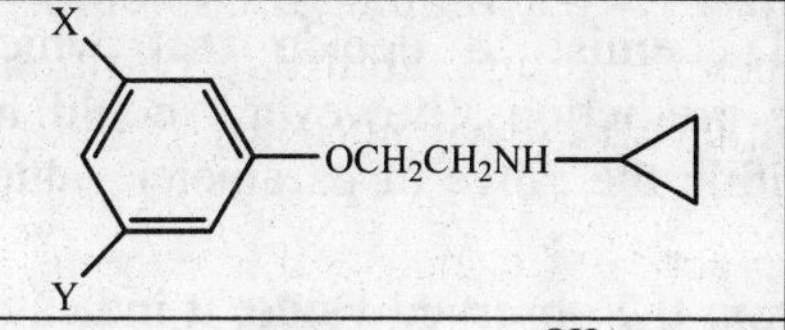	MAO inhibitor (humans)	$\log 1/C = 0.398\pi + 1.089\sigma + 1.03E_s + 4.541$ ($n = 9; r = 0.955$)
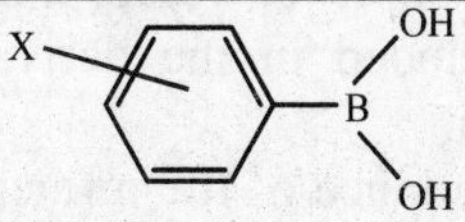	Concentration (C_b) in the brain after 15 minutes	$\log C_b = 0.765\pi - 0.540\pi^2 + 1.505$

Accuracy of a Hansch equation depends on:

1) The number of analogues (n) used; greater is the number, higher is the probability of obtaining an accurate Hansch equation.
2) The accuracy of biological data used in the equation derivation. The degree of variation in biological measurements indicates that a statistically viable number of measurements should be taken for each analogue and an average value should be used in the derivation of Hansch equation.
3) The choice of parameter (Craig plots).

Accuracy of a Hansch equation can be evaluated from the values of standard deviation (s) and regression constant (r) given by the statistical package used to obtain the equation. Smaller the value of 's', better the data fits in the equation. If the 'r' values are significantly lower than 0.9, either unsuitable parameter(s) were used to derive the equation or the compounds used are not related to their activity. Thus, suggesting that the mechanisms of action of these compounds are very different from each other.

Advantages

1) It is the most accurate method.
2) It is accurate for broadest range of solutes (neutral and charged compounds applicable).
3) **It is not necessary that the chemical structure should have to be known beforehand.**

Disadvantages

However, there are drawbacks in the Hansch method:

1) Good fits ($r^2 > 0.9$) can be obtained by manipulating the constants. Therefore, curve fitting should be done for a large number of compounds to ensure that all predictors are considered.
2) The action mechanism may change for drugs within a continuous series, invalidating the comparison of some compounds in the series with the predictor compounds. Such a change cannot be anticipated by the Hansch method.
3) Biological systems are too crude as models for its application or the electronic effects operative in a drug molecule are not sufficiently precise.
4) The method is time and cost consuming.

Applications

1) Hansch equations are used for predicting the activity of an unsynthesised analogue, thus allowing the medicinal chemist to decide that which analogues are worth synthesising. These predictions, however, should be considered valid only if they are made within the range of parameter values used to establish the Hansch equation.
2) When the predicted activity is different from the observed value, it indicates that the activity is affected by factors not included in the derivation of Hansch equation (such as the ease of metabolism).
3) Hansch analysis is also used to indicate the importance of the influence of a parameter on the drug's mechanism of action. **For example,** in a series of analogues whose activity is related to the parameters π and σ by the hypothetical Hansch equation:

   $$\log 1/C = 1.78\pi - 0.12\sigma + 1.674 \quad \text{..... (8)}$$

   Small value of the coefficient for σ relative to that of π in **equation (8)** indicates that the electronic effects do not influence the drug action.

15.2.3.3. Free-Wilson Method

Free-Wilson method assumes that biological activity can be described by additive properties of substituents on a basic molecular structure. In the **Fujita-Ban modification** of this method:

$$\text{Log}1/C = \sum a_i X_i + \mu_0$$

Where, C = Drug concentration for a standardised effect.

a_i = Group contribution of the ith substituent to the pharmacological activity of substituted molecule.

X = Unity if substituent i is present and zero otherwise.

μ_0 =1/C for the parent compound

Regression analysis is used to determine a_i and μ. No such assumptions are made about the relevance of the model parameters to the biological activity of the molecule in the Fujita-Ban modification of the Free-Wilson method. Each substituent's effect is independent of any other, and each makes a constant contribution to the overall activity of the molecule. Therefore, this method can be applied to compounds having more than one variable group. This results in a data matrix that shows the contribution of each substituent in each position to the overall biological effect of the molecule.

The Free-Wilson equation is much similar to the linear Hansch equation, and the results of both equations can be compared. The Free-Wilson method, however, fails to predict the activities of compounds whose substituents are not included in the matrix. This method is limitedly used in drug series where many close analogues are available but their physicochemical data are missing.

15.2.3.4. Topliss Decision Tree Method

Due to the huge cost suffered while synthesising a large number of structural analogues required for the Hansch equation, it has become necessary to limit the synthesis of a lesser number of drug molecules that may be produced in a limited time period having viable biological activity. Based on the outcome of the biological activity, the actual structure of the drug helps in determining the next analogue to be synthesised.

The **Topliss scheme** is an organised **flow diagram** that categorically allows a procedure to be adopted with a commendable success rate.

However, there are **two different Topliss schemes** for aromatic substituents and for aliphatic side-chain substituents. These two schemes were designed by considering the electronic as well as hydrophobicity features (i.e., substituents) to arrive at the optimum biological active substituents.

The Topliss schemes are not a replacement for Hansch analysis. Hence, the former is useful and effective only when a good number of tailor-made structures have been designed and synthesised.

The **Topliss scheme for aromatic substituents (figure 2.6)** is based on the assumption that the 'lead compound' exhibits a single monosubstituted aromatic ring and has been screened for its desired biological activity.

Salient Features

The following salient features the aromatic substituents need to possess with respect to the Topliss scheme:

1) 4-Chloro derivative should be the 'first structural analogue' in this scheme as it can be easily synthesised.
2) The π and σ values are positive as the hydrophobic and electron-withdrawing property of chloro substituent is more than that of hydrogen atom.
3) The biological activity of the synthesised chloro-analogue is measured.
4) The following three situations may arise:
   i) Analogue possessing less activity (L),
   ii) Analogue possessing equal activity (E), and
   iii) Analogue possessing more activity (M).

   Thus, the type of observed activity determines that which 'branch' of the Topliss scheme is to be adopted next.
5) Further line of action towards the synthesis of structural analogues of 4-chloro aromatic substituents are based on the following three options:

Biological Activity	Series Followed	Next Analogues Synthesised
i) Increase	M-series	3,4-Dichloro substituted derivatives
ii) Same profile	E-series	4-Methyl derivatives
iii) Decreases	L-series	4-Methoxy derivatives

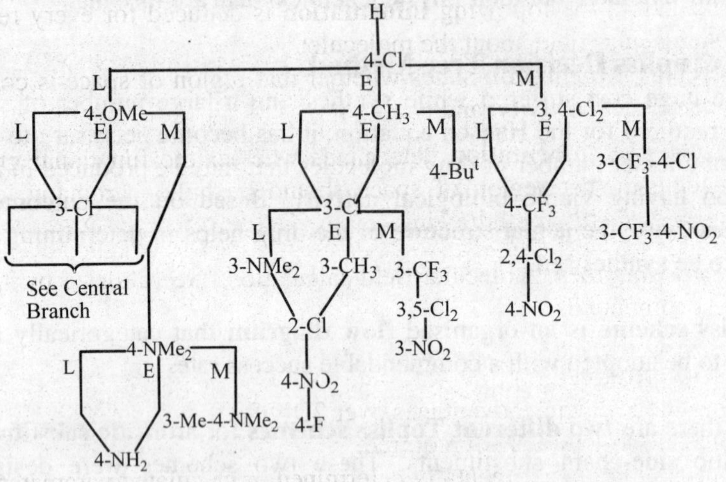

Figure 15.6: Topliss Scheme for Aromatic Substituents

The **Topliss Scheme for aliphatic side chains (figure 15.7)** was adopted in the same way and rationale as the aromatic scheme. The present scheme is expanded in the same manner for the side functional moieties strategically linked to a variety of functional groups, like amine, amide, or carbonyl.

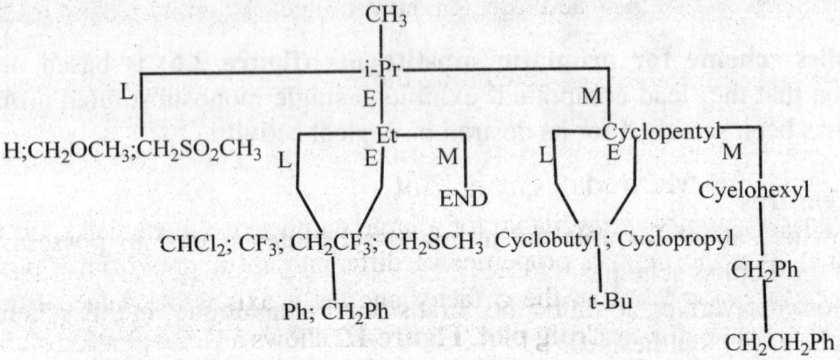

Figure 15.7: Topliss Scheme for Aliphatic Side-Chain Substituents

15.2.4. 3D-QSAR – Comparative Molecular Field Analysis

Like other QSAR forms, the 3D-QSAR starts with a series of compounds having known structures and biological activities. The **first step** involves aligning the molecular structures with alignment algorithms that rotate and translate the molecule in Cartesian coordinate space so that it aligns with another molecule. This starts with the most rigid analogues and progresses to conformationally flexible molecules aligned with the more rigid ones. At the end, all the molecules are aligned on top of each other. The **second step** involves computing a molecular field around each molecule of the training set (based on a grid of **points in space) once they have been aligned.**

Various molecular fields have field descriptors reflecting properties, such as steric factors or electrostatic potential. The field points are then fitted to predict the bioactivity.

A **Partial Least-Squares (PLS) algorithm** is used for this form of fitting. As per this PLS calculation, the following **information** is deduced for every region of space in the molecular field about the molecule:

1) **First piece of information** states whether that region of space is correlated with the biological activity, and
2) **Second piece of information** determines whether the functional group on the molecule in that region of space should be bulky, aromatic, electron donating, and electron withdrawing.

The predictions from these molecular field calculations are validated by applying to a set of test compounds.

15.2.4.1. Advantages

3D-QSAR has the following advantages over 2D-QSAR:

1) The target site structure is not required.
2) The input of either experimentally determined or calculated parameter values is not required.
3) It provides a visual picture whose interpretation is much easier than the mathematical formula of traditional QSAR.
4) It is not restricted to study of similarly structured molecules; it only requires similar pharmacophores.
5) It enables predicting the activities of new molecules without synthesising them.
6) The same general method of generating the 3D-QSAR model is followed for all studies.

15.2.4.2. Analysis Methods - Craig Plot

Tables of π and σ factors are available for a large number of substituents, still it is easier to determine the relative properties of different substituents from a plot in which the y axis is the value of the σ factor and the x axis is the value of the π factor; this plot is known as a **Craig plot**. **Figure 1.2** shows a Craig plot for σ and π factors of *para*-aromatic substituents. A Craig plot holds the following **advantages**:

1) It can be observed from the plot that no relationship exists between π and σ factors. Various substituents are scattered around all four quadrants of the plot.
2) It can be predicted that which substituents have positive π and σ parameters, which substituents have negative π and σ parameters, and which substituents have one positive and one negative parameter.
3) It can be visualised that which substituents have similar π values. **For example,** ethyl, bromo, trifluoromethyl, and trifluoromethylsulfonyl groups are all almost on the same vertical line on the plot. Theoretically, these groups can be interchangeable on drugs where π factor is the major factor affecting the biological activity. Likewise, groups forming a horizontal line are isoelectronic or have similar σ values (e.g., CO_2H, Cl, Br, and I).

4) The plot is used to decide which substituents should be used in a QSAR study. For deriving the most accurate equation involving π and σ, the analogues should be synthesised using substituents from each quadrant. **For example,** halide substituents have increased hydrophobicity and electron-withdrawing properties (i.e., positive π and σ parameters), an OH substituent has more hydrophilic and electron-donating properties (i.e., negative π and σ parameters), alkyl groups have a positive π and a negative σ value, and acyl groups have a negative π and a positive σ value.

5) After deriving the Hansch equation, it can be predicted that whether π or σ should be negative or positive to achieve the desired biological activity. Further developments concentrate on substituents from the relevant quadrant. **For example,** if the equation shows that the π and σ values should be positive, further substituents should be taken from the top right quadrant only. Craig plots can also be drawn to compare other sets of physicochemical parameters, such as hydrophobicity.

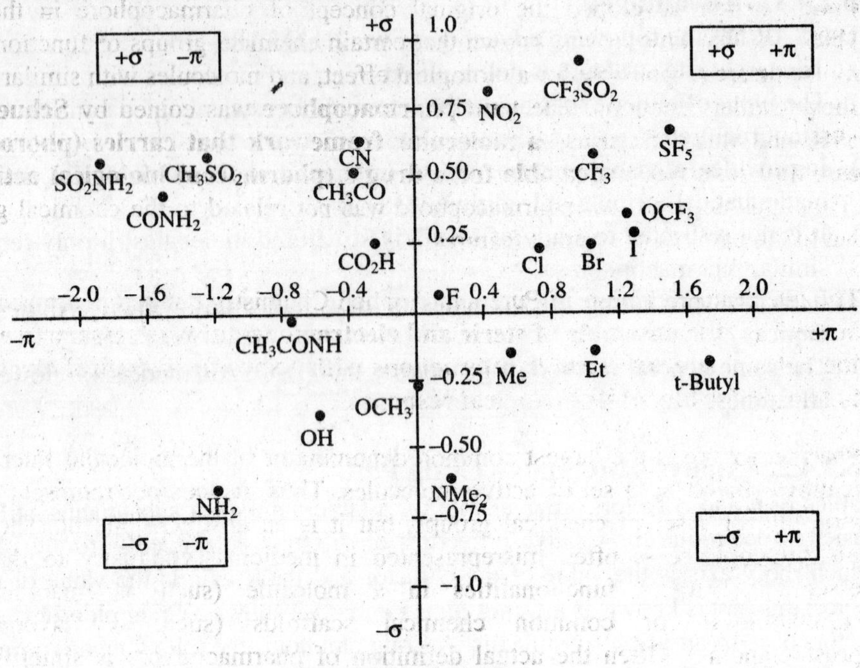

Figure 15.8: Craig Plot

15.2.5. Advantages of QSAR

Quantitative Structure Activity Relationship (QSAR) has the following advantages:

1) It provides a quantifying relationship between the structure and activity on their physiochemical property basis.
2) It is possible to predict designed compounds before the chemical synthesis of novel analogues.
3) It helps in understanding the interactions between functional group of designed molecules and their activity of target enzyme or protein.

15.2.6. Disadvantages of QSAR

Quantitative Structure Activity Relationship (QSAR) has the following disadvantages:

1) It may provide incorrect correlations due to biological data experimental error.
2) If there are less training set of molecules, the data may not reflect the complete property and thus cannot be used for predicting active compounds.
3) In some 3D-QSAR study, ligand binding receptor or protein is not available.
4) It is not necessary that the QSAR study gives successful result on each application.

15.3. PHARMACOPHORE MODELING AND DOCKING TECHNIQUES

15.3.1. Introduction

Paul Ehrlich developed the original concept of pharmacophore in the **late 1800s**. At that time, it was known that certain chemical groups or functions in a molecule are responsible for a biological effect, and molecules with similar effect show similar functions. The term **pharmacophore** was coined by **Schueler** in **1960** and was defined as "**a molecular framework that carries (phoros) the essential features responsible for a drug's (pharmacon) biological activity**". Thus, this definition of pharmacophore was not related to the chemical groups but to the patterns of abstract features.

The International Union of Pure and Applied Chemistry defined pharmacophore in **1997** as "**the ensemble of steric and electronic features necessary to ensure the optimal supramolecular interactions with a specific biological target and to trigger (or block) its biological response**".

Pharmacophore is the largest common denominator of the molecular interaction features shared by a set of active molecules. Thus, it does not represent a real molecule or a set of chemical groups, but it is an abstract concept. The term **pharmacophore** is often misrepresented in medicinal chemistry to describe essential chemical functionalities in a molecule (such as guanidine or sulfonamides), or common chemical scaffolds (such as flavones or prostaglandins). Often the actual definition of pharmacophore is simplified to "the pattern of features of a molecule responsible for a biological effect". Due to this incorrect definition it is believed that a pharmacophore is built from features and not from defined chemical groups.

15.3.2. Pharmacophore Model

Construction of a pharmacophore model involves the following steps:

1) The active compounds binding to the desired target and having the same interaction mechanism are identified by a literature search or a database search.
2) For a 2D-pharmacophore model, essential atom types and their connectivity are defined; while for a 3D-pharmacophore model, the conformations are defined as per the IUPAC nomenclature.

3) Ligand alignment or superimposition is used to evaluate the common features required in binders.
4) The pharmacophore models are built.
5) The pharmacophore models are ranked and the best models are selected.
6) The pharmacophore models are validated.

A pharmacophore model comprises of a few features organised in a specific 3D-pattern. Each feature is represented as a sphere, whose radius determines the tolerance on the deviation from the exact position. The features can be labeled as a single feature or any logic combination consisting of "AND," "OR," and "NOT" to combine different interaction patterns in a label. Additional features can describe forbidden volume interactions to represent the receptor boundary.

Such pharmacophore features are used for screening small molecule libraries in which the compounds are present in their low-energy biorelevant conformations. Each conformation is fitted to the pharmacophore query by aligning the pharmacophore features of the molecule, and the query is composed. A molecule that can be fitted in the spheres representing the query features is considered a hit molecule. Sometimes the pharmacophore query is too complex to find hit molecules from a given library. In such a case, partial matching may be allowed, and only the features essential for activity are matched. These models are also used to align molecules or facilitate molecular docking simulations.

Multiple strategies, depending on the situation and the type of experiment, are available to build pharmacophore models, either manually or using automated algorithms.

15.3.3. Pharmacophore Modeling in Virtual Screening

Pharmacophore modeling is applied to virtual screening for identifying molecules that stimulate the desired biological effect. For this purpose, researchers construct a pharmacophore model (query) that encodes the correct 3D organisation of the required interaction pattern. Different options are available to construct such a query, but it depends on how much is known about the particular protein target.

It is a good practice to divide the ligand data into training and evaluation sets so that the generated pharmacophore query can be validated when multiple active ligands (and inactive derivatives) are known. In all these cases, pharmacophore queries are positive filters to identify compounds, and can also be used as negative filters to avoid side effects.

15.3.3.1. No Protein Structure and No Ligand Structure is Known

Pharmacophore modeling is not possible if the target structure and its ligands are not known. The only option to apply the pharmacophore principle is to design a diverse library using a diversity metric based on pharmacophore fingerprints to ensure optimal diversity of the library having various molecules with different pharmacophore feature composition. Considering the large number of available and potential compounds, the libraries should be designed carefully to efficiently cover chemical space in any search process.

15.3.3.2. No Protein Structure, but Active Ligand Structures are Known

In the case of drug discovery, the structure of the receptor (and any complex with the ligand) is unknown. It is impossible to map the key contributing pharmacophore features onto the molecule if only a single active molecule is known. In such a case, the only option to retrieve similar molecules is to use similarity searches (such as using pharmacophore fingerprints). Once these have been tested, a set of multiple active and inactive compounds may be known and more advanced pharmacophore modeling can be used.

The ligand-based pharmacophore modeling can be utilised if a set of active ligands with known structure and similar or different scaffolds is available. **Interpretation of the pharmacophore** involves two steps:

1) The conformational space of the flexible molecules needs to be covered as the bioactive conformations are not known.
2) The molecules need to be aligned by common pharmacophore features that can be retained in a 3D model.

The features and the permitted steric arrangement of the ligands can be mapped using inactive derivatives. The **Catalyst-HypoGen** algorithm is different from the other tools available for the same purpose. It is a combination of QSAR and pharmacophore method, and it correlates the structure and activity values (K_i or half maximal inhibitory concentration [IC_{50}]) by building a pharmacophore model. Thus, HypoGen identifies a query compound as "active" or "inactive" in the traditional function of a pharmacophore model, and also deduces the activity value based on regression of the training dataset.

15.3.3.3. Protein and Ligand Structures are Known

In this case, structural information for the ligands and the receptor protein are available. A pharmacophore model exhibits the key features of a small molecule that enable it's binding to some receptor molecule; however, this idea can be upturned and pharmacophore queries built from features of a protein active site. These features represent the principle interactions between the protein and its ligands, and can be mapped onto the bioactive conformation of the ligand. An ideal structural model is obtained from crystallographic or nuclear magnetic resonance data, but homology models or other structural data can also be used. A structure for one ligand is considered enough, but still having 3D information for multiple ligands proves to be beneficial for identifying the common interactions. This approach is compatible with most of the pharmacophore modeling methods.

LigandScout is the first software package that automatically constructs a query from one or more Protein Data Bank (PDB) files based on protein-ligand interactions. Such structure-based pharmacophore queries can be used for virtual screening, predicting ligand binding pose, and comparing the binding sites.

15.3.3.4. Only the Protein Structure is Known

In this final case, active ligands are unknown but the structural information for the protein receptor is known. In this case, a putative pharmacophore model is built by analysing the chemical properties of the desired binding site. There are different computational approaches that are used to directly convert 3D atomic structures of protein binding sites into queries. The interaction maps of the De novo drug design tool **LUDI** is used to build a pharmacophore query. **HS-Pharm** is a knowledge-based method, and it employs machine-learning algorithms to order the interacting atoms and to generate an interaction map in the binding site. The interaction map is then converted into pharmacophore features.

GRID package is another approach to analyse the pocket for identifying the key interactions. The desired positions of atomic probes in the binding site can be identified and converted into pharmacophore features by making use of the molecular interaction fields. Although there are many success reports, absence of any ligand structural information is a disadvantage to drug design. This is because in the absence of a molecular scaffold, the features cannot be mapped in 3D space which can still be covered by atoms restrained by bond lengths and angles in the ligands.

In all these **examples**, pharmacophore queries are used to identify active molecules that fulfill some of the geometric and chemical restraints. A pharmacophore query due to its simple and versatile character can be used for identifying active molecules and can also be used as a negative query to identify molecules with undesirable properties.

15.3.4. Applications of Pharmacophores in ADME-tox

Poor ADME-tox majorly contributes to failures during drug development and clinical trials. Therefore, ADME-tox properties should be profiled in the early drug discovery process, and pharmacophore modeling approaches are used for such ADME-tox predictions. Pharmacophore models can be used to identify the probable interactions of drugs with drug-metabolising enzymes by matching the equivalent chemical groups of test molecules to those of drug molecules having a well-known ADME-tox profile.

Cytochrome P-450s (CYP) that initiate drug breakdown is an important enzyme for observing ADME-tox profile. Only six CYP isoenzymes (1A2, 2C9, 2C19, 2D6, 2E1, and 3A4) are responsible for 90% of drug metabolism. Receptor-based pharmacophore models have been built based on the observed interactions of known drugs with the CYP enzymes. These models predict the binding of a drug-like compound to a certain CYP and evaluate the degradation possibility by this enzyme.

ADME-tox pharmacophore models have been built for uridine-5′-diphospho-glucuronosyltransferases enzymes that are related to drug clearance and transporters (such as P-glycoprotein and organic cation transporter).

15.3.5. Pharmacophore-Guided Drug Target Identification

The objective of CADD is to identify and optimise drug-like molecules for a given target. In many cases, the drug molecules are known, but the mechanism of action is not. These compounds are derived from herbal medicines or phenotypically developed drugs. In such cases, CADD assists in the identification of the target. Chemoinformatical fingerprint-based similarity tools identify the close analogue compounds with known mechanism of action. Pharmacophore modeling is also an option, rather than screening compounds with a pharmacophore query. The molecule may become the query and identifies that which pharmacophore model most likely fits the molecule. Such collections of pharmacophore models are built manually or automatically generated from the PDB database. This approach can also be used to identify and optimise drug-like molecules with unknown mechanism of action for a given target.

15.3.6. Limitations of Pharmacophore Methods

Even if there are abundance of successful cases of drug design relying on pharmacophore modeling, as with any method, it is still not reliable and one should be careful about the limitations of this technique.

The **major limitation** of pharmacophore in virtual screening is the **absence of good scoring metrics**. Docking simulations are based on scoring functions trying to predict the affinity, and similarity searches utilise similarity metrics such as the Tanimoto score, the pharmacophore queries still not have a reliable, general scoring metric. The quality of fitting the ligand into a pharmacophore query is expressed by the root mean square deviation between the features of the query and molecular atoms. However, this metric fails to show any similarity with known inhibitors, and also cannot predict the compatibility with receptor protein. Thus, the molecules hitting a pharmacophore query are completely different from other inhibitors and have functional groups that are not complementary with the receptor binding site, thereby making them inactive in spite of being a perfect match.

A **second limitation** is that **a pharmacophore-based virtual screen is dependent on a pre-computed conformation database**. Since these databases contain a limited number of low-energy conformations per molecule, it may be possible that due to the missing conformation an active molecule is not identified. This is the case for many different conformations of rotatable bonds of small molecular functionalities such as hydroxyl groups. Distinguishing different rotations during the conformation generation in terms of root mean square deviation differences is difficult, and thus may not be thoroughly sampled. Often pharmacophore search tools rotate such bonds during the fitting process to obtain conformations with correct directions on the small flexible polar groups.

Another **major limitation** is that **there is no clear way to construct a pharmacophore query**. In many cases, different pharmacophore models work together to retrieve molecules. One **example** is the case of **Christ** ***et al versus*** **De Luca** ***et al***, where a similar but slightly different pharmacophore was created for a similar target. Screenings were performed on a similar dataset, but different molecules were identified. This is also clear from the analysis of various kinase inhibitors that in many cases are very similar to each other and yet have different activity profiles for the kinome. Pharmacophore approaches to identify kinase inhibitors would identify kinase-inhibitor-like molecules; however, it is not sure that these molecules would be active for the targeted kinase.

Successful results demand plenty of experience and a certain dose of serendipity. The influence of expert knowledge for in silico screening (or in cerebro step) has been demonstrated during the virtual screening SAMPL4 challenge. Target identification, prediction of side effects, and ADME-tox profiling are promising applications of pharmacophore modeling; however, its success is limited for new molecule classes as no information is available for such compounds or targets.

15.3.7. Molecular Docking

Molecular docking is a framework to understand drug biomolecular interactions for the rational drug design and discovery. It is also useful in the mechanistic study by non-covalently placing a molecule (ligand) at the desired binding site of the target specific region of the DNA/protein (receptor) to form a stable complex of potential efficacy and more specificity. The information obtained from the docking technique suggests the binding energy, free energy and stability of complexes. The docking technique is used for predicting the uncertain binding parameters of ligand-receptor complex.

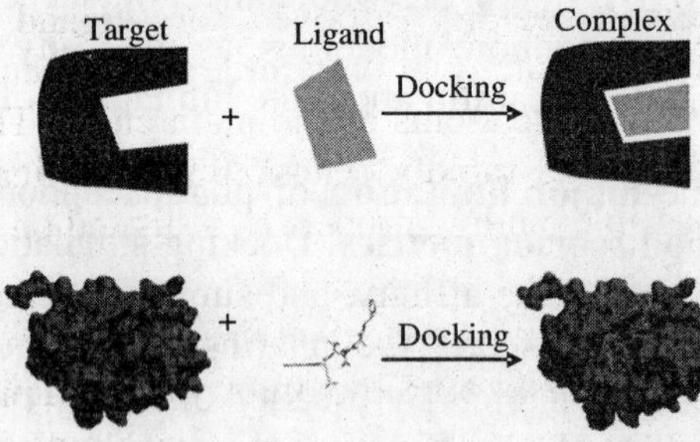

Figure 15.9: Docking Method

Molecular docking aims to attain ligand-receptor complex possessing optimised conformation and less binding free energy. The net predicted binding free energy (ΔG_{bind}) is revealed in terms of hydrogen bond (ΔG_{hbond}), electrostatic (ΔG_{elec}), torsional free energy (ΔG_{tor}), dispersion and repulsion (ΔG_{vdw}), desolvation (ΔG_{desolv}), total internal energy (ΔG_{total}), and unbound system's energy (ΔG_{unb}). Therefore, the general ethics ruling the predicted binding free energy (ΔG_{bind}) should be known as it provides supplementary data on the nature of various kinds of interactions that lead to molecular docking.

15.3.8. Approaches of Molecular Docking

For performing molecular docking, the following two approaches are used:
1) Simulation approach, and
2) Shape complementarity approach.

15.3.8.1. Simulation Approach

In this approach, the ligand and target are separated by physical distance, and the ligand is allowed to bind into groove of target after "definite times of moves" in its conformational space. These moves involve variations to the ligand structure either internally (torsional angle rotations) or externally (rotations and translations). In every move in the conformational limit, the ligand releases energy, which is termed **total energy**.

This approach is advantageous as it is more compatible to accept ligand flexibility; and also it is more real to assess the molecular recognition between ligand and target. This approach, however, takes a longer time to estimate optimal docked conformer due to the large energy dissipating for each conformation. Recently, this drawback has been revolutionised by fast optimisation method and grid-based tools. This has made the simulation approach more user-friendly.

15.3.8.2. Shape Complementarity Approach

In this approach, ligand and target are used as surface structural feature that provides their molecular interaction. The surface of target is shown with respect to its solvent-accessible surface area and ligand's molecular surface is shown in terms of matching surface illustration. Complementarity between the two surfaces based on shape matching illustration aids in searching the complementary groove for ligand on target surface. **For example**, hydrophobicity in protein target molecules is estimated by employing number of turns in the atoms of the main chain. The approach of shape complementarity is quick and rapidly scans numerous ligands (in a few seconds) to find out the possible binding properties of ligand on target molecular surface.

15.3.9. Types of Docking

The widely used docking tools employ search algorithms, such as genetic algorithm, fragment-based algorithms, Monte Carlo algorithms, and molecular dynamics algorithms. Tools, like **DOCK**, **GOLD**, **FlexX**, and **ICM**, are used for high throughput docking simulations. There are various kinds of molecular docking procedures that employ either flexible or rigid ligand/target based on the objectives of docking simulations like flexible ligand docking (target as rigid molecule), rigid body docking (both the target and ligand as rigid molecules), and flexible docking (both interacting molecules as flexible).

15.3.10. Applications of Molecular Docking

Molecular docking is performed before starting the experimental part of any investigation; thus, it demonstrates the feasibility of any biochemical reaction. In some areas, molecular docking has revolutionised the findings. Interaction between small molecules (a ligand) and protein target (an enzyme) may predict enzyme activation or inhibition. Such information provides a raw material for the rational drug designing.

Some major applications of molecular docking are:

1) **Lead Optimisation:** Molecular docking predict an optimised orientation of ligand on its target. It predicts different binding modes of ligand in the groove of target molecule. This is used to develop drug candidates with more potency, selectivity, and efficiency.

2) **Hit Identifications:** Docking along with scoring function is used for evaluating large databases to find out potent drug candidate *in silico*, which can target the desired molecule.

3) **Drug-DNA Interaction:** Molecular docking is important in the initial prediction of drug's binding properties to nucleic acid. The data obtained **establishes the correlation between drug's molecular structure and its**

cytotoxicity. The medicinal chemists are attempting to elucidate the anticancer mechanism of drugs at molecular level by inspecting the interaction mode between nucleic acid and drugs in presence of copper. Medicinal chemists are making *in silico* observations to predict whether the compound/drug is interacting with the protein/DNA.

If the docking programme predicts this interaction, the experimental procedures find out the real binding mode of the complex; this results in a new anticancer drug. This knowledge is also useful in the detection of those structural modifications in a drug that could result in sequence/structure specific binding to their target.

15.3.11. Basic Challenges in Molecular Docking

Some of the basic challenges in molecular docking are:

1) **Ligand Chemistry:** Ligand preparation prominently affects the docking results because ligand recognition by any biomolecule depends on 3D orientation and electrostatic interaction. Thus, conformation of the ligand and ligand preparation is considered important. In the older times, approximate pKa values were deduced by optimising the structure with the removal or addition of hydrogen, but the tautomeric and protomeric states of the molecules which are to be docked remained a major discrepancy. Databases mostly keep molecules in their neutral forms, but they are ionised under physiological conditions; hence, the molecules should be ionised before docking.

2) **Receptor Flexibility:** This is a major challenge in docking, i.e., handling of flexible protein. A biomolecule/protein takes on different conformations depending on the binding ligand. This confirms that if docking is done with a rigid receptor, a single conformation of receptor is achieved. But if docking is done with flexible receptor, the ligands may require many receptor conformations to bind.

   In the studies of molecular docking, the different conformational states of proteins are neglected the most. Protein flexibility is desirable as it achieves a better affinity between a given a drug and target. Another aspect of target flexibility is the active site water molecules that should be rectified to avoid using artefact waters in the docking process.

3) **Scoring Function:** Inadequacy in scoring function is another challenge in the docking process. Search algorithm has the potential to give optimum conformation. In the same manner, scoring function should also differentiate true binding modes from all the other parallel modes. A potential scoring function would be computationally much economical, unfavourable for analysing several binding modes.

   In case of accuracy, scoring functions make a few suggestions to evaluate ligand affinity. The physical phenomenon of entropy and electrostatic interactions are disregarded in scoring schemes. Hence, absence of suitable scoring function in terms of accuracy and speed is the main congestion in molecular docking programming.

15.4. SUMMARY

The details given in the chapter can be summarised as follows:

1) **Drug design** or **tailor-made compounds** aim to develop a drug with high chemotherapeutic index and specific action.
2) **Quantum or wave mechanics** involve some essential principles derived from fundamental assumptions that effectively describe the natural phenomena.
3) **Molecular orbital approach** is based on the assumption that electrons in molecules are directly linked to the orbitals engulfing the entire molecule, and this states the molecular orbital theory.
4) **Molecular connectivity approach** establishes the presence of structural features like cyclisation, unsaturation, skeletal branching, and presence and position of heteroatom in molecules with a series of numerical indices.
5) **Linear free-energy approach** establishes the link between proper selections of physicochemical parameters with a specific biological phenomenon.
6) **QSAR studies** are in part retrospective and predictive, since a training set of compounds of known pharmacological activity should be first established.
7) **Hammet substitution constant** (σ_X) is a measure of a substituent's (i.e., the functional moiety) ability to either withdraw or donate electrons.
8) **Taft steric parameter** (E_s) was the first parameter used to demonstrate the relationship between the shape and size (bulk) of a drug, the dimensions of its target site, and its activity.
9) **Molar refractivity** is a measure of the volume of a compound and how easily it is polarised.
10) **Geometric descriptors** reflect molecular geometry and are conceptually straightforward.
11) **Electronic descriptors** reflect properties that arise from variations in electron distribution throughout the drug molecule framework.
12) **Topological descriptors** describe molecular branching and complexity through notion of molecular connectivity.
13) **Graph theory indices** differentiate between an n-butyl substituent and a tert-butyl substituent.
14) **Physicochemical indices** reflect the drug's ability to partition itself into the lipid surroundings of the receptor micro-environment.
15) **Hansch analysis** majorly contributes in recognising the importance of log P (P = octanol-water partition coefficient), which is the most important parameter for determining the solubility of a drug molecule.
16) **Free-Wilson method** assumes that biological activity can be described by additive properties of substituents on a basic molecular structure.
17) The **Topliss scheme** is an organised **flow diagram** that categorically allows a procedure to be adopted with a commendable success rate.

18) Tables of π and σ factors are available for a large number of substituents, still it is easier to determine the relative properties of different substituents from a plot in which the y axis is the value of the σ factor and the x axis is the value of the π factor; this plot is known as a **Craig plot**.
19) **Paul Ehrlich** developed the original concept of pharmacophore in the **late 1800s**.
20) The term **pharmacophore** was coined by **Schueler** in **1960** and was defined as "**a molecular framework that carries (phoros) the essential features responsible for a drug's (pharmacon) biological activity**".
21) The International Union of Pure and Applied Chemistry defined pharmacophore in **1997** as "**the ensemble of steric and electronic features necessary to ensure the optimal supramolecular interactions with a specific biological target and to trigger (or block) its biological response**".
22) The **major limitation** of pharmacophore in virtual screening is the **absence of good scoring metrics**.
23) A **second limitation** is that **a pharmacophore-based virtual screen is dependent on a pre-computed conformation database**.
24) Another **major limitation** is that **there is no clear way to construct a pharmacophore query**.
25) **Molecular docking** is a framework to understand drug biomolecular interactions for the rational drug design and discovery.
26) In **simulation approach**, the ligand and target are separated by physical distance, and the ligand is allowed to bind into groove of target after "definite times of moves" in its conformational space.
27) In **shape complementarity approach**, ligand and target are used as surface structural feature that provides their molecular interaction.

15.5. EXERCISE

15.5.1. True or False

1) Linear free-energy approach establishes the link between proper selections of physicochemical parameters with a specific biological phenomenon.
2) Verloop's steric parameter substitution constant is a measure of a substituent's ability to either withdraw or donate electrons.
3) Physicochemical descriptors reflect molecular geometry and are conceptually straightforward.
4) Electronic descriptors reflect properties that arise from variations in electron distribution throughout the drug molecule framework.
5) Hansch analysis assumes that biological activity can be described by additive properties of substituents on a basic molecular structure.

15.5.2. Fill in the Blanks

6) _______ was the first parameter used to demonstrate the relationship between the shape and size of a drug, the dimensions of its target site, and its activity.

7) ________ descriptors describe molecular branching and complexity through notion of molecular connectivity.
8) ________ reflect the drug's ability to partition itself into the lipid surroundings of the receptor micro-environment.
9) ________ developed the original concept of pharmacophore in the late 1800s.
10) In ________ approach, ligand and target are used as surface structural feature that provides their molecular interaction.

Answers

1) True	2) False	3) False
4) True	5) False	6) Taft steric parameter
7) Topological	8) Physicochemical indices	9) Paul Ehrlich
10) Shape complementarity		

15.5.3. Very Short Answer Type Questions

1) What do you understand by drug design?
2) Give any two factors governing drug design.
3) Write about the phases of drug design.
4) What are QSAR studies?
5) What is molar refractivity?
6) What are the advantages of Hansch analysis?
7) How 3D-QSAR is advantageous over 2D-QSAR?
8) Define pharmacophore.
9) What is molecular docking?
10) Enlist the topological descriptors used.

15.5.4. Short Answer Type Questions

1) Discuss the various approaches of drug design.
2) Give the Hammet's electronic parameter.
3) Write a short note on partition coefficient.
4) Give the Verloop's steric parameter.
5) Discuss about the Topliss decision tree method.
6) Discuss the advantages of Craig plot.
7) What are the limitations of pharmacophore model?
8) Give the applications of molecular docking.

15.5.5. Long Answer Type Questions

1) Write an exhaustive note on drug design.
2) Discuss any two physicochemical parameters used in QSAR.
3) Write about any two 2D-QSAR techniques.
4) Give a brief review on 3D-QSAR.
5) Discuss the role of pharmacophore models in virtual screening.
6) Briefly discuss about molecular docking.

CHAPTER 16 Combinatorial Chemistry

16.1. COMBINATORIAL CHEMISTRY

16.1.1. Introduction

A technique of synthesising large number of molecules (structurally different) at a time is known as **combinatorial chemistry**. The molecules obtained are submitted for **High Throughput Screening (HTS) assay**. The technique of combinatorial chemistry has been recently developed by the researchers in pharmaceutical industry, so that the time and labour cost required in the production of new drugs can be reduced.

However, this technique greatly affects almost all the branches of chemistry, particularly the drug discovery, as it leads to comparatively faster processing of biologically active compounds. Since the technology of combinatorial chemistry is developing rapidly, screening for novel bioactivities has become possible by the development of compound libraries.

Combinatorial chemistry technique serves the following purposes in pharmaceutical companies:
1) Quick discovery of novel drug candidates,
2) Saves significant amount of money in preclinical developments, and
3) Changes the fundamental approach to drug discovery.

16.1.2. History

A study on combinatorial chemistry entitled **"Use of Peptide Synthesis to Probe Viral Antigens for Epitopes to a Resolution of a Single Amino Acid"** was first conducted in **1984** by **Mario Geysen**.

Furka was another inventor who introduced the **pool-and-split methods**. During the **1980s**, rapid development in the solid phase peptide synthesis was observed and hence the work of **Bruce Merrifield** on **solid phase peptide synthesis** made him the Nobel Prize winner in **chemistry** in **1984**. During this period, preparation of individual peptides was a challenge because automated peptide synthesiser technology was prevailing in its initial stages.

The **tea bag method** was introduced for rapid manual **multiple peptide synthesis** in **1985** by **Richard Houghten**. This and many other developments in multiple peptide synthesis initiated various rapid techniques of bioassays based on molecular biology. However, development of high throughput bioassays was possible due to the mass screening of peptide ligands that function as a tool in drug discovery. Developments in combinatorial chemistry are given in **table 16.1**:

Table 16.1: Milestones in Combinatorial Chemistry

Years	Milestones
1984	Limited peptide library with multi-pin technology.
1985	Limited peptide library using tea bag method.
1986	Approach on solid phase peptide library screening using multi-pin synthesis.
1986-1990	Development of polynucleotide library methods.
1988	Introduction of the split synthesis method on synthesising a limited library of solution peptides.
1990	Light directed parallel peptide synthesis of a library of 1024 peptides on chip.
1990	Successful application of the filamentous phage displayed peptide library method on a huge library of peptides.
1991	Introduction of the one bead-one compound concept and application of this concept to a huge bead-bound peptide library.
1991	Application of the approach on a huge solution phase peptide library.
1992	Synthesis of a limited benzodiazepine-based small molecule library.
1992-1993	Development of encoding methods for one bead-one compound non-peptide library.

16.1.3. Concept

The basic principle of combinatorial chemistry involves synthesis of a wide range of analogues at the same time under the same reaction conditions using the same reaction vessels. However, employing the principle of combinatorial chemistry, the organic chemists develop a large number of compounds at a time rather than only a few compounds using the traditional method. The orthodox chemistry involves usage of basic principles of organic chemistry for stepwise synthesis of a product. **For example**, two compounds (A and B) react via traditional method giving the product AB, which is separated after reaction and further processed for purification.

$$A + B \longrightarrow AB$$

Orthodox synthesis

On the other hand, various combinations of compound A_l to A_n with compound B_l to B_n can be obtained using combinatorial synthesis (**figure 16.1**). Variety of compounds can be generated in combinatorial chemistry by preparing single compounds parallelly or multiple compounds simultaneously in mixtures, using either solution or solid phase techniques. The major outcome of using combinatorial technique is that the productivity has improved and crossed the levels existing from the past hundred years, irrespective of the technique used.

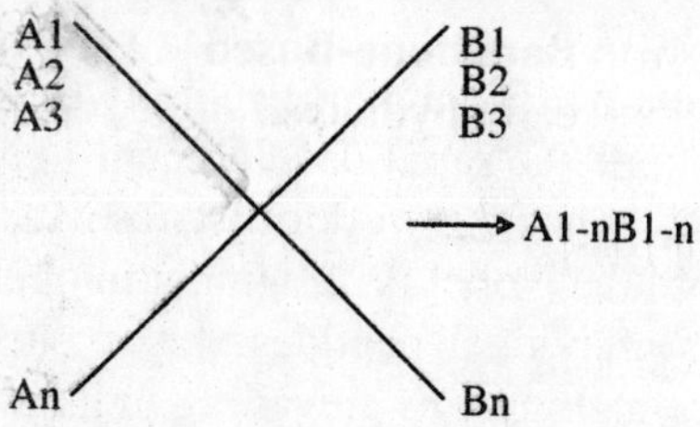

Figure 16.1: Combinatorial Synthesis

16.1.4. Combinatorial Compound Libraries

Collections of finally synthesised compounds are termed as **combinatorial compound libraries**.

These libraries have the following characteristic features:

1) **Size:** Number of reaction steps and the number of building blocks used in each reaction in which a new building block is introduced are the factors on which the size of combinatorial compound libraries depends.

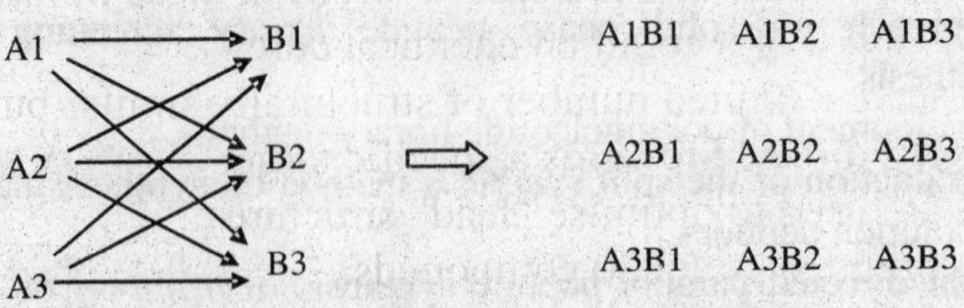

Figure 16.2: Nine Different Compounds

2) **Typical:** 10^2 up to 10^5 compounds.

3) **Types:** The 4 types of combinatorial compound libraries are:

   i) **Scaffold-Based Libraries:** Scaffold is the basic structural element used as a starting point for the generation of chemical libraries and remains common in all the compounds of the library. They consist of several single building blocks, **e.g.,** amino acid and amino benzophenone (**figure 16.3**).

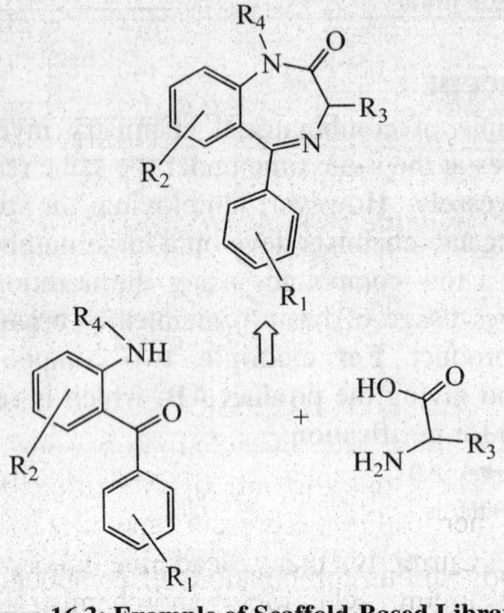

Figure 16.3: Example of Scaffold-Based Libraries

   ii) **Backbone-Based Libraries: Examples** include nucleic acids, carbohydrates.

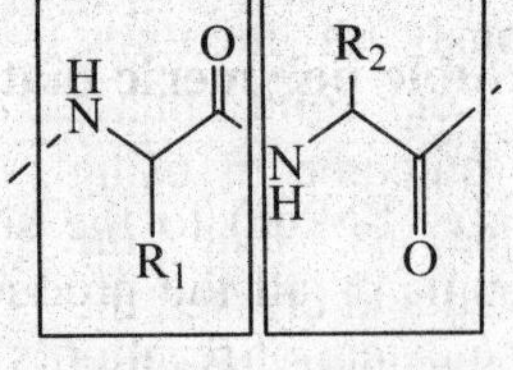

Building block A Building Block B

   iii) **Unbiased/Random Libraries:** Their characteristics include:

      a) They consist of a common chemical core, i.e., the starting point scaffold.
      b) They consist of a large number of highly diverse building blocks.
      c) They act on many targets.

d) They generate "lead" structures.
e) They can produce > 5,000 compounds.
f) They follow solid phase synthesis (one bead screening if possible).

iv) **Directed Libraries:** The features involved in these libraries are:
a) They consist of a common chemical core.
b) They have a limited number of structurally similar building blocks.
c) They are directed towards a specific target.
d) They are used to optimise "lead" structures.
e) They produce << 5,000 compounds.
f) They follow solid plan synthesis in solution.

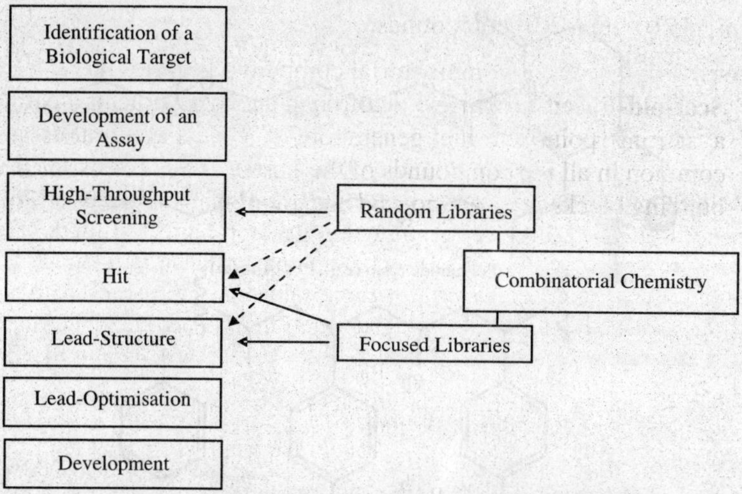

Figure 16.4: Establishment of Combinatorial Libraries

16.1.5. Solid Phase Synthesis

The Solid Phase Synthesis (SPS) technique was introduced by **Merrifield** in **1963**. The SPS concept put forward by Merrifield was initially applied to a developed biopolymer. But at the present time, it is used in every field involving organic synthesis. Currently, many academic laboratories and pharmaceutical companies are developing technologies and chemistry suitable for SPS. This has led in the occurrence of combinatorial chemistry which has modified the approach for developing new drugs, new catalyst, or new natural discovery. Utilising a solid support for organic synthesis depends on the following three requirements:

1) A **cross-linked insoluble polymeric material** must be inert with respect to the synthesis conditions.
2) The **linking substrate** (**linker**) to the solid phase which during synthesis selectively cleaves some or all the products from the solid support. This is done for analysing the extent of reaction(s) and resulting in the final product.
3) The **chemical protection strategy** allowing selective protection and de-protection of reactive groups.

Types of Solid Support

1) Polymeric solid support, 2) Linkers, and 3) Protecting groups.

16.1.5.1. Polymeric Solid Support

The solid support is selected on the basis of the type and chemistry of reaction. However, a stable resin should be used under all the reaction conditions. **Examples** of resins used are polyamide resin, polystyrene resin (Wang resin), etc. (**figure 16.5**). The partially cross-linked hydrophobic polystyrene beads are used for developing the solid support. Nevertheless, folding of peptides in these compounds may result in hindrance of peptide synthesis.

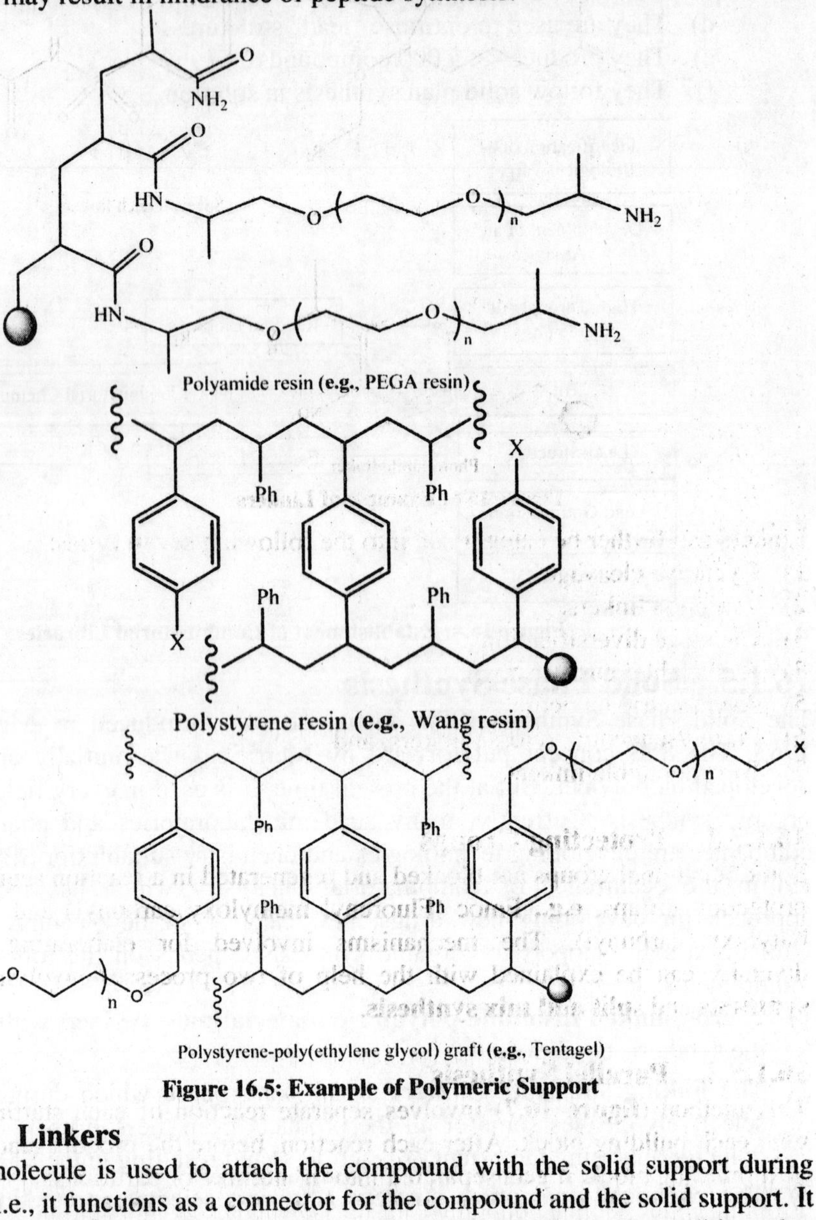

Figure 16.5: Example of Polymeric Support

16.1.5.2. Linkers

A linker molecule is used to attach the compound with the solid support during synthesis, i.e., it functions as a connector for the compound and the solid support. It also enables the cleavage of final product (in high yield) under such conditions that do not cause any destruction of the product (**figure 16.6**). **For example,** *o*-nitrobenzyl photolabile linker is derived from 4-(bromomethyl)-3-nitrobenzoic acid and is used for cleaving peptides from solid support. This linker is the most common photolabile support used for generating peptide acids as well as amides. This linker has also been reported to be containing photolabile amide protecting groups for C-termini of peptides relying on the same basic *o*-nitrobenzyl chemistry.

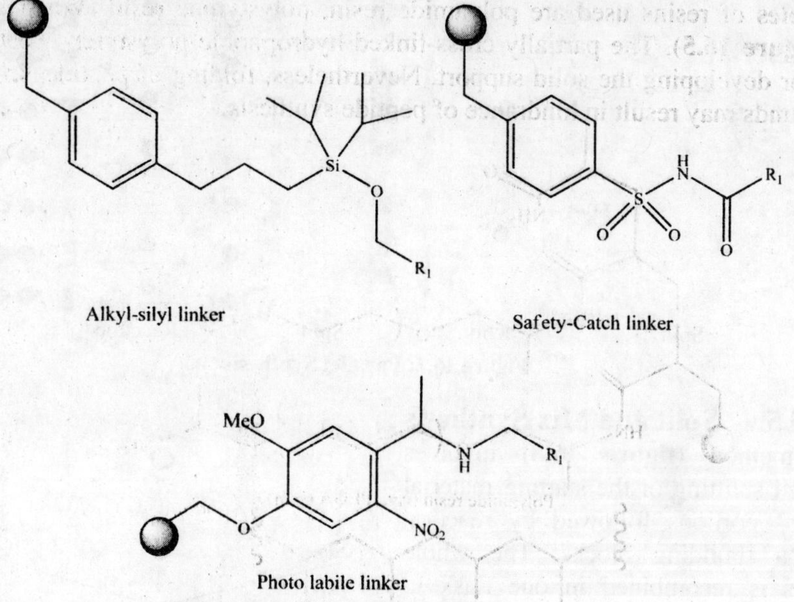

Figure 16.6: Example of Linkers

Linkers can further be categorised into the following **seven types**:

1) Cyclative cleavage,
2) Traceless linkers,
3) Cleavage diversification,
4) Recyclable/reusable resin,
5) Asymmetric induction,
6) Partial/sequential release linkers, and
7) Biocompatible linkers.

16.1.5.3. Protecting Groups

Some functional groups are blocked and regenerated in a reaction sequence using protecting groups, **e.g.,** Fmoc (Fluorenyl methyloxy carbonyl) and Tboc (Ter-butyloxy carbonyl). The mechanisms involved for elaborating molecular diversity can be explained with the help of two processes involving **parallel synthesis** and **split and mix synthesis.**

16.1.5.4. Parallel Synthesis

This method **(figure 16.7)** involves separate reaction of each starting material with each building block. After each reaction, before the product reacts with the next building block, it gets separated into 'n' number of partitions.

Advantages

1) De-convolution is not required.
2) Synergistic effects which may give false positive results during screening do not occur.

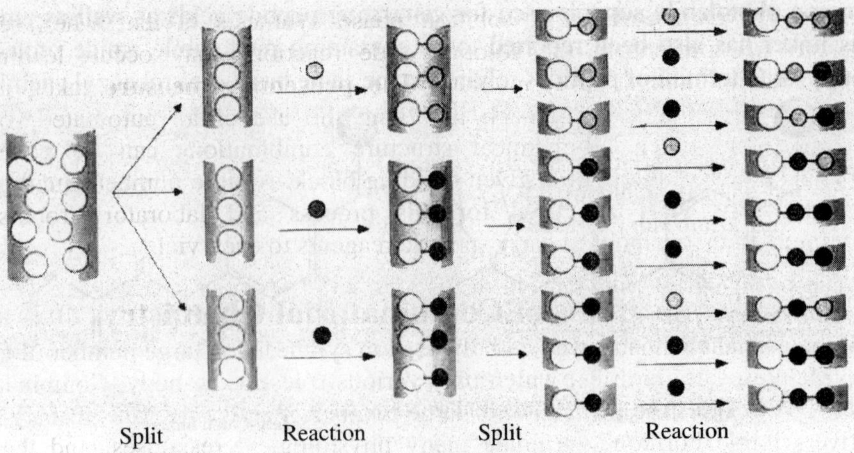

Figure 16.7: Parallel Synthesis

16.1.5.5. Split and Mix Synthesis

This method (**figure 16.8**) involves repeated splitting of the starting material into 'n' portions followed by reaction with 'n' building blocks. The whole process is recombined in one flask to carryover the second step. However, the whole procedure is repeated and is particularly used for solid phase synthesis (**figure 16.8**).

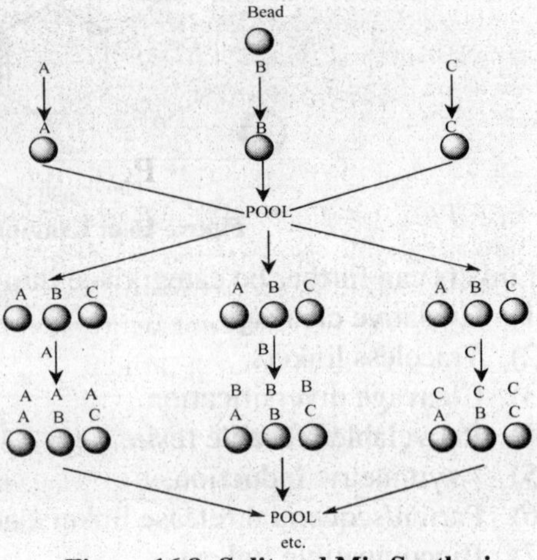

Figure 16.8: Split and Mix Synthesis

Advantages: Split and mix synthesis is advantageous as large libraries are available easily.

Limitations

1) Formation of complex mixtures,
2) Need of de-convolution (de-convolution is the method of identifying the active component in a mixture) or tagging, and
3) Synergistic effects which may give false positive results are observed during screening.

16.1.6. Solution Phase Synthesis

In this synthesis, chemical reactions are simultaneously conducted in well-ordered sets (arrays) of reaction vessels placed in the solution, **e.g.**, preparation of small array of amides. In the method of amide preparation (arrays), different acid chlorides and amines, along with tertiary amine for neutralising the effect of liberated hydrochloric acid are contained in each reaction vessel.

The chemical reactions occur simultaneously in these previously incubated vessels to perform liquid-liquid extraction. The solvent evaporates giving crude amides which are directly tested in biological assay.

The major **disadvantage** of solution phase synthesis is that when several reagents are present in the solution, side reactions may occur, leading to polymerisation and a tarred product. The **preventive measure** taken is the development of a new approach involving the use of an automated robotic apparatus by which all-chemical structure combinations can be generated separately and parallelly on a given building block. A large number (hundreds to thousands) of vials are used for this process and laboratory robots are programmed in a manner to carry specific reagents to each vial.

16.1.7. Applications of Combinatorial Chemistry

Combinatorial chemistry was initially used in synthesising large number of active peptides (peptide libraries) which play various roles in the body. Combinatorial chemistry enables the generation of large number of active peptides. Biologically active peptide hormones regulate many physiological responses, and the low molecular weight bioactive peptides act as a hormone receptor either against or as antagonists. Peptide structure is present in molecules which inhibit enzymes catalysing proteolysis, phosphorylation and other post translational protein modifications. These enzymes might play an important role in pathogenesis of various disease states.

16.1.7.1. Synthesis of Peptoids

Enzymes used for treating AIDS and cancer, like kinase and protease, are inhibited by some polypeptide libraries. Since the bioavailability and pharmacokinetic properties of these peptides are not adequate, synthetic peptide-mimetic like peptoids are being developed. **Simon** along with his colleagues has developed one of such peptoids.

Peptoids (poly-N-substituted glycines) are a group of peptido-mimetics whose side chains are attached to the N-atom of the peptide backbone, and not to the α-carbons (as in amino acids). From **figure 16.9**. the peptides and peptoids can be compared.

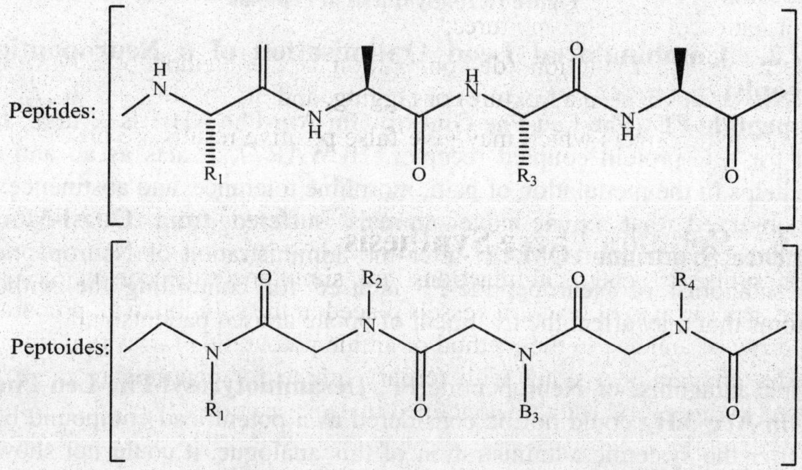

Figure 16.9: Comparison of Peptides and Peptoids

Peptoids result by formal polymerisation of a basic set of monomers N-substituted glycine units and can be **synthesised** by either of the two methods (**figure 16.10**):

1) Full monomer oligomers synthesis, and
2) Sub-monomer oligomers synthesis.

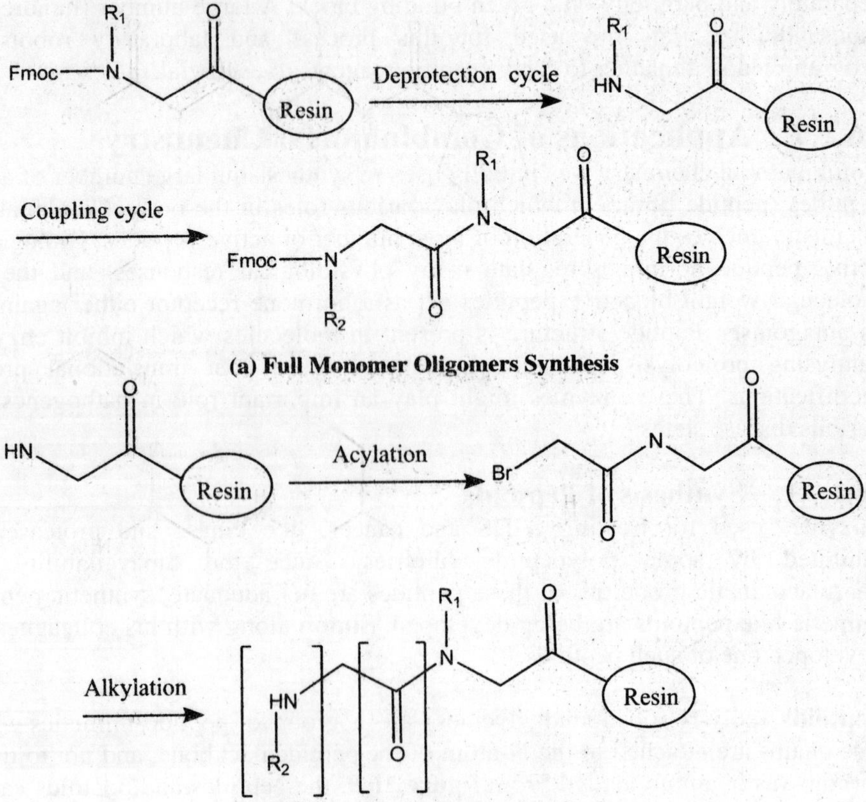

(a) Full Monomer Oligomers Synthesis

(b) Sub-Monomer Oligomer Synthesis

Figure 16.10: Synthesis of Peptoids

16.1.7.2. Combinatorial Lead Optimisation of a Neuropeptide-FF Antagonist

Neuropeptide-FF (Phe-Leu-Phe-Gln-Pro-Gln-Arg-Phe-NH_2) is a high affinity ligand for a G-protein coupled receptor, HLWAR77. It acts as an anti-opioid which helps in the modulation of pain, morphine tolerance, and abstinence. It has been observed that opiate-naive animals suffered from **Quasi-Morphine Abstinence Syndrome** (**QMAS**) after the administration of Neuropeptide-FF. Thus, antagonist of Neuropeptide-FF is used for controlling the withdrawal symptoms that may affect the treatment of opiate abused patients.

The first antagonist of Neuropeptide-FF, **Desaminotyrosyl-Phe-Leu-Phe-Gln-Pro-Gln-Arg-NH_2**, could not be considered as a potent lead compound because even after the systemic administration of this analogue, it could not show CNS bioavailability. However, an antagonist with lipophilicity sufficient enough to cross the BBB has been developed by derivatisation with 5-(dimethyl amino)-l-naphthalene sulfonyl (dansyl) at the secondary amino group of the N-terminal proline residue of the tripeptide Pro-Gln-Arg-NH_2 (obtained from the sequence of Neuropeptide-FF).

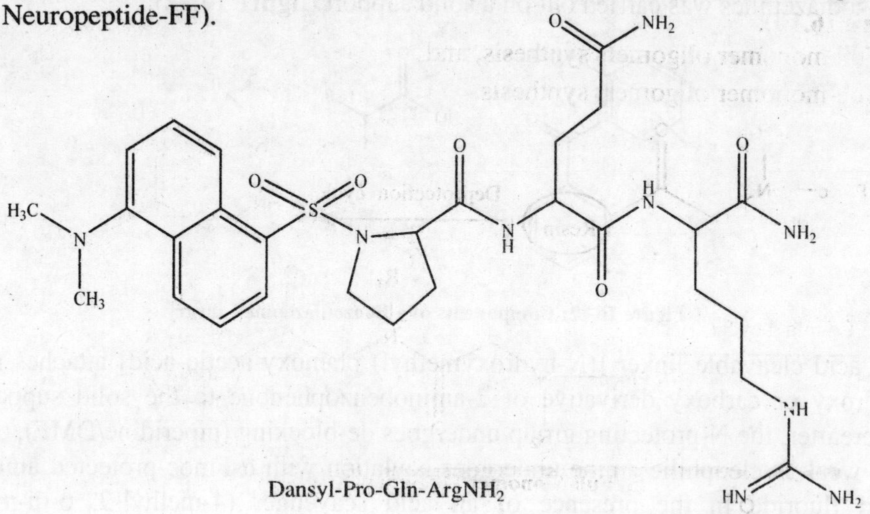

Dansyl-Pro-Gln-ArgNH2

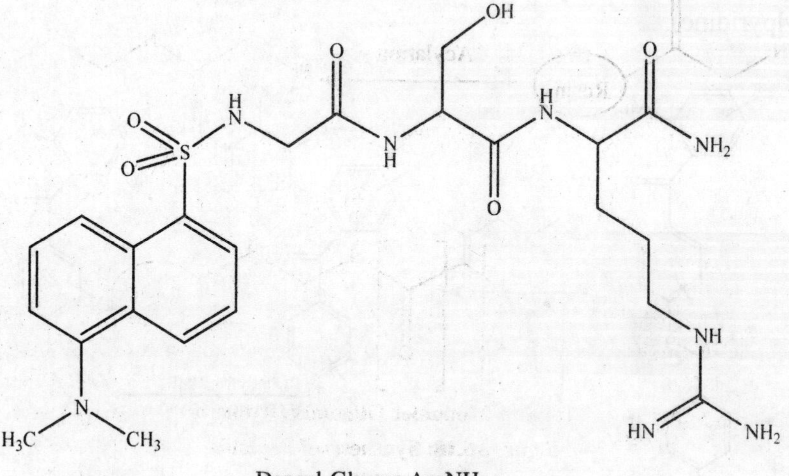

Dansyl-Gly-ser-ArgNH2

Figure 16.11: Structure of Neuropeptide-FF Antagonists

The proline and glutamine residues of this lead compound (obtained by solid phase split and mix method using coded amino acid as building blocks) were replaced by the libraries for improving the potency. **5-(Dimethyl amino)-l-naphthalene sulfonyl-Gly-Ser-Arg-NH_2 (dansyl-GSR-NH_2)** having high affinity to Neuropeptide-FF receptor and increased CNS bioavailability as compared to the lead compound, has been developed after screening for competitive binding against a radio-iodinated Neuropeptide-FF analogue (**figure 16.11**).

16.1.7.3. Generation of a Benzodiazepine Library

Studies conducted by **Ellman** on solid phase synthesis of 1,4-benzodiazepine laid the principle for developing small molecules library. This work has been a big progress in the field of medicinal chemistry and was the first example of applying combinatorial organic synthesis to non-polymeric organic compounds.

Using three building blocks of different chemical families, the synthesis of benzodiazepines was carried out on a solid support (**figure 16.12**).

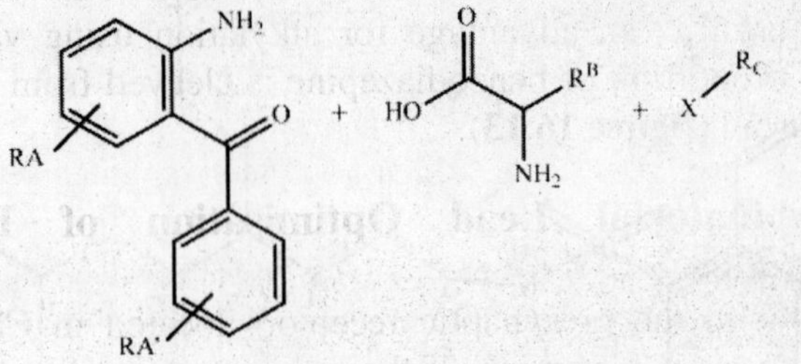

Figure 16.12: Components of a Benzodiazepine Library

An acid cleavable linker [(N-hydroxymethyl) phenoxy-acetic acid] attaches the hydroxy or carboxy derivative of 2-aminobenzophenone to the solid support. Thereafter, the N-protecting group undergoes de-blocking (piperidine/DMF), and the weak nucleophilic amine undergoes acylation with α-Fmoc-protected amino acid fluoride in the presence of an acid scavenger (4-methyl-2, 6-di-*tert*-butylpyridine).

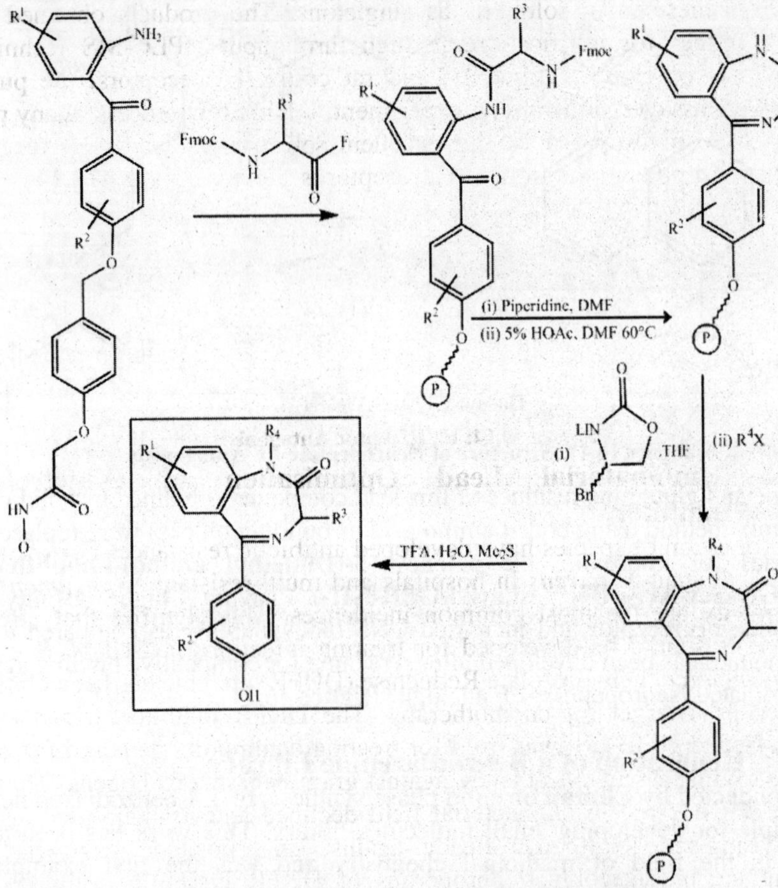

Figure 16.13: Synthesis of Benzodiazepine Library

Fmoc is treated with 5% acetic acid in the presence of DMF, thereby resulting in its de-protection. This causes cyclisation of the intermediate lactam. Lithiated 5-(phenyl methyl)-2-oxazolidinone can selectively deprotonate the anilide NH_2. This property is used as an advantage for alkylation using various alkylating reagents. A large proportion of benzodiazepine is cleaved from the solid support using an aqueous acid (**figure 16.13**).

16.1.7.4. Combinatorial Lead Optimisation of Histamine H_3 Receptor Antagonist

H_3 receptors found in the presynaptic receptors located in CNS, controls the production and release of histamine. If these receptors are blocked, the pre- and post-synaptic H_3 receptors are affected and the level of histamine and other neurotransmitters in brain increases. Due to its wide distribution in mammalian CNS, the H_3 receptor has many physiological roles to play. It can be used therapeutically as a novel drug development target. Thus, its use has been suggested in many neurological (like Alzheimer's disease, Parkinson's disease, and epilepsy) and metabolic (like obesity) disorders.

Some selective H_3 blockers have been generated using a series of biaryl derivatives. 49 biphenyl-O-propylamine amides library, shown in **figure 16.14 (a)**, were synthesised in solutions as singletons. The products obtained were processed further for purification by high throughput HPLC-MS techniques. With the help of cloned human H_3 and rat cortex H_3 receptors, the purified products were assayed in a binding experiment. During this process, many potent inhibitors were investigated having excellent selectivity towards H_3 receptors. One of the most potent inhibitors of H_3 receptor is shown in **figure 16.14 (b)**.

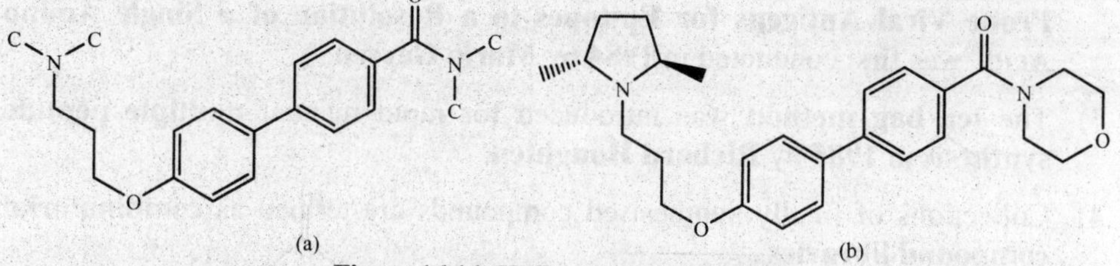

Figure 16.14: H_3 Receptor Antagonists

16.1.7.5. Combinatorial Lead Optimisation of Dihydrofolate Reductase Inhibitor

A large proportion of species have developed antibiotic resistance. **For example**, methicillin resistant *S. aureus* in hospitals and multi-resistant *S. pneumoniae* in the community are the most common incidences. This signifies that effective anti-bacterials should be developed for treating infections caused by *S. aureus* and *S. pneumoniae*. Dihydrofolate Reductase (DHFR) enzyme has been clinically established as a target for chemotherapy. The DHFR inhibitor, trimethoprim, shown in **figure 16.15 (a)**, was used for treating community-acquired infections and UTIs having maximum potency against gram-negative pathogens. Thus, the use of DHFR enzyme in antibacterial field declined and its inhibitors are now being investigated for their efficacy against gram-positive pathogens. For improving the pharmacokinetic properties of DHFR inhibitors some specific researches are being conducted currently.

After the synthesis of a library of 1392 compounds in solution, the products obtained were checked for their ability to inhibit the bacterial enzymes from TMP-sensitive *S. aureus*, TMP-resistant *S. pneumonia*, and human DHFR. Many potent inhibitors were discovered.

Figure 16.15 (b) shows one of the most potent inhibitors possessing IC_{50} value of 42nM against *S. aureus* and 550nM against *S. pneumoniae*.

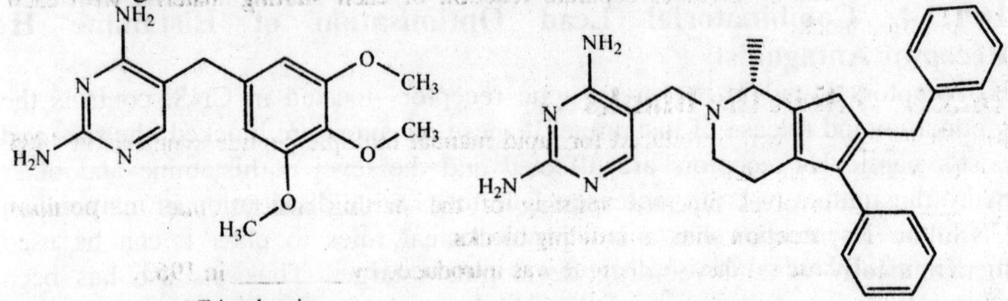

a) Trimethoprim b)

Figure 16.15: Dihydrofolate Reductase Inhibitors

16.2. SUMMARY

The details given in the chapter can be summarised as follows:

1) A technique of synthesising large number of molecules (structurally different) at a time is known as **combinatorial chemistry.**
2) A study on combinatorial chemistry entitled "**Use of Peptide Synthesis to Probe Viral Antigens for Epitopes to a Resolution of a Single Amino Acid**" was first conducted in **1984** by **Mario Geysen.**
3) The **tea bag method** was introduced for rapid manual **multiple peptide synthesis** in **1985** by **Richard Houghten.**
4) Collections of finally synthesised compounds are termed as **combinatorial compound libraries.**
5) **Scaffold** is the basic structural element used as a starting point for the generation of chemical libraries and remains common in all the compounds of the library.
6) The Solid Phase Synthesis (SPS) technique was introduced by **Merrifield** in **1963.**
7) A **linker molecule** is used to attach the compound with the solid support during synthesis, i.e., it functions as a connector for the compound and the solid support.
8) **Parallel synthesis** involves separate reaction of each starting material with each building block.
9) **Mix and split synthesis** involves repeated splitting of the starting material into 'n' portions followed by reaction with 'n' building blocks.

16.3. EXERCISE

16.3.1. True or False

1) Collections of finally synthesised compounds are termed as descriptors.
2) Linker is the basic structural element used as a starting point for the generation of chemical libraries and remains common in all the compounds of the library.
3) Parallel synthesis involves separate reaction of each starting material with each building block.

16.3.2. Fill in the Blanks

4) The ________ was introduced for rapid manual multiple peptide synthesis in 1985 by Richard Houghten.
5) ________ involves repeated splitting of the starting material into 'n' portions followed by reaction with 'n' building blocks.
6) The solid phase synthesis technique was introduced by ________ in 1963.

Answers

1) False	2) False	3) True
4) Tea bag method	5) Mix and split synthesis	6) Merrifield

16.3.3. Very Short Answer Type Questions

1) What is combinatorial chemistry?
2) What are Scaffold-based libraries?
3) Enlist the types of linkers.
4) Give the advantages and limitations of mix and split synthesis.
5) What is parallel synthesis?

16.3.4. Short Answer Type Questions

1) Discuss the history and concept of combinatorial chemistry.
2) Write a note on combinatorial compound libraries.
3) Discuss about the types of solid support used in solid phase synthesis.
4) Give the application of combinatorial chemistry in lead optimisation.

16.3.5. Long Answer Type Questions

1) Discuss solid phase synthesis in detail.
2) Give any four synthetic applications of combinatorial synthesis.

Index

A

B

C

D

F

M

P

Q

Bibliography

- Block, Roche, Soine, Wilson, *Inorganic Medicinal and Pharmaceutical Chemistry*, Varghese Pub.
- Singh H., Kapoor V.K., *Organic Pharmaceutical Chemistry*, Vallabh Prakashan.
- Pandeya Surendra N., *A text book of Medicinal Chemistry (Synthetic and Biochemical Approach) Vol - I*, S.G. Publisher.
- Pandeya Surendra N., *A text book of Medicinal Chemistry (Synthetic and Biochemical Approach) Vol - II*, S.G. Publisher.
- Beckett A.H., Stenlake J.B., *Practical Pharmaceutical Chemistry (Fourth Edition - Part One)*, CBS Publishers.
- Beckett A.H., Stenlake J.B., *Practical Pharmaceutical Chemistry (Fourth Edition - Part Two)*, CBS Publishers.
- Ali Mohammed, *Text book of Pharmaceutical Organic Chemistry*, CBS Publishers.
- Kar Ashutosh, *Medicinal Chemistry*, New Age Pub.
- Block John H., Beale John M., *Wilson and Gisvold's text book of Organic Medicinal and Pharmaceutical Chemistry*, Lippincott Williams and Wilkins.
- Chatwal G.R., *Medicinal Chemistry (Organic Pharmaceutical Chemistry)*, Himalaya Publishers.
- Ahluwalia V.K., Chopra Madhu, *Medicinal Chemistry*, ANE Books India.
- Sriram D., Yogeswari, *P. Medicinal Chemistry*, Pearson.
- Qadry J S, SQadry S and Budhiraja Asha, *Organic Pharmaceutical and Medicinal Chemistry Vol I*, B S Shah Prakashan.
- Lemke Thomas L., Williams David A., Roche Victoria F., Zito S. William, *Foye's Principle of Medicinal Chemistry 6th Edition*, Lippincott Williams and Wilkins.
- Nadendla Rama Rao, *Principles of Organic Medicinal Chemistry*, New Age Publishers.